Remodeling Your Temple

Restoring Your Physical and Mental Well-Being to Glorify God

Laurie K. Dahle

I AM F.E.D.

ISBN-13: 978-1-7323946-1-2

Library of Congress Control Number: 2018906506

Scripture references are from the following sources:

Scripture quotations marked (NIV) are taken from THE HOLY BIBLE, NEW INTERNATIONAL VERSION®, NIV® Copyright © 1973, 1978, 1984, 2011 by Biblica, Inc.® Used by permission. All rights reserved worldwide.

All unmarked Scripture quotations are taken from the Holy Bible, New Living Translation, copyright © 1996, 2004, 2007, 2013, 2015 by Tyndale House Foundation. Used by permission of Tyndale House Publishers, Inc., Carol Stream, Illinois 60188. All rights reserved.

Cover and Temple Diagram Designed by Andrew Dahle
Photograph of Temple by Laurie Dahle

I am honored that God had the confidence in me to write these books. He never gave up on me even when I was discouraged or felt overwhelmed. God has shown me that when I trust Him, He will show me His glory and can do amazing things in my life. God can use my weakness to show His power.

Thank you Dr. Brenda Miano for sharing your love of God and nutrition with me. The information you have shared with me is invaluable. Thank you for being a consultant on the nutrition chapters of this book.

Thank you Andrew Dahle for all your work in designing the cover and temple drawings as well as all the support you gave me as I undertook this project.

Thank you Mary Ann Chase, Lisa Ulrich, Yvonne Twillman, and Amy De La Hunt for helping with editing this book and all your encouragement.

*** Disclaimer: All information contained within this book is for reference purposes only and not intended to substitute the advice given by a pharmacist, physician, or any other licensed health-care professional. Every person needs to be responsible for his or her well-being; therefore, they should research all advice or information so they can make an informed decision as to how they are going to enhance their lifestyle. Although the author has made every effort to provide accurate and complete information we assume no responsibility for errors, inaccuracies, omissions or any inconsistencies herein.

TABLE OF CONTENTS

Appendix

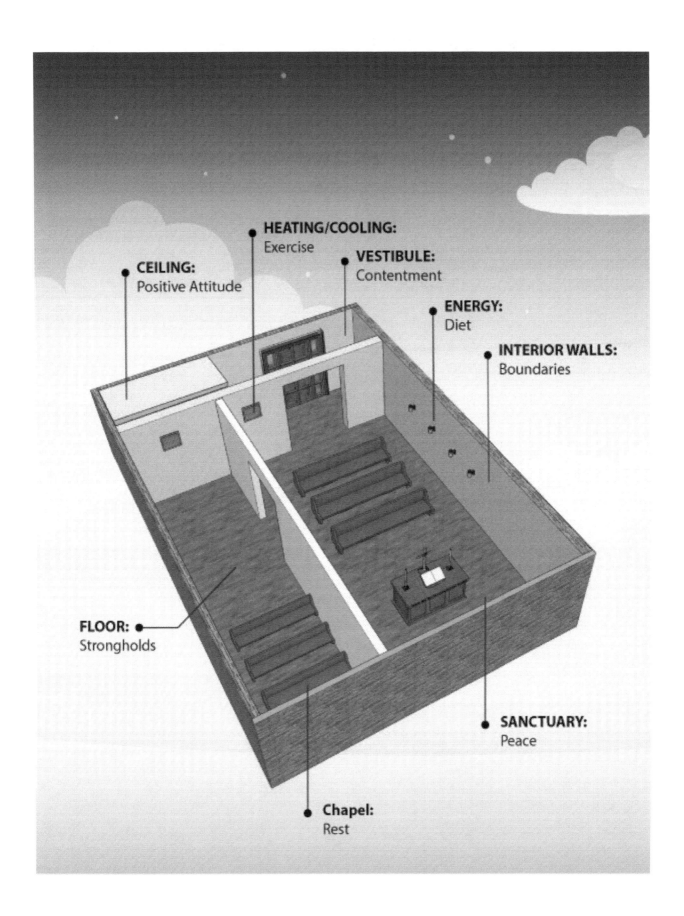

CEILING:
Positive Attitude

HEATING/COOLING:
Exercise

VESTIBULE:
Contentment

ENERGY:
Diet

INTERIOR WALLS:
Boundaries

FLOOR:
Strongholds

SANCTUARY:
Peace

Chapel:
Rest

Blueprints: *For God is working in you, giving you the desire and the power to do what pleases him (Philippians 2:13).*

Trusting The Architect: *Since we respected our earthly fathers who disciplined us, shouldn't we submit even more to the discipline of the Father of our spirits, and live forever (Hebrews 12:9)?*

Walls (Boundaries): *A person without self-control is like a city with broken-down walls (Proverbs 25:28).*

Ceiling (Attitude): *A cheerful heart is good medicine, but a broken spirit saps a person's strength (Proverbs 17:22).*

Sanctuary (Peace): *"Have the people of Israel build me a holy sanctuary so I can live among them. You must build this Tabernacle and its furnishings exactly according to the pattern I will show you (Exodus 25:8-9).*

Floor (Strongholds): *Now I stand on solid ground, and I will publicly praise the LORD (Psalm 26:12).*

Vestibule (Contentment): *For the Kingdom of God is not a matter of what we eat or drink, but of living a life of goodness and peace and joy in the Holy Spirit (Romans 14:17).*

Chapel (Rest): Those who live in the shelter of the Most High will find rest in the shadow of the Almighty *(Psalm 91:1).*

Energy source (Diet): *At the end of the ten days, Daniel and his three friends looked healthier and better nourished than the young men who had been eating the food assigned by the king (Daniel 1:15).*

Heating and cooling (Exercise): *Dear friend, I hope all is well with you and that you are as healthy in body as you are strong in spirit (3 John 1:2).*

Preface

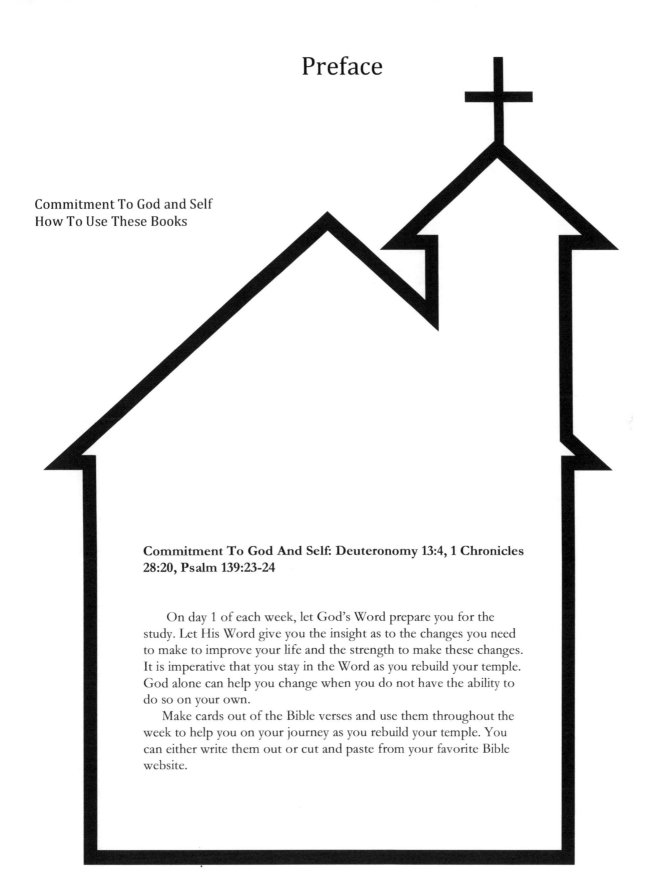

Commitment To God and Self
How To Use These Books

Commitment To God And Self: Deuteronomy 13:4, 1 Chronicles 28:20, Psalm 139:23-24

On day 1 of each week, let God's Word prepare you for the study. Let His Word give you the insight as to the changes you need to make to improve your life and the strength to make these changes. It is imperative that you stay in the Word as you rebuild your temple. God alone can help you change when you do not have the ability to do so on your own.

Make cards out of the Bible verses and use them throughout the week to help you on your journey as you rebuild your temple. You can either write them out or cut and paste from your favorite Bible website.

My eyes will be open and my ears attentive to every prayer made in this place. For I have chosen this Temple and set it apart to be holy—a place where my name will be honored forever. I will always watch over it, for it is dear to my heart (2 Chronicles 7:15-16).

The temple is of great important to God. He went into great detail as to the specifications and layout of the temple as this was to be God's primary meeting place with His people. In Exodus 25:8, God tells Moses to have His people build a temple so He could live among them. Since the Israelites were roaming in the desert for forty years, God designed the temple to be mobile. As we become more familiar with Scripture, we find that a temple does not have to be a physical structure. A temple is a meeting place between God and His people as well as a place for the atonement of sin.

When Jesus ascended into Heaven after His resurrection, He gave us the gift of the Holy Spirit to be our helper and abide with us forever (John 14:16). When we accept the gift of the Holy Spirit, He can help us achieve our goals of improving or maintaining a healthy lifestyle. Since the Holy Spirit lives in us, our bodies are to be a temple for Him. Because of Jesus' death and resurrection, we now have the ability to be in God's presence at all times. Therefore we need to care for our bodies so that they honor God.

God has put the same careful planning into the construction of our temples as He did for the temple the Israelites built. *I praise you because I am fearfully and wonderfully made; your works are wonderful, I know that full well (Isaiah 139:14 NIV)*. The Israelites were responsible for following God's plans and erecting the temple and then maintaining it. The Bible is our guide as to how to care for our bodies. In 1 Thessalonians 5:23 God tells us to keep holy our spirit, soul, and body. In *Rebuilding Your Temple* we discussed how we could improve our faith to maintain our spirit. In this book we are going to address the soul and physical body. After all, *And what union can there be between God's temple and idols? For we are the temple of the living God. As God said: "I will live in them and walk among them. I will be their God, and they will be my people (2 Corinthians 6:16)*. We should offer God the best temple possible for Him to dwell.

So, are you ready to remodel the inside of your temple? Making changes and seeing results can be exciting. God created you with a specific purpose in mind. He has plans for your life and wants you to live your life to the fullest. You were not created to live a mediocre life. Unfortunately, many people let their physical and emotional health deteriorate, and this hinders their living a life that is pleasing and glorifies God. It is essential that both the external and internal structures of the temple be maintained. For some people, their outside of the temple (spiritual) can be structurally sound, but the inside (the physical and/or emotional components) of the temple is in disarray.

If you completed the *Rebuilding Your Temple* study, I hope you had a chance to appreciate all the hard work you have done to rebuild the outside of your temple and now are ready to tackle the remodeling of the inside of your temple. I pray that you are seeing God more active in your life and have an increased dependency on Him. By building a strong external structure, you trust that God can and will give you the strength and willpower to make the changes necessary to live a healthy lifestyle. If you did not do the first part of this study, I hope that after completing this one you will find the time to do it because faith and a relationship with God are essential to living a healthy life. We cannot make the changes on the inside of our temple if the outside is falling down. Faith and trust in God are the keys to changing and living productive lives. We can have healthy physical bodies by eating a nutritious diet, and physically strong, but we are not completely healthy until we have a strong faith and bask in the love of our Father.

In this book, we are going to tackle our diet and exercise after we look at many of the emotional factors that can affect how we live our lives to their fullest. How we perceive things determines how we react to various situations as well as to how we worship and honor God. Many times our eating habits can be affected by how we deal with stress, our contentment with our lives, and feelings of our self-worth. When we seek God's help and trust Him, He can make us aware of and correct some of the underlying factors that keep us from remodeling our temple. God can give us the strength to overcome our strongholds. Until we seek Him, we will continue to fight the same battles.

When I initially started writing these books, I was going to address mainly diet because I felt that it was the most crucial part of healthy living. As I began my journey on improving my lifestyle, diet was my primary focus followed by exercise. My most significant changes came after I allowed God to take over my life and become my primary focus.

God and I battled when I started teaching classes about healthy living because I wanted to address diet first. Most of the people who joined my classes were coming for the nutritional information. Each week I wanted to tackle nutrition and God wanted me to address faith first. God kept telling me that although many of the participants may already have a great faith foundation, they had not completely surrendered this area of their life to Him. Living a healthy lifestyle is not only about having the knowledge as to proper nutrition and exercise but also having the ability to utilize it. This includes surrendering this aspect of our lives entirely to God. How many people do you know who preach healthy living are overweight, have illnesses that are worsened or caused by poor diet, or have cigarette, food, or alcohol addictions? For many, this is because they lack the willpower or have an inability to surrender this aspect of their life to God. We will address nutrition in depth once we address other areas that may affect diet.

I would like for you to review how you rebuilt the outside of your temple and the significance of each part of the temple. You have to have faith (footings) to develop a relationship with God (foundation). Jesus Christ is the cornerstone of your faith. The Holy Spirit (rebar) enlightens you and helps you understand scripture. The Holy Spirit can guide you in prayer (bolts) to keep you connected to God. By building a relationship with God, you can experience His love. When you know God's love, your external walls are structurally sound. The more secure you are in God's love, the better you will be able to love yourself. When you know you are loveable, it is easier to make changes in your life because you see yourself as worthy of change. Christian fellowship (grout) supports you and can hold you accountable for your actions and sharpens your faith. God's Word (roof) is what allows you to build your faith, know God's love and help you stay strong against temptation. Knowing you have a purpose and calling in life (the door) gives you a reason to want to change and to see the necessity for having a healthy body, mind, and spirit. Shame and guilt (windows) can leave you feeling as if you are in a dark place, suffocating, and unworthy of God's love. This can hinder your ability to make changes. Unforgiveness (stairs) blocks your entrance into seeing all God can do in your life. Forgiveness and repentance help you draw closer to God and restore peace and joy. Accepting God's gift of grace (bells) lightens the load you carry throughout life, and you can improve all the other components of your temple. The final piece of the outside of your temple is salvation (steeple). Knowing that you have an eternity in Heaven makes all the struggles and battles you face on earth worth fighting.

Now that you have the outside structure of the temple erected, it is time to attend to remodeling the inside of your temple. By choosing to make healthy living your hobby you will see greater results because hobbies are things we enjoy doing, so we want to spend time enjoying them and will often let them take over our lives. Spend as much of your free time as you can on this new hobby, allowing God to help you improve your skills and habits. At first, this may take extra effort to pull yourself away from unhealthy habits that have controlled your life. With the help of God, these patterns will be replaced. You will see that living a healthy lifestyle is a joy and will draw you closer to God.

Spending a mere 30 minutes a day on your new hobby will not allow you to develop new habits and change your lifestyle. This study addresses many areas of healthy living and takes additional commitment if you are going to see life-changing results. Therefore, be willing to incorporate what you learn throughout your day. Your dedication to this study will be well worth it. The effort you put into it will have a direct correlation to the outcome you will see. For some of you, this is your first attempt at making healthy changes in your life. Just reading the material may be the place for you to begin. We all have to start somewhere. I hope that once you become familiar with the material, you will revisit the chapters and utilize the information to make healthy changes.

When making changes in your life, first obtain the necessary information, then process it, and finally, apply it to your life. In order to make these applications habits, spend time re-establishing the norms of your life. Being successful requires you to be honest with yourself, be willing to look at your life with an open mind, and have a desire to change the unhealthy areas.

Six years ago, God began working in my life to make many of the changes I have addressed in these books. At first, it was not easy, but as I got more comfortable with my relationship with God, I learned to trust that He could and would help me change. I then began to enjoy the journey. It has since become my passion. My life has become more fulfilling, and I have found the peace and joy that only God can give. I hope that you too will allow God to work wonders in your life.

I am asking you to commit these next 7 weeks to God. Tell Him you want to be His willing and obedient servant. Let Him know you are willing to do what it takes to not only build a stronger relationship with Him but also to make changes in your life so you can better serve Him.

As I wrote these books, God spoke very clearly to me. He told me that His Word is the most crucial part of this study. Unless you know and live by His Word, trying to live a healthy life will be very difficult. You may be able to clean up some areas, but until you completely surrender to Him and use His Word as your footings, you will continue to miss the most critical part of healthy living. It is crucial that you have a relationship with your Father and know His love. God created you and therefore understands every aspect of your complex and wonderfully made life. When you surrender to Him and accept His love, you will find you can live your life the way He envisioned for you. Then you will reap the benefits and see other areas of your life improve.

In the first book, I asked readers to become more aware of their diets, eating habits, and toxins that they encounter. I have included these same questionnaires in the back of this book for you to review. If this is the first study you are doing, you can answer them over the next few weeks so when you begin the diet sections, you are more aware of some of your habits.

HOW TO USE THESE BOOKS

You made all the delicate, inner parts of my body and knit me together in my mother's womb. Thank you for making me so wonderfully complex! Your workmanship is marvelous—how well I know it. You watched me as I was being formed in utter seclusion, as I was woven together in the dark of the womb. You saw me before I was born. Every day of my life was recorded in your book. Every moment was laid out before a single day had passed (Psalm 139:13-16).

God has given each one of us a plan to live a healthy and productive life. He has a specific calling for each one of us. However, you must be willing to follow His plan if you want to live the life He has intended for you. Your body is a beautifully constructed temple that was designed to be able to fulfill your calling on earth. In doing so, you honor God, your Creator. To live the life God has specially designed for you, you must be willing to keep your temple in good shape. Healthy living is so much more than just eating a clean diet and exercising. Over the next seven weeks, as you study God's Word, you will learn how it can help you to lead a healthy, spiritually based life.

These books contain information that you can immediately begin utilizing in your daily life. Sometimes, people join a healthy living group or read a book on this topic with expectations that it is going to give them all the answers and not require much work. Although many of us like to think we can make these changes quickly, the reality is that change takes time and hard work. It is not something we can wish to happen and then reap immediate benefits.

I have given basic information to get you started on this journey. I recommend that if something is not clear or you do not feel you have enough information, research it in more depth. There is plenty of literature out there on all the topics I have covered in these books. Read the book slowly, so you can take time to digest it.

No two people will travel along the same path. We are all unique individuals who have different needs, levels of determination, financial resources and abilities. As I researched each topic, I have shared the things that I found most valuable for my journey, and I have given different options that have worked for others. Know that you too will have to pick and choose what works best in your life. You, like me, will have to experiment with how you can incorporate what works best in your life. You, like me, will have to experiment with how you can incorporate healthy living into your lifestyle. It will take time to find and become comfortable with a routine that works for you. Don't be hard on yourself when you struggle or make a mistake. Instead, enjoy the journey, and know this is all part of growing and improving your life.

8

I feel nutrition is essential to living a healthy life. The food we eat determines whether our bodies will receive the proper nutrients, maintain healthy body weight, help with our ability to think clearly, manage our emotions, and give us the energy to fulfill our callings. When I first started teaching healthy living classes, many of the people came to learn about their diet, but they found it difficult to make changes until they addressed other areas of their lives By turning our hunger towards God, He will help us to break our addiction to food and change our dietary habits. He will make us aware of the emotional issues that may be standing in the way of us changing our diet.

Food plays a vital role in our society. For many, it is a way to socialize. People get together and share a meal. However, eating is also a way people mask emotional pain. When a person cannot quiet their mind, eating diverts the attention. Food helps to combat boredom and loneliness, which leads to poor habits and addictions. Our brains begin to associate food with comfort. Eating can bring us pleasure as well as fill many voids in our lives. For some, food has become a crutch to avoid addressing unhealthy matters in their lives. Healing is needed if food has become a crutch in a person's life.

Before we can make nutritional changes, it is best to address issues that may be causing us to overindulge or eat poorly. I have chosen to address nutrition later in the book so that readers can first identify any other factors that may hinder their making changes in the diet and keeps them from being successful. By allowing our hunger to be for our faith and God, we can break our addiction to food and change our dietary habits.

- Before beginning each chapter, pray that God guides your thoughts and gives you the wisdom to be able to improve your life. Pray that you grow physically, emotionally, and mentally as well as spiritually. Know that you are not a disappointment to God and that He chose to create you to be the person you are. By making these improvements, you are honoring God.

- To start each week, I have given you a list of Bible verses to review. I suggest you write out the verses on index cards. By doing this you let God prepare your heart so that you are ready to study the week's lessons. By familiarizing yourself with God's Word, you will find the encouragement and strength to address the various issues. He can give you the strength to help you break strongholds that prevent you from living the life He intended for you to live. Let His Word be the first thoughts that awake you each morning and the last thoughts that bid you a good night. When God becomes first in your life, you will reap the rewards that He has promised you, and you will see His glory.

- The verses can also be prayers to God, asking Him to help you in a specific area. Use Scripture to remind you of God's promises. By seeking God's Word first, He can reveal things to you that you would otherwise wish to keep buried or not address.

- Take time to answer the questions throughout the chapter. The questions will help you to understand the material better and give you direction as to where you need to make changes in your life. Some of the questions have been repeated throughout the study because as you make alterations to your lifestyle, your answers may also change, and you will be able to answer the questions more thoroughly.

- You will be asked to set goals, and by doing so, you will be able to establish a game plan. Without establishing goals, your time will be spent jumping from one idea to another. By having to think about and write the goals, you are telling yourself that you are ready to make a change. You also need to make sure the goals you set are realistic and attainable. By making short-term goals as well as long-term goals, you will be able to see progress and keep a positive attitude. It is easy to get discouraged and quit when you set unrealistic goals. Spend some time thinking about your goals and being honest with yourself. Don't ignore challenges that are causing you pain or hindering you as you set these goals. You will have to address these concerns if change is to occur.

- I recommend you use a journal as you read this book. After each chapter, record your thoughts. Write your story on these pages. These notes may be something you can look back on and realize how far you have come on your journey. They can also help you design your game plan. It may one day serve as a testimony as to how much you have grown in your faith. Include "God moments" so that you can see just how active He is in your life during this time. Write down subjects you want to further research and new things you want to try and implement in your life. Include your feelings, good things that have occurred, and struggles you have had. I found that by writing things down, it helped me put into words what I was thinking, made it possible for me to address questions I had as I learned new information, and it helped me to see the changes that I had made but forgotten. When I was struggling, I could look back and see the effort I was putting forth was making a difference.

- On the first day of each week, there is an exercise to help you start incorporating healthy lifestyle changes into your daily routines. Give your best effort to try and complete these assignments. When you get to the diet chapters, there is a lot of information, and it can be overwhelming if you think you need to make all the changes at once. Becoming more aware of your diet and environment, you can start incorporating small changes, which will lead to the bigger ones. There are also a few bonus exercises throughout the week that will help you to establish new habits in various areas of your life.

- Conclude each chapter with a prayer, asking God to help you understand what you have just read.

- Use the resources I have referenced at the end of the book when you are ready to delve deeper into a subject.

You must be willing to do your homework if you are going to see the best results and adopt a healthy lifestyle. Use the tools I have given you and decide what works for you.

Please know that it is all right if you cannot do everything in this book. Small changes will eventually lead to more significant changes. Do what you can at this time. As you begin to make progress, you may want to try to add more changes to your life.

As you work through these books, you will realize that with God's help, you can take control of your life. Your choices will affect your outcome. I pray that you build a stronger relationship with our loving Father and that you see God's blessings and experience God's glory on this journey. If you keep your eyes fixed on our loving Father, He will not disappoint you.

Week 1

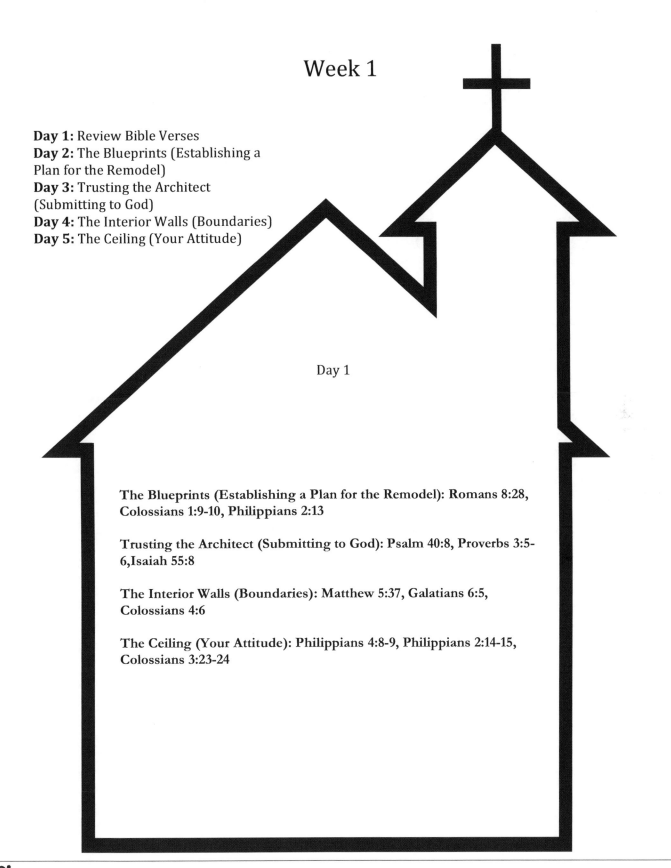

Day 1: Review Bible Verses
Day 2: The Blueprints (Establishing a Plan for the Remodel)
Day 3: Trusting the Architect (Submitting to God)
Day 4: The Interior Walls (Boundaries)
Day 5: The Ceiling (Your Attitude)

Day 1

The Blueprints (Establishing a Plan for the Remodel): Romans 8:28, Colossians 1:9-10, Philippians 2:13

Trusting the Architect (Submitting to God): Psalm 40:8, Proverbs 3:5-6, Isaiah 55:8

The Interior Walls (Boundaries): Matthew 5:37, Galatians 6:5, Colossians 4:6

The Ceiling (Your Attitude): Philippians 4:8-9, Philippians 2:14-15, Colossians 3:23-24

Weekly exercise: Give up food that has sugar, sugar substitutes or high fructose corn syrup for 2 days. Sugar can be hard to give up, but is essential to do, if you want to clean up your diet. By doing it for a short period at first, it can encourage you to be able to do it for a more extended period of time. Doing this in the middle of the week may be easier when there may be less temptation to eat junk food. If you have medical restrictions, you should consult your doctor before making significant changes.

THE BLUEPRINTS
(ESTABLISHING A PLAN FOR THE REMODEL)

A blueprint is a technical drawing or plan designed by the architect to show how to build the temple. It is a vision with which to set your goals so that you can achieve them. Just as we established a blueprint to rebuild the outside of our temple, we now have to develop one for the inside.

Nugget of the day: In his grace, God has given us different gifts for doing certain things well. So if God has given you the ability to prophesy, speak out with as much faith as God has given you. If your gift is serving others, serve them well. If you are a teacher, teach well. If your gift is to encourage others, be encouraging. If it is giving, give generously. If God has given you leadership ability, take the responsibility seriously. And if you have a gift for showing kindness to others, do it gladly (Romans 12:6-8).

Sometimes people spend so much time admiring other people's gifts, that they do not appreciate their own custom-designed gift. God handpicked each one of us to fulfill a particular role in the body of Christ. He did not randomly give us talents and dreams. God chose each one of them and carefully placed them in our hearts. God selected these gifts for us before our conception. We may let our gifts or talents go unappreciated or don't think they are as important as someone else's gifts. When we do not utilize these gifts to the best of our abilities, there is a hole in the body of Christ. Even though a job may seem small or of little importance to people, it is significant to God. He did not give us our skills based on salary or prestige. He handpicked them determined on how we could best further His Kingdom.

My prayer is that you take the time to appreciate the gifts and talents God has given you. He has entrusted you with the responsibility of using these gifts to further His Kingdom and to bring others to Christ. Spend some time thanking God for believing in you and allowing you to be His ambassador. It is an honor to serve God. Ask the Holy Spirit for guidance so you can use these gifts to make a difference in this world. Can you imagine how much better this world would be if we all used our gifts and talents to further God's Kingdom and to honor God?

****

A builder cannot begin a project without a plan. The plan gives the builder an overview of the project. The blueprints tell him the exact materials he will need, the precise measurements and the order in which to build. If the builder does not have plans, he will spend extra money buying supplies he does not need or waste time correcting his mistakes and trying to figure out what step he needs to take to complete the project. The same is true with your choosing to change your lifestyle. You have to see the big picture so that you know what your plan of action will be so that you do not waste money on buying food that is not healthy or time trying to figure out each step. When you investigate and gain knowledge on what healthy living entails and then design a course of action, you will have a higher success rate. You, like the builder, also need to be willing to commit to making changes, and when you have an overall plan, you can keep your sights on the end results. You will be less likely to start the project and then quit in the middle of it because it is too overwhelming or you are unsure of the course you need to take to see the results you desire.

How often do you try to impress people with your appearance or behaviors? When you go to work, do you make sure you have on a cute outfit, comb your hair, and do your makeup correctly? What about your first date with someone? Do you repeatedly try on different outfits until you are satisfied with the look, right down to the last detail? People are very conscious of their outward appearance and how others perceive them. Many of us also have a different way of acting when we first meet someone. We let them see our "good side." We speak kindly, we act happier, and we do things we know will please this person. We love to make good first impressions because we know that is often the image a person will have of us. As time goes on, though, and we get more comfortable with the person, we often let our guards down. We spend more time in comfy clothes and even let people see us with our "hair down." After a married couple is together for a while, they no longer try and impress one another by dressing up. They are used to the other person seeing them in their sweats and tee shirts. They also no longer feel as if they have to let the other person always see their good side. At times, they grumble about things more and find fault with what is happening in their home. They save their good side for when they go out in public.

When a person decides they need to lose weight or get into shape, they often devise a plan that will get them to their desired weight or allow them to have more energy. However, if the person is not invested in this new way of life or they do not make it part of their daily routine, they will eventually return to eating an unhealthy diet and not working out as frequently. Sometimes the return to old habits is so gradual the person does not realize they are reverting to their old ways.

People often find that they revert to old habits with their relationship with God as well. God is the driving force of our behaviors and our emotional well-being. When we first get to know God, we spend a lot of time in His Word, make time for prayer, are excited to go to a place of worship, and spend time with other believers. We try to live by the commands of the Bible and take to heart the Words that Jesus spoke. As time goes on, we get comfortable with our faith and let other things take priority in our lives. Before long, the Bible often remains unopened, or it might even be covered with dust. We miss Sunday service more frequently. We justify it by saying we had a long week and sleep is more important than going to church. The more lenient our attitude, the more careless we become with our inner and outer appearance before God. Before long, we find we are struggling to find the peace and joy that only God can give us in our lives.

Now it is time to make the changes and spruce up our lives, so we present to God a temple that is pleasing and worthy of housing the Holy Spirit. Just as you did in *Rebuilding Your Temple*, I am asking you to review the following areas that you are going to address in this book. In the areas you struggle, I am asking you to write down the struggle and then a goal as to how you want to change this area in your life. It helps to make both a short-term and long-term goal so that you can see the progress you are making. Feel free to come back to these goals and add to them as the Holy Spirit reveals more changes to you. Writing out these goals will give you something tangible to work toward and use as a reference. When you need a reminder, you can look at the goals. Research has shown that people who write down their goals have a much higher rate of achievement. (Not all these areas will pertain to you. Skip the ones that are not causing you struggles in your life.)

Before you tackle this job, spend some time in prayer and ask God to reveal to you changes you can make. Be open to listening to God. He has your best interest at heart and will help you to find greater joy and peace in your life when you trust Him to help you make these changes. God has created you with a specific purpose in mind. When you rely on Him to help you grow and make changes in your life, you will see how much more productive your life will become. Remember that God already knows what areas you need to work on; He is waiting for you to approach Him so He can help you. God wants to show you His glory and let you see how He can transform your life when you trust Him.

If you are doing this study in a small group, you may be able to use your strengths to help those who are weak in areas in which you are strong and vice versa.

Example: Rest struggle: I tend to get only 5 hours of sleep a night and fall asleep at work frequently.
Short-term goal: I will prepare my lunch and get my clothes ready the night before so that I can sleep later in the morning.
Long-term goal: I will get to bed earlier at night and get 7-8 hours of sleep.

Trusting God struggle: Strongholds struggle:
Short-term goal: Short-term goal:
Long-term goal: Long-term goal:

Boundaries struggle: Attitude struggle:
Short-term goal: Short-term goal:
Long-term goal: Long-term goal:

Stress struggle: Contentment struggle:
Short-term goal: Short-term goal:

Long-term goal: Long-term goal:

Rest struggle: Diet struggle:
Short-term goal: Short-term goal:
Long-term goal: Long-term goal:

Exercise struggle:
Short-term goal:
Long-term goal:

Environmental toxins struggle:
Short-term goal:
Long-term goal:

Journal your thoughts.

Day 3

TRUSTING THE ARCHITECT
(SUBMITTING TO GOD)

When we hire an architect, we do so because we trust him and want his advice. If we do not follow our architect's guidance, we will still not build a temple that is solid and capable of fulfilling its purpose.

Nugget of the day: And we know that God causes everything to work together for the good of those who love God and are called according to his purpose for them *(Romans 8:28).*

Our human nature desires to control everything. At times, this is a strength, but for the majority of the time, it is a weakness. Our trying to control everything causes much stress. To control everything in our life, it often requires us to attempt also to control other people's lives. Many times, the person we are trying to control is also fighting to be in control and it becomes a vicious cycle. If we heed God's advice and allow Him to be in control, our lives would be less hectic. We find that when God is in control, miracles happen. We have a choice: We can trust that God knows what we need to do to improve our quality of life, or we can believe we know what we are doing and attempt to make changes on our own. When we accept that God has plans, then submit to Him: life becomes less stressful. Doors will open, and we will see dreams become a reality.

My prayer is that you ask the Holy Spirit to give you the ability to commit your life to God and let Him take command. Rather than trying to control situations, put your needs in prayer and let God guide you. He sees the big picture. He can change hearts, break addictions, and remove obstacles that are out of your control. God will far exceed your dreams and expectations. With God in charge, He will bring peace and joy. Giving up control is no easy task. Spend some time asking the Holy Spirit for guidance and strength. Let God do what He does best, lead His children.

****

An architect is essential to make the project complete. He does not only understand one piece of the project. He knows the whole picture. He has a vision as to what the end result will be, and he puts all these plans on paper. When a problem arises, the project manager will consult with the architect to correct the problem.

As Christians, we have hired God as our Architect. We need to trust that He has a plan to help us live healthy and productive lives. While Jesus lived His life as a human, He consulted with God often throughout His day. Jesus knew that God would guide Him and help Him to make the right decisions to fulfill God's plan for His life. In turn, we are to imitate Jesus and model our lives after Him because Jesus came to teach us how to live. Therefore, we must trust He knows the answers. When we do not follow Jesus' advice, we will have difficulty de-stressing and finding rest. When we run into problems, we will not always find the answers by looking to people, as God is the One who intricately designed us and placed our calling on our hearts. Let's study how Jesus submitted to God so that He could live a life that was pleasing to God. We too can remodel our temple so that we live a healthier life, find peace, and fulfill our calling.

Then Jesus said, "Come to me, all of you who are weary and carry heavy burdens, and I will give you rest. Take my yoke upon you. Let me teach you, because I am humble and gentle at heart, and you will find rest for your souls. For my yoke is easy to bear, and the burden I give you is light" (Matthew 11:28-30). We can easily forget that before Jesus ascended into Heaven, He walked the earth as a man. He faced many of the struggles and temptations that we face in this world. Jesus understands how we feel. Jesus not only came to save us but to help us relate to Him, and He personally invites us to find rest by coming to Him. Jesus knows what it is like to live in this world. Even though He is the Son of God, He was not exempt from the struggles of life. Jesus spent His life ministering to others. Because He had people continually needing His attention, He had to set boundaries. Jesus faced temptations from Satan, and He knew what it was like to be exhausted and need to find rest. Jesus had to perform the duties of daily living as well as fulfill His ministry that was His career. Jesus also knows what it is like to be mistreated as He was mocked, ridiculed, belittled, and beaten. Then Jesus hung on a cross and died for our sins though He was sinless. When we face adversity, feel unable to keep performing our daily chores or fulfill our calling, Jesus is willing to listen to our needs and will be our intercessor asking God to intervene on our behalf.

Before Jesus was crucified, He literally sweat blood. He prayed, asking God to take away the cup He was about to be served. *"Father, if you are willing, please take this cup of suffering away from me. Yet I want your will to be done, not mine." Then an angel from heaven appeared and strengthened him. He prayed more fervently, and he was in such agony of spirit that his sweat fell to the ground like great drops of blood* (Luke 22:42-44). Hematidrosis is a medical condition that occurs when a person is under extreme stress. The capillary blood vessels that supply the sweat glands burst and cause blood to be excreted in the sweat. [1] The Son of God was in such extreme emotional distress that it caused Him to sweat blood, and it was no coincidence that Luke, the physician, recorded this.

Notice how Jesus dealt with the stress. Jesus went to His Father. He left the disciples and went to be alone with His Dad. Jesus knew where His strength came from, and He knew that only God could get Him through such a difficult time. Although God knew He could not change this course of history, God did provide Jesus with the strength to go through with His calling. Have you ever thought about what would have happened had God answered His prayer and stopped the crucifixion? We all would have been lost. We would have only known Jesus as a historical figure. Instead, Jesus listened to His Father. He went through the trials of this earth, died on a cross, rose from the dead, and ascended into Heaven to spend eternity with His Father. Because of Jesus' death and resurrection, the whole world has the opportunity to spend eternity with Him.

We all have struggles in this world. While we are going through these trials, we often miss the blessings. We get wrapped up in our problems letting stress overcome us as we look for all kinds of outlets and try many solutions. Rather than prayer being our first defense, we often exhaust all other options before turning to prayer. We may even make the mistake of getting angry with God when He does not change the situation for us. If God has allowed us to go through a particular struggle, it is because He knows we have to learn a lesson, the situation will draw us closer to Him, or it will be our testimony that God can use to minister to others.

What if prayer were our first line of defense when we fought a battle? What if the moment we face adversity, we get down on our knees and pray without ceasing? Our outlook would be different. Prayer helps us to cope with pain and suffering, giving us the strength to face the trials that lie before us. Prayer changes lives and provides hope.

God, in His infinite wisdom, knew from the beginning of time that we would need to experience struggles to draw close to Him. God knows that it is in trials that we will seek Him and build a relationship. God has also proven time and time again that when we remain faithful, we will enjoy His blessings. Who would have believed that God could part the Red Sea for the Israelites? Who would have thought Daniel would emerge victorious from the lion's den? Who would have guessed David could slay Goliath? Without these trials, these Bible greats would not have witnessed God's glory.

In the book of Philippians, Paul speaks of holding onto our faith to get us through tough times. He reminds the Philippians to keep their eyes on Heaven. If they lose sight of their ultimate goal, they will experience distress and less peace in life. The same is true for us. When we don't keep our eyes firmly fixed on God and surrender to Him, we will experience unrest.

Read Philippians 4:1-9

What is Paul's command in verse 1?

What should we always do?

Write verse 6 in your own words.

What will your reward be for obeying verse 6?

As you are changing your lifestyle, know our Lord is walking with you every step of the way. Know that God's ways have a divine purpose. *"My thoughts are nothing like your thoughts," says the Lord. "And my ways are far beyond anything you could imagine (Isaiah 55:8).* God has a plan for your life. If you allow Him, He will use your trials to show you His glory. Do not be afraid to go to our Lord and tell Him how you are feeling. Share your fears with Him. He understands. Remember, He is fully human and fully God. Lay it all out before Him. You do not have to be afraid of sharing your innermost thoughts because He already knows them. Share with God what changes are hard for you and where you need guidance. Then, trust Him. By changing your lifestyle to better honor, you will have a testimony to share with others and draw you closer to God.

How often do we tell other people to let God be in control? He knows what He is doing. God sees the big picture. Yet, when it comes to our lives, we somehow think differently. Let us follow our own advice. Once we give God our problems, we should be able to trust that He will get us through difficult times.

The only way we can relinquish control is to submit ourselves to the Lord. Submission can be a scary word. Many of us think submission means losing control. In actuality, when we submit to God, we allow Him to take charge of our lives. We admit God knows what He is doing and can help us improve our lifestyle, which enables us to be free. We no longer have to fight to change what is happening in our world because we can accept it and trust that God will get us through the challenges we face. God will give us the strength we need to fight the battles. *'For the Lord your God is going with you! He will fight for you against your enemies, and he will give you victory' (Deuteronomy 20:4)!* Our Lord will provide us with the peace to be able to think clearly and heed His direction. *The Lord gives his people strength. The Lord blesses them with peace (Psalm 29:11).*

How do you describe submission?

Read the following verses and paraphrase them.

James 4:7

Job 22:21

1 Peter 5:6

After reading these verses, how do you see that submitting to God is a blessing?

Faith is powerful when we utilize it. Our faith makes our footings firm. By having firm footings, we can erect a stable foundation by building a relationship with God, our Father that helps us to trust and believe His Word. God knew that we could not face the challenges of this world alone, and He knew there would be times when we would be at a loss as to how to pray to our Father. He gave us a secret weapon to combat our doubt and fears by allowing the Holy Spirit to be our anchor bolts. These bolts strengthen our faith, enabling us to build a stable relationship with our Lord. This relationship enables us to submit our lives to God. *And the Spirit of the LORD will rest on him-the Spirit of wisdom and understanding, the Spirit of counsel and might, the Spirit of knowledge and the fear of the LORD (Isaiah 11:2).*

Most of us do not utilize the Holy Spirit in our lives. We have heard sermons about His power, and yet we do not allow the Spirit to help us take control of our lives. The more we know our God, the more we know of His love. Our external walls are then sturdy to help us deal with the challenges of life. Knowing God loves us, supports us, and wants the best for us gives us the strength to make changes. The more time we take to make sure the outside of our temples are solid, the better our quality of life will become. When our outside is secure, we will find the strength to remodel the inside of our temple so that we can live a healthier life emotionally, physically, and spiritually. It all starts with the footings.

Changing your lifestyle can cause stress. You have disrupted your routine to establish a new one. When challenged, choose to look to God and submit to His will to restore your peace. Your stress level will decrease when God is in control. At times fear may get the best of you, but when you give your worries to God, He will get you through. Many unexpected blessings will be given to you. *Be joyful in hope, patient in affliction, faithful in prayer (Romans 12:12 NIV).* Once you start investing time and effort into building a relationship with God Jesus and the Holy Spirit, you will experience peace and joy amidst the trials. *And this righteousness will bring peace. Yes, it will bring quietness and confidence forever. My people will live in safety, quietly at home. They will be at rest (Isaiah 32:17-18 NLT).*

Food for thought:

1. How does prayer help you deal with fear and anxiety?

2. Do you turn to prayer as your first line of defense? If not, what do you do first when you are worried?

3. What Bible verses give you comfort during these times?

4. Think about your journey so far. What blessings have you seen? (Take some time to think about this. There may have been some blessings you have overlooked because you allowed stress to control your life.) I urge you to keep a diary of these blessings. One day you may want to share them with others who are struggling.

5. How can you use this time to bring others to Christ?

6. Do you see how your temple is coming together?

Journal your thoughts.

THE INTERIOR WALLS
(BOUNDARIES)

Walls within a building set the boundaries of each area. The sanctuary is separated from the vestibule by the walls. Depending on the placement of the wall, it can be load bearing or non-load bearing. A load bearing wall is part of the structure of the building and offers support. A non-load bearing wall is only a partition. Walls can provide security when a person is within the confines of the room.

Nugget of the day: *Dear brothers and sisters, if another believer is overcome by some sin, you who are godly should gently and humbly help that person back onto the right path. And be careful not to fall into the same temptation yourself. Share each other's burdens, and in this way obey the law of Christ. If you think you are too important to help someone, you are only fooling yourself. You are not that important. Pay careful attention to your own work, for then you will get the satisfaction of a job well done, and you won't need to compare yourself to anyone else. For we are each responsible for our own conduct* (Galatians 6:1-5).

While studying this verse, I gained more insight as to the true meaning of carrying one another's burdens. We often get so wrapped up in trying to help someone else that we lose sight of our responsibilities. Usually, we try to change a person or try to solve the problem for them, but this is not what we are supposed to do. We should allow each person to fight their own battles and solve their problems because these situations draw the person closer to and teach them to rely on God. When we try and step in and be the "savior," we can deter the person from looking to the real Savior. We are to be a support system for people. We can help point them in the right direction, and we can let them know when they are going down the wrong path. We all have our challenges in life, and when we assume someone else's, it can be overwhelming. We can lose focus in our lives and not complete our callings.

My prayer is that you realize we are not responsible for other people's problems or actions. I pray that when you encounter someone who needs assistance or is going down the wrong path, you first go to God in prayer to determine your role in helping them. God can give you the insight you cannot get on your own. We are to assist one another, but we cannot fix them. I also pray that you release yourself from any guilt you carry from not "fixing" another person's problem. When faced with helping another person, point them in the right direction and help them to look to the One who can help them. Also, do not to place your burdens on another person. If you have trouble letting go of another person's struggles, go to God tonight and ask Him to give you clarity as to how to deal with the situation. Release the other person to God. It is exhausting trying to be someone we cannot be. We have enough on our plate just dealing with our own lives. Likewise, instead of looking forward to others to fix your life, look up to our Lord and Savior who can heal you, guide you, and help you succeed.
****

When a builder remodels a temple and wants to remove a wall, he first has to determine whether on not the wall is load bearing. If it is, he needs to take the appropriate measures to secure the beams above it. Otherwise, when he removes the wall, the roof could cave in on him.

The walls of your temple establish boundaries so that you do not become overwhelmed by other people's problems, take on jobs that are not yours to accept, lose your own identity, or frustrate yourself trying to control things you cannot change. There are two types of walls in our temples: load bearing and non-load bearing.

The load bearing walls are our responsibilities and needs that have to be met. Sometimes these responsibilities include taking care of ourselves, family, assisting aging parents, running a household, holding down a job, and being a good spouse. We cannot remove the load bearing walls or our temples will fall.

The non-load bearing walls are the needs and responsibilities of others or extra responsibilities we add to our lives. At times these responsibilities can be delegated to others or even eliminated. It is imperative we maintain our load bearing walls first and then address the issues of the non-load bearing walls. We frequently assume responsibility for things that we should not address. We feel pressure from family members, coworkers, friends, or organizations. We feel as if we say no or wait until our needs are met to help others, we are not good parents, friends, or coworkers. People have a way of making others feel guilty when they say no to a particular task or do not accept a volunteer job. There are times we put other people's needs ahead of ours and, in doing so, cause chaos in our lives. Family members know how to make us feel guilty when we want alone time, to go out with friends, or to spend time on a hobby. For many, being able to admit we cannot volunteer for or take on another job is difficult. It may make us feel weak, or like we are not a team player. We can feel cruel or uncaring by not stepping in to help someone else or making time for ourselves. Therefore, we do not set boundaries.

At times, being unable to say no limits your ability to fulfill your role in the body of Christ. When you don't set boundaries, people can take advantage of you and add so much pressure on your life that you cannot accomplish your work. We all have people in our lives who want us to fix everything for them or to do their jobs. Even when they see that we are busy taking care of our business, they want us to stop and help them. Sometimes their requests are legitimate, and they need our assistance. There are times we must step in and help another person, be a support for them, or get them through a difficult time. Other times, they are avoiding the task, or they are too dependent on us to take on their own responsibilities. At these times, our stepping in enables them. You should recognize when a person truly needs your help or when they have an unhealthy dependency on you. Many of us know when we need to step in and help someone and when we should step back and let the person handle the situation. Therefore, it is essential to build boundaries into our temples. We need to know it is okay to say no when we are overwhelmed or need a break and tell someone else that their responsibilities are not your responsibilities.

We too, can overstep our boundaries. There are times we put too much pressure on ourselves. Being a parent, working a job, and being involved in extracurricular activities can cause chaos in our lives. Trying to keep up with the neighbors or another parent can put unrealistic expectations on us. Accepting that we are not supermoms or dads, that our jobs are not our entire lives, or that we do not have to volunteer for every job at our church, work, or school can be very freeing. It is healthy for you to recognize your limits and know when you cannot take on another responsibility. It is also all right for you to have quiet time when you are not doing anything or for you to do something you enjoy. It is in your best interest for family members to see that your life is valuable, and sometimes you come first. If you do not establish boundaries for yourself, others will continue to take advantage of you.

Parents have an added burden not only to try and help meet the needs of their spouse but also their children. Without setting clear boundaries with their children, they can interfere too much, prohibiting them from growing into responsible young adults. Parents can teach their children to be dependent on them rather than realize they can be in control. Rather than teaching their children to pray and seek God, the parent tries to handle all their problems. As adults, these children will continue to be needy and emotionally drain the parents. The children will not recognize that their parents have a life too and need help every once in a while. Parents need to know it is all right to say no to their children. Children need to know parents have needs and responsibilities that also need to be met, which also teaches the children how to transition into adulthood and set their boundaries. Parents do their children a disservice by letting them think they are the most important people in the family. As they grow into adulthood, they will often continue to put themselves first and not acknowledge others' wants and needs. They will continue to demand attention even when they are capable of doing things for themselves. Not teaching children to turn to God in prayer for guidance takes away from them developing a relationship with God.

Spouses can learn helplessness when we do not relinquish some of the responsibilities of our household to them. Initially, saying no to unrealistic demands or asking for help when needed is difficult. After the first few times, when you see how it frees you up to meet your needs and to take care of your responsibilities, you will be more confident in saying no when appropriate.

To live a healthy life, you need to establish boundaries for yourself as well as for others. Do you acknowledge you have needs and set boundaries with your spouse and children? Explain.

Instead of enabling another person, try to empower them. Encourage them to address their problems. Give them examples or demonstrate how you handle situations. If their needs are beyond your scope, direct them to a pastor, counselor, or someone who is equipped to help them. By doing so, you do not take on the responsibility of making their changes, but you are a support system.

You must remember that your strength does not come from yourself, but God. The best way to find the strength to deal with your problems is to pray for guidance. You can ask the Holy Spirit to let you know when to intervene with another person and when to step back. Recognize that your job is to please God. In pleasing God, you may not always have the approval of another person. You have a role to fulfill, and God will help you do this. Lean on God as you learn to be assertive and set your boundaries.

Just as you had to learn to lean on God, it is imperative others do too. The best way to help another person make changes in their life is to pray for them and guide them toward God. We can thank God for putting them in our lives, acknowledge their struggles, ask God to guide them, and help them find the strength to improve their lives.

In what areas do you have trouble setting boundaries?

How does this hinder following your calling or improving your lifestyle?

Who do you feel responsible for in your life, and how does this feeling stand in the way of you changing your lifestyle?

In what areas do you need to release control of others?

Giving too much of ourselves to others can burn us out so that we are not helpful to anyone or ourselves. The work we do becomes sloppy and incomplete. Instead of trying to help everyone and assume everyone else's responsibility, we need to release this control to God and let Him help them in the manner He sees fit. After all, God knows His children, and He knows how to help them much better than we do.

How can you relinquish the control of others to God?

When you try and control another person, or make changes for them, you can become a hindrance in their life. When people tend to rely on you to give them advice or do their work, they never find their inner strength. More importantly, you hinder their relationship with God because they become dependent on you rather than God.

How does your support for this person limit them from becoming the person they could become?

Take some time to pray for this person now and ask God to help you encourage them. By letting go of the added stress in your life, you can continue to grow and make the healthy changes you need to address.

Just as we cannot control another person, we should not let someone else control us. We often allow those we love to influence how we handle our circumstances and the way we see and address various issues. This influence is often a significant deterrent when we try to make healthy changes in our lives. People interfere for several reasons. People feel threatened when we make changes, and they do not. They are afraid that if we make changes, we will become more independent and they will lose any control they think they have over us. Some people cannot find happiness, so they like it when others are just as miserable as themselves. For others, when they see us living unhealthy lifestyles, it helps them to justify their unhealthy habits. Using the following verse, examine the motives of someone who appears to be trying to control us. *Love is patient and kind. Love is not jealous or boastful or proud or rude. It does not demand its own way. It is not irritable, and it keeps no record of being wronged (1 Corinthians 13:4-5).*

I often hear people say they cannot make changes in their lives because family members are unwilling to make the same changes in their lives as well. This is going to be the case frequently. Most family members will not buy into your new lifestyle. Although they do not choose to make these changes now, it does not mean our loved ones will not follow this path later in life. At this time, they are just not ready. After they witness the changes in our lives, they might see how much healthier we are and how much better we feel. It is at this time that they may decide that they too want to live a healthy lifestyle.

How do family members control your life or influence your decisions?

How does this keep you from living the lifestyle you know you should be living?

How does their control contradict 1 Corinthians 13:4-5?

You should realize that you do not need the approval of others. When someone compliments you, it feels good. However, you should not allow this to be the driving force behind your behavior. Once you realize it is God you need to please and not people, it frees you to live up to your full potential. How has criticism limited your ability to change your lifestyle?

We all see things from a different perspective, so what might be suitable for one may not work for another. God, on the other hand, knows His children and He knows what they need. When you finally realize it is God alone you should want to please, you take the pressure off yourself. Trying to please others can be tiring. No one can please everyone all the time. Every person has different expectations as to what pleases them. God is consistent. When we know His Word, we know His expectations.

I have realized this in my job that requires me to visit several locations. Trying to please many supervisors can be tiring. They each have different expectations, and they also each have their flaws. To satisfy each supervisor, I would have to change how I performed my job at each location. When I finally came to the realization that I work to please God, this took the pressure to please each supervisor off of me. I know God's expectations, and I know what is morally and ethically the right way to work. When I am doing my best to please God, I am trying to adhere to a higher standard because I enjoy doing my Father's will. *For none of us lives for ourselves alone, and none of us dies for ourselves alone. If we live, we live for the Lord; and if we die, we die for the Lord. So, whether we live or die, we belong to the Lord. For we will all stand before God's judgment seat. It is written: "'As surely as I live,' says the Lord, 'every knee will bow before me; every tongue will acknowledge God.'" So then, each of us will give an account of ourselves to God* (Romans 14:7-8,11-12 NIV).

There is an inner peace that comes when you no longer live for another person's approval. This peace enables you not to take their criticism personally. You can spend more time focusing on the positive comments rather than the negative ones you hear. Often a person hears only the negative, but you do yourself a grave injustice when this happens because you never truly appreciate your accomplishments or enjoy your success. When you hear a negative comment, look for any truth in the response and use that piece to better your life, and release the hurtful aspect.

When you are going to offer someone else advice, be mindful of how you speak to them. Words have power, and they can build up or tear down a person. Try to model your life after Christ. Before saying anything, determine whether or not your words will help or hurt. A good guideline to use is Galatians 5:22-23. *But the fruit of the Spirit is love, joy, peace, forbearance, kindness, goodness, faithfulness, gentleness, and self-control. Against such things there is no law* (NIV). Speaking your mind often feels right at the moment, but later, these same words may come back to haunt you after they are spoken, causing regret and anxiety.

Jesus knew to set boundaries. He knew when He needed to retreat to spend time with His Father (Matthew 6:6). Jesus made sure His needs were met first so that He could better serve God and His followers. When Jesus faced the pressures of this world, He sought God's advice. He recognized that God was the One He needed to please (John 5:44). Jesus stood up for what He believed and did not let others dissuade Him from going about His business (Matthew 16:23).

How does knowing Jesus set boundaries encourage you to do the same?

- Set boundaries for others and yourself. Setting these boundaries will make your temple more pleasing to God. What are some of these boundaries?
- When you say no, mean it.
- When asked to do something that goes against your lifestyle change, you need to stay the course you have set for yourself.
- When you know someone is capable of dealing with their problem or situation, you need to step back and let them.
- If a person tears you down or does not respect your decisions, you need to take a break from that relationship.
- Let others assume responsibility for their own actions.
- Do not let anyone or anything interfere with your relationship with your loving Father or fulfilling your calling.

At this time in your life, if you are attempting to make changes in your lifestyle, your focus should be on you. Eating right, getting adequate sleep, relaxing, and exercising are essential to staying healthy and require an investment of your time. You will not see improvements in these areas if you do not make the time to deal with them. Set your boundaries and let others know that you are addressing your needs. As you adopt a healthier lifestyle, you will find you will have more energy to help those that need it. Do not feel guilty that at this time you are the person whose needs you are addressing.

Food for thought:

1. Has reviewing this material taken any pressure off of you so that you can focus on your needs? How has this helped you?

2. Why are establishing boundaries important?

3. What are some boundaries you need to establish in your life?

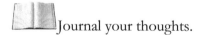Journal your thoughts.

THE CEILING
(YOUR ATTITUDE)

The ceiling in our temple has to be well planned because it can change the atmosphere of the sanctuary. Many temples have vaulted ceilings, which make the room look larger and feel airy. The ceilings can be inspirational and uplifting with painted murals or beautiful architectural designs.

Nugget of the day: Give thanks to him who killed the firstborn of Egypt. His faithful love endures forever. He brought Israel out of Egypt. His faithful love endures forever. He acted with a strong hand and powerful arm. His faithful love endures forever *(Psalm 136:10-12)*.

We always have something for which we can be thankful. At times, we may have to make an effort to see our blessings because we are in the midst of a storm- but even then, we receive blessings. The Israelites overlooked many of their blessings because all they could focus on was what they did not have. The Israelites' negativity cost them the Promised Land. Their offspring received the gift that they forfeited since they were so focused on grumbling. They had many signs and witnessed many miracles, and yet all they could do was complain? God parted the Red Sea, delivered them from slavery, their shoes did not wear out, rocks provided water, and they were supplied with food daily. Still, they chose to remain focused on the negative.

My prayer is that you realize you receive blessings every day from our God. Focus on these blessings instead of your problems. Most of the time we will realize our storms are light showers when we change our attitude and look at the positive rather than the negative. Even in our darkest days, we miss many blessings when we do not open our eyes and hearts to see them. You do not want to miss your promised lands because you grumble too much. You have a lot at stake, so you must choose: do you complain or do you count your blessings?

****

When the architect designs the temple, he places much emphasis on the dimensions of the ceiling. There are many factors to be considered. Many people congregate inside the church that causes the place to get warm. If the ceilings are high, the hot air will rise to make the people more comfortable. The acoustics are also affected by the ceiling, and because good worship is essential to a service, the ceiling needs to accommodate this need. Most importantly, a high ceiling in a church acknowledges the awesomeness of God and declares God's house is the most important building in the town. Tall ceilings can make a person feel small, allowing them to see how big and powerful God is in their lives.

No one wants their temple to feel closed in and confining. Our attitude is like the ceiling. People love to walk into a beautiful church and stand in awe of the ceiling and how uplifting it can be. They love to look up toward Heaven and see the splendor. The ceiling can change the entire atmosphere of the sanctuary. Looking up in our temples will point us to God, and if we keep our eyes fixed on God, He can change our attitude and help us see things more positively leading us to live lives that reflect Him. *For God is working in you, giving you the desire and the power to do what pleases him. Do everything without complaining and arguing, so that no one can criticize you. Live clean, innocent lives as children of God, shining like bright lights in a world full of crooked and perverse people. Hold firmly to the word of life; then, on the day of Christ's return, I will be proud that I did not run the race in vain and that my work was not useless. But I will rejoice even if I lose my life, pouring it out like a liquid offering to God, just like your faithful service is an offering to God. And I want all of you to share that joy. Yes, you should rejoice, and I will share your joy* (Philippians 2:13-18 NIV).

When we have a positive attitude, we can see the good in our lives, work through struggles, and be intent on winning the battle. We can see how God uses various challenges and struggles to draw us closer to Him. On the other hand, when we allow negativity to guide our lives, not only will our relationships with others suffer, but also our relationship with God. When a temple has negative energy, a person will find it hard to find comfort in this place. By having a ceiling in our temple that helps to restore the positive energy one needs, we will be able to draw closer to God. Gaze at the ceiling of your temple often and reassess how you are living your life. *A cheerful heart is good medicine, but a broken spirit saps a person's strength (Proverbs 17:22).*

The brain is the powerful control center of the body. Our thinking, whether it is positive or negative, can assist or hinder our lives, improve our health, and alter the way we look at life. Too often, we do not allow the brain to work to its full capacity because we put limits on what it can do. There are many ways we can enhance how our brain functions. We can use prayer, positive thinking, and visualization. When we attempt to make changes in our lives, we need to enlist all the resources at our disposal.

Keeping a positive attitude does not mean we deny the challenges or difficult times in our lives. Positive thinkers admit they have battles, but they plan to win them. They do not let others fill their heads with defeating thoughts. At times, doubts may creep in, but the difference between positive and negative people is that positive thinkers may allow themselves a moment of self-pity and then they will use prayer, self-talk, or visualization to change their attitude, and then they move forward. They will once again be ready to fight and persevere. Negative people let negative thoughts define their lives, and even though they may have good intentions, they always seem to focus on the downside of life.

Making changes in your lifestyle is no different. You have to decide how you are going to look at these changes. When you see that these changes are right for you, you will see the value of exercising and eating right. You will want to establish boundaries and find peace. When you understand their importance, you will find the time to address these changes. When you view the work needed to make changes as a burden, you will find it hard to incorporate the changes in your life. You may even make excuses as to why you cannot exercise or try to justify your poor eating habits. Being positive, looking for, and celebrating the small changes that occur gives you the motivation to keep working rather than giving up.

Positive thinking is nothing new. The Bible has given you many verses to help you keep a positive attitude in your everyday living or when faced with the unexpected challenge. God knows you will face challenges at some point in time so He has given you guidance on how to handle these situations. God looks at things differently than you do and sees these challenging times as teachable moments. These moments will help define where you are in your Christian walk. *Consider it pure joy, my brothers and sisters, whenever you face trials of many kinds, because you know that the testing of your faith produces perseverance. Let perseverance finish its work so that you may be mature and complete, not lacking anything (James 1:2-4).*

When you face a trial, you have a choice. You can accept the challenge and use it to bring you closer to God, learn how to deal with adversity, and let God's glory shine through you, or you can allow the challenge to hinder or destroy you. *And we know that God causes everything to work together for the good of those who love God and are called according to his purpose for them (Romans 8:28).* For many, the very thing we thought would break us makes us stronger. We develop better coping skills, grow in faith, and become stronger people.

If you accept Christ as your Savior and believe the Bible is the ultimate Word of God, then you must trust that God has a plan for your life. God is using this period of your life as you work to improve your lifestyle to bring you closer to Him, which is a mark of an excellent father. God knows what is best for you, and He will stand by you as you go through this challenge and will show His glory throughout, always remaining faithful. Remaining positive and staying the course will bring you many blessings: having more energy, being in better physical shape, having a stronger faith, and experiencing a happier life.

What negative thoughts inhibit your ability to make lifestyle changes?

How can you retrain your brain to think positively about these issues?

The Bible cautions us to "lean not on our own understanding." We only have a small glimpse of God's plan. We only see the present. We do not know what tomorrow will bring, so we need to trust God, who sees the whole picture, to guide us through to the end. *Trust in the LORD with all your heart and lean not on your own understanding; in all your ways submit to him, and he will make your paths straight (Proverbs 3:5-6 NIV).*

Look up the following Bible verses about trials and record what they mean to you personally.

Psalm 91:1-2:

Romans 8:38-39:

1 Peter 1:6-9:

If you are going to accept God's truths, then you also need to remember that there will be blessings as you go through these trials. Allow God to work in your life, and you will see His glory. Keep your eyes, ears, and heart open to these blessings, or you may miss them. Some blessings are subtle, such as a beautiful sunrise greeting you after a difficult night. Maybe it is a friend calling at just the right moment to offer words of encouragement. You may stumble upon the perfect Bible verse when you feel you are not strong enough to make changes or face trials. In 2 Corinthians 6:3-10, Paul tells us how he saw the good in his struggles and was able to share his faith and help bring others to Christ. *We live in such a way that no one will stumble because of us, and no one will find fault with our ministry. In everything we do, we show that we are true ministers of God. We patiently endure troubles and hardships and calamities of every kind. We have been beaten, been put in prison, faced angry mobs, worked to exhaustion, endured sleepless nights, and gone without food. We prove ourselves by our purity, our understanding, our patience, our kindness, by the Holy Spirit within us and by our sincere love. We faithfully preach the truth. God's power is working in us. We use the weapons of righteousness in the right hand for attack and the left hand for defense. We serve God whether people honor us or despise us, whether they slander us or praise us. We are honest, but they call us impostors. We are ignored, even though we are well known. We live close to death, but we are still alive. We have been beaten, but we have not been killed. Our hearts ache, but we always have joy. We are poor, but we give spiritual riches to others. We own nothing, and yet we have everything.*

When you keep a positive outlook, you will find good no matter what stage of your life you are currently experiencing. In the Bible, Paul freely admits he faced struggles. He recognized these struggles were bringing him closer to his God. Paul found joy in his salvation and in knowing He would spend eternity in God's presence.

What blessings has God given you this past week? If none come to mind, take some time to reflect on your week.

We live in a cynical world. All one has to do is read a newspaper, watch the news, look at Facebook, or spend time listening to the conversation of others. People love to outdo one another when sharing their troubles and woes and seem to enjoy sharing negative gossip about others. Seldom do we hear praise reports, rejoice in other's accomplishments, or hear the good works others are doing. Let us try to put an end to all our negative talk and start looking for the good in others and ourselves. By doing so, we take hold of our thoughts. Let's allow our lights to shine amid the challenges and find the courage to rejoice as we endure trials.

In the same way, let your good deeds shine out for all to see, so that everyone will praise your heavenly Father (Matthew 5:16). We all have the ability to experience life to its fullest. Be grateful for the opportunities life presents and look for the blessings hidden within life's challenges. *For you are all children of the light and of the day; we don't belong to darkness and night. So be on your guard, not asleep like the others. Stay alert and be clearheaded (1 Thessalonians 5:5-6).*

Food for thought:

1. How does it make you feel when you realize God is in charge?

2. What holds you back from submitting your life to God?

3. When you allow God to be in control of your life, do you find peace?

25

4. What are some of the positive outcomes you will witness in your life when you improve your lifestyle and live healthier?

5. Take some time to contemplate these verses and then write a prayer to God asking for strength to endure, eyes to see good in others and the ability to maintain a positive attitude each day. *The LORD is my strength and my defense; he has become my salvation. Shouts of joy and victory resound in the tents of the righteous: "The LORD's right hand has done mighty things! The LORD's right hand is lifted high; the LORD's right hand has done mighty things"* (Psalm 118:14-16 NIV)!

Journal your thoughts.

Week 2

Day 1: Review Bible Verses
Day 2: The Sanctuary (Restoring Peace)
Day 3: Laying the Floor (Letting Go of Strongholds)
Day 4: The Vestibule (Contentment)
Day 5: The Chapel (Rest)

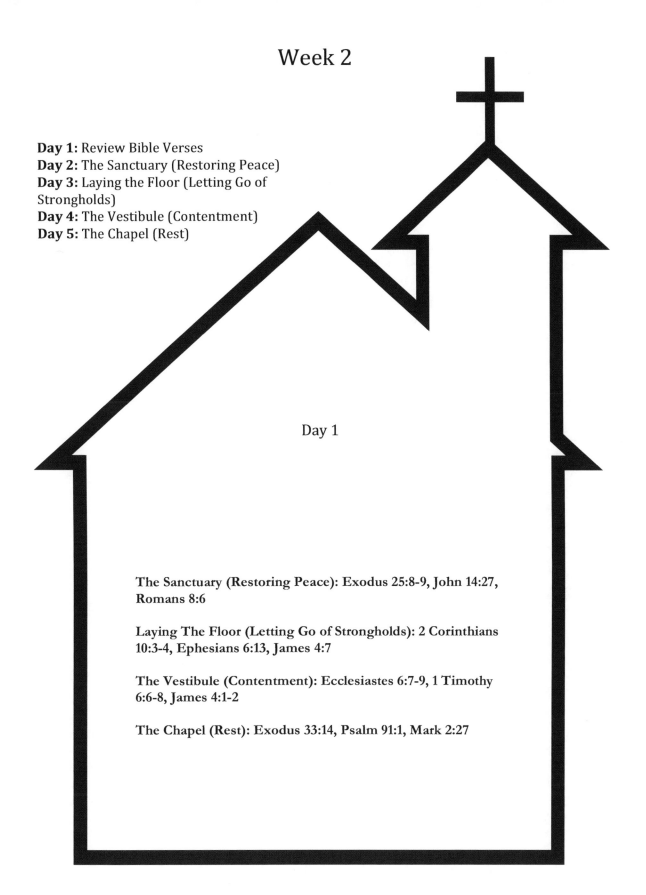

Day 1

The Sanctuary (Restoring Peace): Exodus 25:8-9, John 14:27, Romans 8:6

Laying The Floor (Letting Go of Strongholds): 2 Corinthians 10:3-4, Ephesians 6:13, James 4:7

The Vestibule (Contentment): Ecclesiastes 6:7-9, 1 Timothy 6:6-8, James 4:1-2

The Chapel (Rest): Exodus 33:14, Psalm 91:1, Mark 2:27

Weekly exercise: Take some time this week to work on decreasing the stress in your life. Try to incorporate one of the techniques mentioned in this study into your daily schedule for the next week. Write how you felt about the activity afterward.

THE SANCTUARY
(RESTORING PEACE)

Every temple needs a sanctuary. It is the holiest place in the temple. A sanctuary is also a refuge or a place that offers protection.

Nugget of the day: The one thing I ask of the Lord—the thing I seek most—is to live in the house of the Lord all the days of my life, delighting in the Lord's perfections and meditating in his Temple *(Psalm 27:4).*

Can you imagine living in God's house all your days? Life would be beautiful. Right now, we may not be in the physical presence of the Lord, but spiritually we can be. We can experience life as God intended for us to live. We all have a choice as to how we live our lives. When we choose to live a fast-paced, hectic life we can lose sight of God. We can choose to slow our days down and experience God. When we decide to live according to God's Word, our lives become less stressful. We can calm our lives by sitting in God's presence and meditating on His Word as we hear Him speak to us and guide us. We can focus on the good and count our blessings instead of focusing on the things we cannot control. We can speak words of encouragement instead of being critical and reach out and help others instead of focusing on ourselves. We can ask God to accompany us throughout our day and have Him in our house.

My prayer is that you make spending time in God's presence your priority. There are so many things you can do throughout your day to stay connected to God and live a less stressful life. You have a choice. You can choose to live a life of kindness and giving, or you can let your world be self-centered. Each time you model your life after Jesus' life, you move a little closer to the house of the Lord.

✱✱

Every temple has a sanctuary, as it is a holy place that is set aside for worshipping God. God directed Moses to build a sanctuary where He could dwell among the people (Exodus 25:8-9). From the beginning of time, God wanted to interact with His people as the original sanctuary was the Garden of Eden in which God walked (Genesis 3:8). God had specific requirements for building and maintaining His sanctuaries so that He could reside in them. A sanctuary is also a place for people to go when they need protection.

We all need a place where we can go and find peace. Our sanctuary is the place where the Holy Spirit resides. This place needs to be a peaceful and comforting place so that we can hear the Holy Spirit speak to us. This should be a place where we can stop, take deep breaths, and relax while spending time in the Word of God. *Don't you realize that all of you together are the temple of God and that the Spirit of God lives in you (1Corinthians 3:16)?* When we allow stress to control our lives, it disrupts our peace, and our lives can be in turmoil. Stress can make it hard to hear the Holy Spirit speak to and can prevent us from spending time in God's Word.

Everyone experiences stress. No one is exempt from it, and it affects each person differently. How people deal with stress can have a significant effect on their overall health and quality of life. Stress in life can be from external sources such as the environment, our lifestyles, or from relationships with other people. There are also internal sources that cause stress such as illness, worry, anger, unforgiveness, poor behaviors, or negative attitude. People handle stress in a variety of ways, and it can affect both the mind and body. The body responds to stress by releasing hormones that increase blood pressure, heart rate, and can raise blood sugar levels. The neural pathways of the brain can be damaged or the brain may shrink by too much stress. These changes in the brain affect emotions, memory, and the ability to think rationally.

There are two main types of stress: acute and chronic stress. Acute stress is temporary and can be beneficial. It has the potential of being exhilarating when in small amounts or exhausting when too much. We experience this type of stress when we are in danger or when we challenge ourselves. It allows us to activate the fight or flight response so that we can meet deadlines, get a competitive edge such as in sports or workplace and get thrills out of life such as riding a roller coaster or downhill skiing. This type of stress is also called an adrenaline rush.

The second type is chronic stress. This kind of pressure is the most detrimental to the body because it is ongoing and may cause a person to think they have little hope of things changing. Chronic stress takes a toll mentally and emotionally as well as physically. People who experience chronic stress typically get so used to it that they never deal with it. They let this type of stress follow them throughout life and do not understand why they are always tired, cranky, or have trouble focusing. Chronic stress can also cause problems with fertility, increased muscle tightness, pain, digestive and urinary systems, weight gain, sleep, heart problems, depression, and the immune system.

Acute stress can boost our immune system, but chronic stress can weaken it. When our immune system is weak, the body cannot defend itself from germs or illnesses. A study by Meridian Stress Management Consultancy in the UK reports almost 180,000 people die a year from stress-related illnesses. In the United States, emotional stress is a major contributing factor in deaths from six areas: cancer, heart disease, respiratory disorders, cirrhosis of the liver, suicide, and accidental deaths. [1]

Stress builds up in a person as they go through life with its many responsibilities, challenges, and struggles. Every decision, every obstacle, and even happy events have the potential to cause us stress. When we make educated choices with God's guidance, we need to trust in those decisions. Stress comes when we begin to second-guess ourselves. Attempting to make changes in our lifestyle and alter our habits can also add pressure to our lives. If we do not recognize this and address it, stress can limit our ability to make necessary changes.

Often stress can cause us to resort to "comfort foods" or to eat more frequently as we attempt to take our minds off of what is worrying us. Eating this way adds to our stress level. While we are trying to make changes, it is imperative that the body remains strong to not compound our problems. As we embark on our journey, our bodies and minds need to be prepared to fight the battles we will encounter as we attempt to make changes. We do not want to make these changes harder by adding undue stress. We want the body to run like a well-oiled machine, and it cannot do this if we allow stress to control our lives. Letting stress have control causes us to be run down physically, spiritually, emotionally, and mentally, straining our relationship with God.

In what areas of your life does stress play a role?

If you are affected by stress, what are some of the symptoms you experience?

How do you deal with this stress?

How does stress alter your relationship with God?

You should recognize how stress affects your body. From my own experiences, I know how it affected my body. My muscles in my shoulders and back were in constant spasm, which caused chronic pain. I held my breath, and it wasn't until after I had gone through the cancer treatment that I realized I had forgotten how to take a refreshing breath. I woke up after a night's sleep groggy and not well rested - the "what ifs" kept me awake. Stress took the peace and joy out of my life. I was so focused on all that I had to do and all my problems that I forgot to keep my eyes on the One who could restore that peace and joy. Rather than spending time in God's Word and believing His truths, I believed what the world was telling me. I would let people's opinions and actions change how I felt about things. I spent many sleepless nights worrying about things I had no control of and often would never come true.

"Be careful, or your hearts will be weighed down with carousing, drunkenness and the anxieties of life, and that day will close on you suddenly like a trap (Luke 21:34 NIV). We should take stress more seriously and recognize how it manifests in our own bodies rather than letting it control our lives. By having tactics in place to deal with stress, you can keep it from wreaking havoc in your life. To relieve stress, I have found the following strategies to be beneficial:

- Remind yourself to breathe deep cleansing breaths.
- Focus on relaxing your tense muscles. (This is addressed in a later chapter)
- Use positive self-talk to remove negative thoughts.
- Rehearse beforehand how you can handle a stressful situation you are going to face.
- When dealing with others, stay calm, speak in a quiet tone, keep your composure if there is disagreement, and maintain a relaxed posture.

- Stay in God's Word and use it as a weapon. Seek His guidance.
- Exercise regularly. While exercising, listen to praise music to keep your mind from wandering and focusing on your struggles.

As you can see, the best way to deal with stress is by trusting God to help us handle our problems. We have to be able to use His Word to ward off the stress and find comfort. When we realize God is in control, and we relinquish our worries and cares to Him, we will restore peace. When our world appears to be spinning out of control, we have lost our ability to trust that God will get us through. Trusting God takes practice. If we learn to trust God with the small things, it will be easier to give Him control over the more significant challenges. *You can make many plans, but the Lord's purpose will prevail (Proverbs 19:21).* We cannot control everything in life, but we can control how we react.

If you are going through a difficult time in your life or have just emerged from a struggle, you may have some side effects of stress. Take some time to recognize how stress is affecting your life. Answer these questions honestly.

1. Do you find yourself holding your breath or taking quick, short breaths rather than taking full breaths?
2. Do you have constant muscle tightness or keep your shoulders in shrugging position?
3. Do you have persistent or frequent headaches?
4. Do you clench or grind your teeth or have jaw tightness?
5. Do you hold your hand in a clenched fist or exhibit nervous habits?
6. Do you get aggravated by insignificant things and let them bother you all day?
7. Do you get angry quickly?
8. Do you hold grudges?
9. Do you frequently experience sleep disturbances or spend much of the night worring about things?
10. Do you feel overwhelmed, have an inability to concentrate, or feel out of control?
11. Do you find yourself withdrawing and no longer being interested in yourfavorite activities?
12. Do you have panic attacks or increased heart palpitations?

Although, understandably, that stress will be present in our lives, we will have to address it if we are going to be successful in changing our lifestyles. Here are some ways that might be helpful to lessen stress.

Identify what is causing stress in your life. It might include: the changes you are attempting to make, relationships, finances, your job, loss of free time, decreased energy, or illness. List these factors now.

Prioritize the things you need to accomplish. Focus on the things that matter the most, family, health, and career. Having lofty goals can be overwhelming. When you establish small, obtainable goals, you will be more successful in achieving them. What are some of the priorities you need to focus on at this time?

Avoid scheduling conflicts. Plan and prioritize what needs to be done each day accordingly. Make sure to take time for fellowship.

Know your limits. It is okay to say no to the demands that prevent you from making necessary changes in your life. Find time to spend with God, exercise, and prepare healthy meals. If you are fatigued, stop to rest. Not only are you helping yourself, but you are also setting a good example for your family. Are there any limits you need to set?

Ask for help. Most of the time, people are willing to help you if you would ask. When you allow the right people to be part of your life, you improve your relationships, lessen your stress, and make the journey more enjoyable.

Prioritize your finances. Finances are often a significant contributor to stress. Set up a budget and live by it. When you live within your means, you reduce the stress in your life. Spending money you do not have may be fun at that moment, but it leads to many sleepless nights of worry. By prioritizing, you will spend money on things you need and not waste your money. Instead of eating out, prepare food at home. Not only will you save money, but you will also enjoy healthier meals. Rather than go to the movies, enjoy visiting the free activities your city offers and explore parks and museums, or utilize the library and all its free resources. Also, you will have some exciting adventures, get much-needed exercise and meet new people.

1. What needs do you spend your money on (tithing, home, utilities, transportation)?

2. In what areas can you decrease your spending?

3. What can you do for fun and entertainment that will not hurt your budget?

Let go of the things you cannot control. Learn how to cope with things that cause stress in your life, such as traffic situations and changes in schedules that you cannot control. Turn these things over to God and let Him deal with them. Worrying about things only brings more stress and could make the situation worse. Worry and stress can interfere with your healthy lifestyle.

Incorporate exercise into your daily routine: Exercise produces endorphins. Endorphins are hormones that help to reduce stress, act as painkillers, improve sleep, and improve focus so that you can clearly address your problem and come up with a solution. [2] Some studies have shown that establishing a consistent exercise routine can alter our moods and help us to be more upbeat. A person does not always have time to perform a full exercise routine every day. On days when time is an essence, even five minutes of aerobic exercise can start to alter a person's mood.

Food for thought:

1. What are you worried about that you cannot control?

2. How can you handle these things when they disrupt your schedule or upset you?

3. What changes can you make to decrease stress?

4. Are there people in your life who cause you stress? What are you doing to handle this situation?

5. Give these things over to God. Write a prayer relinquishing the control of these things and ask God to guide you.

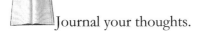Journal your thoughts.

LAYING THE FLOOR
(LETTING GO OF STRONGHOLDS)

Laying the proper floor takes skill. The floor needs to be stable so that a person can walk safely.

***Nugget of the day: All of them ate the same spiritual food, and all of them drank the same spiritual water. For they drank from the spiritual rock that traveled with them, and that rock was Christ. Yet God was not pleased with most of them, and their bodies were scattered in the wilderness** (1 Corinthians 10:3-5).*

Have you ever taken the time to think that most of us miss our promised land because we spend a significant portion of our time complaining and finding fault with our lives rather than seeing the good? God has given each of us a unique calling with special blessings, but instead of appreciating these, we often want what another person has, or we are jealous of their talents. It is up to us to accept our gifts and talents and use them for God's glory. Social media is so prevalent that it is easy to get caught up in all the negativity. All one has to do is spend some time on the Internet to see people who are unhappy with their lives and who are willing to find fault with everything and everyone. We need to rise above this. We need to take time to appreciate our lives, spend time in thanksgiving, accept our gifts and talents, and utilize them for the good of all.

My prayer is that we all live a good life here on earth and make it to our promised land. I pray you learn to see the good in life, in yourself, and in those around you. Make a conscious effort to see the blessings God has bestowed on you and take the time to enjoy them. God wants you to have good things in this life. Spend some time in thanksgiving and let God know you accept and appreciate the gifts He has given you. Your whole outlook changes when you look at your life positively. As you change your attitude, you will see doors open and will enjoy your promised land.

✴✴✴

The flooring in a temple is important. There are many factors the architect needs to consider when he decides on the material he will use. If the floor is not level, all the furniture may slide, and it can be more difficult for people to walk on as they could trip and fall. The flooring can alter the appearance of the temple. If the floor is worn, it will make the church look run down and uninviting. The material has to be durable to withstand all the wear and tear of people walking on it and tracking debris into the temple. The final consideration is its ability to be an acoustic barrier. If the floor creaks or causes an echo when walked on the noise could be a distraction to the other people in the temple.

We all need a solid ground on which to stand. *Now I stand on solid ground, and I will publicly praise the LORD (Psalm 26:12).* Our temple is no different; there needs to be a durable, level floor on which to stand. Strongholds can be either positive or negative. These strongholds can let us stand securely or stumble through life. When God is in control, and we look to Him for our stability, this is a good stronghold. Our floor is solid, and we can maneuver through our world accomplishing the plans God has set before us. When a floor is uneven or is sagging, a person will find they lose their balance and fall. When a stronghold is negative such as when we hold onto anger, guilt, shame, and stress, it can disrupt our relationship with both God and people making our floor unstable. Our instability will cause us to lose our focus. This instability will make it hard for us to find peace in our lives and fulfill our callings. Trying to stabilize ourselves, we tend to grasp for anything that we can use to try to catch our balance. When we grasp something positive such as prayer, Christian fellowship, or healthy habits, we can stabilize our lives. When we hold onto negative strongholds such as food, alcohol, or immoral behavior, we cause chaos in our lives.

What do you try and use to stabilize yourself when you feel insecure?

People who dwell on their past failures or struggles allow these things to become negative strongholds, and this enables past problems to define who they are as people. Satan knows our weaknesses, and he will use our struggles to keep us beaten down and unable to let go of our past. When we are feeling good or have successfully moved forward in our lives, Satan will remind us of past failures and try to get us to dwell on them rather than our successes. We are no threat to the devil when we are struggling. He knows that when we are fighting internal battles, it makes it hard for us to advance the Kingdom of God. Satan knows that when we feel unclean on the inside, we will be less likely to clean up our physical body. He loves to tell us we are not capable of being successful, are unlovable, or that we have no self-worth. All of these are LIES. We know that Satan is the master of lies and deceit.

If you are going to release these strongholds, you will need a structurally sound external temple. Only when you look to God to define who you are and develop a relationship with Him, will you be able to shed your negative self-image and see yourself as God sees you. When you dwell in God's presence and stay in His Word, He can shed light on who you indeed are and how valuable you are to Him. You are not fighting worldly battles, you are fighting spiritual battles, and thus you must arm yourself with the right weapons if you are going to be victorious. (2 Corinthians 10:3-5) God has provided this weaponry for you in the form of His Word. His Word is more powerful than Satan's lies. Learn to correctly use this weaponry if you are going to be victorious.

Your brain is a sophisticated computer, and it is programmable. Every time someone criticizes you, your brain retains this data. Each time you think an unkind thought about yourself, the mind processes this information. The key to letting go of the harmful strongholds is to fill your mind with God's Word. Continue to combat and replace the negative data with the positive. *You must have the same attitude that Christ Jesus had (Philippians 2:5)*. You cannot stop all the information from getting into your brain, but you can quickly replace it with the word of God.

Not all strongholds are from Satan. At times we can be our own worst enemy. When we hold onto hurt, guilt, and shame, or let anger control us, they become our negative strongholds. These emotions can also limit our ability to change unhealthy habits and see the good in life. Learning to change our attitude in response to stress, anger, shame, guilt, and unforgiveness is a lifelong project. We all have to deal with these issues at some point in our lives. When you allow these emotions to control us, our bodies are in a constant state of alertness and are working overtime. The body is in a continuous guarded position causing the muscles to tighten up. Your temple will be in disarray if you do not address these issues. Here are some techniques to help calm the body and fight the strongholds. Along with prayer and using God's Word, there are ways to relax your body and rid it of stress so that you can focus more easily on the Word.

Pray without ceasing. Prayer has a calming effect on your mind and body. Use prayer in every situation. When you let God be part of your solution, you will have a more positive attitude. Trusting God and knowing that He is in control and has a plan for you, will allow you to see His glory. Including God in your everyday life and spending time in His Word helps to hear Him speak to you and draw you closer to Him. God alone can give you the peace and joy you desire in life. Remaining in contact with your Creator will allow Him to nourish you and give you the strength to get through difficult times. *"Yes, I am the vine; you are the branches. Those who remain in me, and I in them, will produce much fruit. For apart from me you can do nothing"(John 15:5)*.

Do you see Jesus as your vine, and how do you allow Him to nourish you?

Practice meditating on God's Word. Meditation is a way to focus the mind on one thing and has to be practiced to be effective. It is best when done for short periods of time at first, then expanded upon as you become more comfortable with the technique. Prepare a quiet place removed from all distractions. Sit or lie down in a comfortable position and be able to maintain this position throughout the session. You can find meditation programs on the Internet as well as CD's to use in your home. While meditating, it is an excellent time to practice listening to God: *"Be still, and know that I am God" (Psalm 46:10)*. Spend time reading and rereading Bible verses until you know them by heart. By thinking about each verse and memorizing them, when stress starts to creep into your life, you can call them to mind.

Appreciate change. Look for positive changes that are occurring. They do not have to be large ones. Enjoy the small changes that will lead to the big ones. Look at the positive things you have accomplished: you passed on an unhealthy food even though you wanted to eat it, exercised when you wanted to watch television, or you felt more energized on a particular day. Take time to meditate on how your life has changed since you began this journey. Sometimes you need to make time to think about the changes you've made. What are some of the bright moments on your journey so far?

Incorporate laughter in your life. Hang out with friends who make you laugh, or watch a funny movie. We have all heard the phrase "laughter is the best medicine," which is true in so many ways. Research has shown that laughter has many effects on our bodies. [1] Some of the benefits include: stimulating many of our organs, increasing the intake of oxygen to the heart, lungs, and brain, relieving stress, improving circulation, and allowing muscles to relax. Laughter may help in enhancing the immune system, coping with stressful situations, and assisting people to forget about their pain.

Look up the following Bible verses and write what they mean to you.

Proverbs 17:22

Job 8:21

Proverbs 15:13

Nehemiah 8:10

God knows the importance of laughter and how it can be a source of healing, which is why He included it in the Bible.

What are some ways you can include laughter in your day?

God showed His sense of humor in the Bible. *They have left the straight way and wandered off to follow the way of Balaam son of Bezer, who loved the wages of wickedness. But he was rebuked for his wrongdoing by a donkey-an animal without speech-who spoke with a human voice and restrained the prophet's madness (2 Peter 2:15-16 NIV).* Balaam may have been shocked initially, but after he obeyed God, he had to appreciate God's way of getting his attention.

Being able to find humor in our struggles and mistakes can make the trials of life more manageable. God has a sense of humor, and He uses it frequently. I often see God using humor in my life to teach me a lesson or to help me get through a rough patch. There are times when I ask Him a question or pray to Him requesting something, and He gives me my answer in a humorous way. If God can use humor to get us through life, we too should try to find humor in difficult or stressful situations. Though it may not ease all the pain, it can dull it or can give us temporary relief, allowing us to think more clearly.

Watch how you speak to yourself: Let your mouth speak only kind words. You can be your own worst enemy. That small, inner voice can destroy you if you let it. When you talk to yourself, talk the way you expect others to speak to you. If you tell yourself you will never lose weight or make changes, then that is precisely what will happen. If you hear these words, either from others or your lips, you will eventually start to believe them. They become a self-fulfilling prophecy. God, in His infinite wisdom knows that our thoughts can defeat us, and He gave us verses to guard against this. *Guard your heart above all else, for it determines the course of your life (Proverbs 4:23).* He also gave us a solution to combat our negative thoughts. *And now, dear brothers and sisters, one final thing. Fix your thoughts on what is true, and honorable, and right, and pure, and lovely, and admirable. Think about things that are excellent and worthy of praise (Philippians 4:8).*

Look up the following Bible verses. Record how they might change your mindset regarding how you speak to yourself.

Romans 12:2

Colossians 3:2

2 Corinthians 10:5

1 Peter 5:8

John 6:68

What are some of the negative thoughts you need to remove from your life?

Below are some Bible verses you can use to retrain your inner voice.

When your inner voice says: "I have messed up so bad that God cannot forgive me this time."
Respond: But God died for me while I was still a sinner (Romans 5:8).

When your inner voice says: "I am not loveable."
Respond: My God is in my midst; He will save me and rejoice over me with gladness. He quiets me by His love and will rejoice over me by loud singing (Zephaniah 3:17).

When your inner voice says: "I am not worthy of God's love."
Respond: God so loved me that He gave His only Son so I will have eternal life (John 3:16).

When your inner voice says: "I cannot do this."
 Respond: For God has not given me a spirit of timidity, but of power, love, and discipline (2 Timothy 1:7).

When your inner voice has negative thoughts.
Respond with: I will submit my thoughts to God and the devil will flee from me (James 4:7).

When your inner voice says: "I cannot break my strongholds."
 Respond with: I will seek the Lord and His strength; I will seek His face continually (1 Chronicles 16:11).

It's your turn. Write out the negative thoughts that consume you and replace them with the authoritative Word of God. Keep them near you so that you can use them every time you have to correct the negative thoughts that are trying to hold you captive. Perhaps you can place these verses in your phone, so they are readily available.

Exercise regularly: You need to exercise at least three times a week. Research shows that exercise affects your attitude. When you are physically active, it releases neurochemicals into your brain. The primary neurochemicals are dopamine, norepinephrine, and endorphins. These three neurochemicals have been shown to improve mood, increase alertness, and improve cognitive function. Exercise also helps remove adrenaline and cortisol, which are stress hormones. Exercise requires you to focus and therefore, can distract you from the struggles you are facing.[2]

Eat well. Diet is critical. Foods can alter your mood and increase the stress in your body. Some of the foods that are good for combating stress are green leafy vegetables, salmon, oatmeal, blueberries, pistachios, cashews, seeds, dark chocolate, avocados, raw carrots, and celery. Stay away from sugar, gluten, and processed food. [3]

Remove yourself from negative conversations. People can drag you down, and they can fill your head with negativity. You must guard against negativity at all times, which may entail changing your daily habits. For example, if at work you eat lunch with a group of people who are continually belittling others, spreading gossip, or just speaking negatively, you may have to find an alternative group or spend this time with God. Set boundaries for your family and friends who bring negativity into your world. When someone wants to tell you a negative story, stop the person immediately. Do not let people fill your head with negative comments. You have the power to control what you allow your mind to hear.

Enjoy music. Listen to your favorite upbeat music. Christian music is not only uplifting, but it also fills a spiritual need.

Get adequate sleep. Sleep is essential for your brain to function at optimal capacity. When you lack sleep, your mind has a difficult time functioning. Receiving adequate rest, allows your body to wake up refreshed. You can look at a situation from a different perspective. Lack of sleep alters some parts of the brain's activity, which in turn can have an impact on attitude.

Use aromatherapy: There are many essential oils that can be used for relaxation, and there are many ways to dispense them. The easiest way is to use a diffuser, which can be purchased online or in stores. You can use cotton balls with several drops of essential oil placed in the vents of your car. I recommend only pure essential oils. (Aromatherapy is addressed to a greater extent in a future chapter.)

Make an "I am thankful list." Many things happen every day that are good. When you struggle, it is so easy to miss these things. Each day list at least five good things that happened to you. They can be as simple as seeing a beautiful sunrise or noting the fact that you woke to see another day. Life is good, and when we take the time to look, we can recognize this.

Become aware of how you are holding your body and the muscles. Learn to recognize when you are guarding yourself by tightening your muscles. When you are tight, utilize some relaxation techniques.

Stop clenching your teeth. Become aware of when you are doing this and make a conscious effort to stop. Often people clench their teeth when sleeping. An easy way to prevent this is by using a mouth guard. Custom ones made by a dentist are best as they are often more comfortable to wear. However, they are much more expensive than an over the counter mouth guard, which can be molded to fit a person's teeth. Many sporting goods stores have them.

Rehearse how you will handle situations. Do this frequently. If you know you are about to enter a situation that is going to cause you to stress, address it beforehand. Talk to yourself about how to stay calm and how best to react to the situation.

Practice your deep breathing. When people are stressed, they tend to take short, quick breaths rather than deep, relaxed breaths, which decreases blood oxygenation. You can do deep breathing throughout the day. Breathe in through your nose and feel your stomach rise and then slowly exhale. Do this ten to twenty minutes a day. Make sure that when doing the breathing, you are getting the deep breaths that cause the abdomen to rise and fall. When your body is stressed, breathing is shallow and occurs more in the upper lungs, which are located in the top of the rib cage. This shallow breathing decreases the oxygen intake. It hinders your ability to expel carbon dioxide, which causes a build up toxins within your body. Shallow breathing also affects a person's posture because of the recruitment of the neck muscles to allow this type of breathing. The neck muscles become tight, putting pressure on the upper ribs and causing a head forward posture. Relearning the proper way to breathe may take some time to master. Doing this while driving or sitting at your desk is an excellent time to practice. Deep breathing is also very effective when done in conjunction with yoga and meditation.

Here is a deep breathing technique. Get into a comfortable position, either sitting or lying down. If lying down, it may be best to place a pillow under the knees. Place one hand on your abdomen. It is often easier if the eyes are closed to avoid distractions. Breathe in through the nose, letting the belly rise so that it is pushing the hand up. Breathe out through the mouth, allowing the abdomen to come back down. Start slowly, doing it for two to five minutes and increase the time as the technique becomes more comfortable. If this method is going to be effective in handling stress, it must be practiced first when one is relaxed. Try using the 4-7-8 breathing technique. (Breathe in for a count of 4, hold for a count of 7, and exhale for a count of 8.) This technique will help stop the negative thought process because the counting pattern will act as a distraction.

Do yoga. This practice incorporates deep breathing, meditation, and light exercise into one session. Studies have shown that yoga helps to combat stress. It also reduces fatigue, improves flexibility, increases muscle tone, gives mental clarity and awareness, and improves circulation and cardiovascular health. Many yoga programs are available on the Internet that you can do in your home, or many gyms offer classes. You must attend more than one class to receive the benefits. As with every program, there can be both good and bad instructors. If you do not like one instructor, try another until you find one with whom you are comfortable. Make sure that this is a Christian-based program.

Use visualization. Visualization is a great technique to decrease stress. Picture yourself in a peaceful setting such as walking on a beach or sitting on a mountain with Jesus by your side. Before beginning visualization, get into a comfortable position either sitting cross-legged or reclined in a chair. Be cautious about lying down because it can lead to falling asleep. Use deep breathing with the eyes closed. Once relaxed, imagine a place or spot that elicits peace or serenity and try using all the senses to imagine the scene. One of my favorite images is sitting on a mountain reading the Bible while watching the sunrise with a cool breeze blowing and birds chirping. There are Christian websites to find visualization techniques that also provide sounds to enhance the experience.

Try acupuncture. Acupuncture can offer deep relaxation. The needles used are very thin. It is not painful, and most of the time, you do not even feel the needle being inserted. The needles are often left in for 20-30 minutes. Acupuncture is an ancient form of Chinese medicine and operates on the principle that Qi is the energy force that controls the body's health. These forces move through pathways called meridians. When the body is stressed, these meridians can become disrupted. While getting acupuncture, the heart and breathing rate may slow, muscle tension decreases, and the people may go into a very relaxed state. I recommend this both for stress release and pain relief. I find acupuncture very relaxing. Often, while receiving acupuncture, I use the quiet time to pray. Because I am relaxed, I can focus on my prayer and have quality time with our loving Father.

Get a massage or do a self-massage working on tight muscles. Massage helps to reduce the tension in the muscles, relieves pain caused by muscle tightness, and can reduce your stress. It is not always economically feasible to get a professional massage. However, you can do a self-massage on tight muscles. Use coconut oil combined with a relaxing essential oil to help reduce tension even more. Working on the neck, low back, and face can be very beneficial, as we tend to tense these muscles when we are stressed.

Learn progressive muscle relaxation. By tensing and relaxing muscle groups, you can relieve tension in your body. With this technique, you tense and relax muscles one at a time as you use a deep breathing technique. There are many scripts for this on the Internet.

Practice relaxing and destressing techniques frequently. By practicing these techniques when you are in a relaxed state, you learn to do them correctly. They will become a habit, and you will more readily use them when you need to calm yourself.

Get a punching bag. Set up a punching bag in the basement or use a punching ball, which can help to get rid of anger and frustration.

Schedule social activities. When there is something to look forward to, the anticipation can occupy your thoughts. Socializing is very important to help ward off depression.

Take a walk and enjoy nature. Getting in the sunlight along with the walking can do wonders for your body. Sunlight increases serotonin and facilitates vitamin D production. This helps to improve your mood.

Seek the help of a Christian therapist. If you find you are unable to break the negative patterns in your life or feel you are dealing with depression, get professional help.

Food for thought:

1. Do you see yourself as a positive person or a negative person?

2. What can you do to change your attitude so that it is more positive?

3. Write a prayer or letter to God, telling Him exactly how you feel. Don't hold anything back. Talk to Him as you would a parent or close friend. In the prayer, ask for help in dealing with these feelings. Invite the Holy Spirit to enlighten you and help you deal with the issues that are holding you back from being positive.

4. Did you find any of the above suggestions useful in helping manage your stress? Which ones?

5. How are you going to incorporate these suggestions into your life?

6. Start your thankful list. When you count your blessings, you can see how active God is in your life.

Journal your thoughts.

THE VESTIBULE
(CONTENTMENT)

The vestibule is a small chamber that opens into the sanctuary, serving as the entrance hall. How a person is greeted in the entrance hall can affect their attitude and how they enter the sanctuary.

Nugget of the day: Trust in the Lord with all your heart; do not depend on your own understanding. Seek his will in all you do, and he will show you which path to take *(Proverbs 3:5).*

Contentment can be summed up in eight words: trust in the Lord with all your heart. We do not have superpowers or the ability to foretell the future. Therefore, we need to rely on God to lead us in this world. Most children do not fret over the problems they will face during their day. They live for the moment and trust that their parents will take care of any problem that may arise. It would help us to follow this example. Let us learn to place our faith in God so that when issues arise, we turn them over to our Father. When we put expectations on our lives and believe we will not find contentment until these factors are a reality, we cannot be at peace. Our world is unpredictable. There are too many variables that can change everything in a matter of minutes. Trusting God is the only way we will find contentment in an uncertain world. Satan loves to rock our world and shake our faith in God. God is the only One that can foresee the future. He is the only One that knows what His plans are for our lives. We experience contentment when we accept that God is in control and trust that He will provide for our needs. Contentment is not something we can buy or achieve on our own. It is when we change our attitude from self-centered to God-centered that we will find peace.

My prayer is that you realize God is the key to living a content life. By trusting God, you can appreciate what you have, and live within your means. When we look to God and live our lives accordingly, we know that we are on course to serve our purpose on earth and glorify God. I pray we adopt a childlike attitude and look for God's blessings in all situations. Contentment is only attained when you trust in the Lord with all your heart.
****

The vestibule is the reception area and helps the people transition from their everyday life to focus on why they came to the temple to worship. The vestibule can be one of the hardest areas to design so that it is welcoming and a place where people want to enter. First impressions are difficult to break, so the architect wants the person to enter the building and feel comfortable. Often this is the first thing the people see when they enter the temple. If it is warm and inviting the people want to proceed into the place of worship. Many temples have greeters standing at the door to welcome the visitor. The people may congregate in this area to visit with one another or get to know some of the members. If the vestibule is cluttered or run down the people may be distracted or uncomfortable.

When a person is not content with life, the vestibule can be cold and uninviting. It makes it hard for a person to want to enter the sanctuary because they are not comfortable with where they are in life. There are many external and internal pressures on every one of us. At times, the world can make us feel guilty that our lives are not like everyone else's. Often, people put so much value on materialism and doing things in a specific manner that when we veer away from the so-called norm of society, it can be hard to accept the Christian lifestyles we have chosen. When we are greeted warmly in the vestibule, we will understand it is not about what we have, rather who we are as Christians that allows us to live the lives God specifically designed for us.

I know what it is to be in need, and I know what it is to have plenty. I have learned the secret of being content in any and every situation, whether well fed or hungry, whether living in plenty or in want (Philippians 4:12). Being content with all of our circumstances is the secret to life. We live in a world that values material things and is becoming more "I" centered every day. Too often we are made to feel as if we are not living a complete life unless we drive a new car, take a lavish vacation, have the latest television, live in a large house, or have a prestigious career.

What keeps you from being content?

Why do you feel this way?

Then he said, "Beware! Guard against every kind of greed. Life is not measured by how much you own" (Luke 12:15). The Bible contains over 2,000 verses in regards to finances, which is 15 percent of the Bible.(1) God knew that money would be something that could control our lives. He has given us ample teachings as to how it can either destroy us or further His kingdom. God does not tell us that money itself is evil. *For the love of money is the root of all kinds of evil. And some people, craving money, have wandered from the true faith and pierced themselves with many sorrows* (1 Timothy 6:10). The problem comes when we love money and put it above all else in our lives. It is how we go about attaining possessions that can destroy our lives. When we are dependent on money for our happiness or security, it stands in the way of our relationship with God. This dependency on money weakens our foundation. Rather than trusting God, we trust the almighty dollar.

Lack of contentment is not limited to material things. We often put conditions on our lives such as I will be happy when I get to be a manager at my job, I will enjoy life more when I go on vacation or retire, I will be content when I have children or grandchildren.

What conditions do you think need to exist for you to be content?

We spend so much time wishing our lives away that we never really get to experience all life has to offer. The journey to reach our goals is actually where we learn the skills to develop our trust in God. This experience is essential to building our temples. We worry so much about getting to our destination that we do not see all the blessings God is bestowing on us along the way. We do not appreciate the work, the people we are meeting, and miracles that are taking place. God uses these opportunities to draw closer to us. He knows that once we have all we want, we tend to forget Him. *I consider that our present sufferings are not worth comparing with the glory that will be revealed in us* (Romans 8:18 NIV). We need to take time to appreciate all the blessings we receive as we work towards our goals. Rather than celebrating only the end victory, take time to celebrate each milestone. Are you happy when you lose one or two pounds? Are you happy when you can walk further than the last time? Are you happy when you eat less junk food? When will you be happy?

As you are working toward changing your lifestyle, are you putting conditions on the outcome?

What are these conditions?

One of the reasons we may fall short of attaining our goals is we cannot live up to the expectations we put on ourselves. We may lose five or ten pounds, plateau, then get discouraged and give up. We don't take the time to appreciate the changes we made and the effort it took to attain a specific goal. Another issue is that if we lose weight or improve our fitness, but we are not satisfied with who we are, we will still not be content. We can improve the outer appearance, but we also need to fix the inside if we are going to live a healthy lifestyle. Where do we find this contentment? It comes from knowing who we are in Christ, and knowing our Creator loves us. It hinges on trusting God wholeheartedly and giving Him control of our lives.

What do the following Bible verses tell you about contentment and how you should live your life?

Matthew 6:25-26

Matthew 6:32-33

1 Timothy 6:6-7

There is nothing wrong with having goals and dreams for your life. In truth, God wants you to grow and to become a better person. God has placed dreams and goals in your heart. He has given you specific gifts and talents so that you can be successful in answering God's call for your life. God wants you to use your abilities for

His glory, not for yours. Living a healthy lifestyle needs to be one of your goals. God wants this for you because He knows when you are healthy, you will be able to achieve the plans He has for you.

Contentment is much more than having everything you desire in life. When you are content, it will be easier to continue to make changes necessary to improve your health. You will enjoy the journey when you enthusiastically celebrate the accomplishments. This recognition of small victories will help you not to be discouraged when change is slower than anticipated or you take a step backward.

Contentment in earthly things will never last. Things break or become outdated, goals change, careers come to an end, and people let you down. Your satisfaction must come from your faith, trusting God will provide for you and will guide you on your journey. *Wherever your treasure is, there the desires of your heart will also be* (Matthew 6:21). When you finally surrender your life to God, you find the peace and contentment for which you have been searching. It is then you will see how rich and fulfilling your life can be. *For the Kingdom of God is not a matter of what we eat or drink, but of living a life of goodness and peace and joy in the Holy Spirit. If you serve Christ with this attitude, you will please God, and others will approve of you, too* (Romans 14:17-18).

Contentment is:

- Finding the good in every situation and seeing God's blessings, even in your trials.
- Being thankful for what you have.
- Appreciating every gift you receive from God.
- Relishing the moment and taking time to celebrate it before looking ahead to the next milestone you want to achieve.
- Having a calling and knowing you are serving a divine purpose.
- Trusting God will guide you, giving you strength and abilities to help fulfill your calling.
- Living within your means and being satisfied.
- Living a life that is pleasing to God and when you fail seeking and accepting God's forgiveness.
- Forgiving those who have hurt you.
- Sharing your talents and wealth.

Contentment is not:

- Worrying about your problems.
- Comparing your gifts to others and feeling as if you have been cheated or you are not living up to your potential.
- Putting conditions on what you think will give you peace.
- Letting material things dictate who you are and your self-worth.
- Holding onto anger or hatred.

And people should eat and drink and enjoy the fruits of their labor, for these are gifts from God (Ecclesiastes 3:13). How can you apply the above verse to your life?

Food for thought:

1. How has your idea of contentment changed as you work through this study?

2. In what areas of your life do you lack contentment?
How can this be addressed?

3. Do you compare your gifts and talents to other people's gifts? If so, how is this stealing your contentment?

Journal your thoughts.

THE CHAPEL
(REST)

Many churches have a smaller room called a chapel where members can retreat to in order to find peace and spend some quiet time with God. Here they can worship privately or in a small group.

Nugget of the day: Those who live at the ends of the earth stand in awe of your wonders. From where the sun rises to where it sets, you inspire shouts of joy (Psalm 65:8).

Have you ever wondered why God gives us night and day? At times, I think I would be so much happier if I didn't have to sleep. There is so much to do in this world, and I could accomplish so much more if I did not have to stop what I am doing to rest. Then I witness a beautiful sunrise and realize our God, in His infinite wisdom, knows we need the newness of each day. Each morning He gives us a display of His wonder. He greets us with a cheerful good morning telling us, " I Am thinking of you." Each sunrise is a reminder that we have a brand new start. We can put our mistakes and troubles behind us and look forward to a new day and a clean slate. It is God's way of telling us He is not giving up on us. The sunrise is a reflection of our Dad's love for us. It lets us witness another wonder only God could create. It tells us life is good. Each sunset is God's way of telling His children good night. He gives us a way to end the day and put our worries to rest. It is at night that we can quiet our minds, spend some alone time with God, and relax. We can lay our bodies down and recharge.

My prayer is that each morning you accept the gift of a new day and leave your past behind. Each evening, take the time to enjoy the sunset, breathe, relax, and let the stress of the day melt away. God has blessed you with these beautiful displays of His awe and wonder. It is a gift given to you every morning and every night. There are no requirements for you to accept them, and every day they are different. They welcome you to the start of a new day, and then they wish you a good night.

****

The chapel is usually a smaller place of worship. Many of the larger churches have both a sanctuary and the chapel. There are times a person comes to the chapel to find rest and to sit in God's presence. Other times worship service is performed in this area when the leader wants a more intimate setting. The smaller area can make a person feel closer to God. The fewer distractions may give the person the ability to focus their mind and thoughts on God.

There is a difference between rest and sleep. Rest is a time to quiet the mind and let the body calm down and be in a relaxed state. Everyone needs a place of rest because in this hectic day and age, we often find it hard to have a place where we can relax. We run ourselves ragged and do not take the time in the day to recharge, which can lead to having a difficult time getting through the day, having a short temper, and being restless. Rest is essential for people to be able to perform their duties, which God has assigned.

Resting in God's presence is essential as well to quiet of our minds. When we pray and find the time to sit quietly and talk with God, He can give us the confidence to tackle our fears, give us answers to our problems, help alleviate worry, and reduce our stress in life. We all need a room that allows us to sit in God's presence and recharge. God designed us to need rest, and so our temples must have a chapel.

On the seventh day God had finished his work of creation, so he rested from all his work. And God blessed the seventh day and declared it holy, because it was the day when he rested from all his work of creation (Genesis 2:2-3). God knew the importance of rest. He also took the time to rest and appreciate what He had accomplished. If the Creator of the universe recognized the importance of rest, shouldn't we?

Read Exodus 20:8-10. Why do you think God established the Sabbath?

Do you take time to rest and enjoy your day? ____ What do you do during this time?

We live in a society that values busyness. People often place their self-worth on how much they accomplish in a day, week, or year. They love to outdo one another and show everyone how productive they are throughout the day. I too once fell into this group of people as I felt my children and I always had to be busy. I thought I was not a good mom unless we were involved in all the activities in school, scouts, and sports. After my children got older, I was busy from the moment I jumped out of bed until late in the night when I collapsed back into bed. I seldom took time to eat a nice meal or relax. I did not understand why I became sad when the evening came and the darkness was present. Then I had that "aha" moment when I realized the dark was a reminder that in a few hours I would fall into bed exhausted. Rarely did I have the energy to even change out of my clothes. I had to get a few precious hours of sleep before I would have to get up and do it all over again. At the time, I enjoyed our active life, but it took a toll on me physically, emotionally, mentally, and spiritually. I was always tired, and if I sat down for a few moments in a meeting or to visit, I would fall asleep. How many of you make this same mistake? Maybe it is not with your children, but with your job or your social life.

What activities in your life interfere with your ability to relax and cause you undue stress?

How do the following verses speak to you personally?

Matthew 11:28-29

Mark 6:31

Psalm 37:7

I have since learned that the key to living a fulfilling life is also taking the time to sit and appreciate all that is around me. I live in the moment rather than wondering what precious time I am wasting sitting still. I enjoy quiet moments with God, sitting in His presence or reading His Word. *He says, "Be still, and know that I am God" (Psalm 46:10)!* This command was not only given so God could spend time with His beloved children but also so we can recharge our minds and bodies. I have learned the importance of sitting with family and friends and enjoying their company. I love watching the sunrise and sunset. I enjoy taking walks while listening to praise music or sharing a good conversation with a friend. I have also learned that taking time to relax has helped me become more productive. I am now more creative, and although my projects may take longer to accomplish, I enjoy the activity rather than pushing myself because it is something I must do. Most mornings before taking on the day, I sit in God's presence and read His Word before going off to work. I find the time to do Bible studies so that I become more familiar with the Word. In the evenings, I look forward to the darkness because I know most of the time I will have a peaceful evening and get a good night's sleep.

How do you make time to sit in God's presence and connect with Him?

Do you find it important to make the time even when your schedule may be hectic?

If so, how does this help to prepare you for the day ahead?

Sleep is also a key component to living a healthy lifestyle. Sleep allows our bodies to slow down more than when they are in a state of rest and occurs for a longer period of the day, usually seven to eight hours. While a person is asleep, the brain can filter the information it had gathered throughout the day to help a person retain this information and their memories. A person who has adequate sleep is more likely to make good decisions and focus more clearly throughout the day. Our metabolism is also dependent on a good nights sleep. We all need sleep, and when we are sleep deprived, our body, mind, and spirit suffer. Sleep research has shown that the lack of sleep or poor quality of sleep affects every tissue and system in our body. Our brains, hearts, lungs, immune system and metabolism all suffer when we lack sleep. It also causes us to have an increased risk of some diseases and disorders. These include cardiovascular disease, diabetes, high blood pressure, depression, and obesity. [1] When we are sleep deprived, we can become moody and irritable. We tend to eat more, activating the hunger hormone ghrelin, causing us to crave sugary and fatty foods. (2) This, in turn, causes weight gain. People also exhibit a lack of focus, poor coordination, poor decision-making, and increased impulsivity when sleep deprived. Impulsivity causes a person to react differently than they would have had they not been fatigued. Other physical signs of sleep deprivation are poor skin condition, impaired eyesight due to tired eye muscles, slurred speech and susceptibility to sickness. A person may also experience micro-sleep, which causes them to nod off for several seconds, allowing for a lapse in their attention to a task. (3) According to the NHSA, falling asleep while driving is responsible for at least 100,000 crashes, 71,000 injuries, and 1,550 deaths each year in the United States. (4)

The amount of sleep an individual needs varies from person to person. Most adults require seven to nine hours of sleep each night. However, after the age of sixty, the amount of sleep needed tends to decrease. If you are striving to live healthy lives, recognize the importance of a good night's rest.

We also need to have a place where we can get the best possible sleep so that our bodies can function correctly. If we do not have a room that is conducive to getting a good night's sleep, we will awaken groggy and lethargic. Sleep can be interrupted for a variety of reasons. One of these reasons is due to the blue light emitted from electronics and LED lights. The blue light can suppress the secretion of melatonin. (5) Another contributing factor can be the type of mattress we sleep on or the bedding we use. Many toxic chemicals have been added to mattresses to make them flame resistant. Some substances that may be used are boric acid, formaldehyde, and flame-retardants. (6) For some people, these chemicals can cause skin irritation, restless sleeping, or breathing problems. Alcohol can cause sleep problems. (7) Foods can also cause us to lose sleep. Spicy foods can cause indigestion and possibly change our body temperature due to capsaicin. High-fat diets can cause fragmented sleep and more daytime sleepiness. (8)

Ways to enhance sleep:
- Reduce stress in your life. Perform meditation or deep breathing techniques before bed.
- Keep the room temperature cool.
- Make sure the room is dark. You may need to use light-blocking curtains or blackout shades.
- Keep your bedtime consistent, so the body is familiar with a sleep pattern.
- Don't drink fluids within two hours of going to bed, and make sure to use the bathroom before sleeping.
- Maintain a healthy body weight. Excess weight can cause or worsen sleep apnea. (9)
- Avoid drinking alcohol before bed.
- Take a hot bath or shower before bedtime.
- Reduce your caffeine intake.
- Use your bed only for sleeping. When you do work or watch television in bed, it is harder to fall asleep.
- Avoid looking at bright screens two to three hours before bedtime. Some electronics have controls to turn off the blue light in the evening.
- Keep electronic devices away from the bed. Charge your phone on the other side of the room.
- Exercise daily. Research has shown one hundred and fifty minutes of moderate to vigorous exercise weekly improves sleep quality up to sixty-five percent. (10)
- Use essential oils.
- Replace worn mattresses.

Foods and drinks that help promote sleep are as follows:
- Tart cherry juice, which is rich in melatonin.
- Foods that contain an abundant amount of calcium such as kale and collards.
- Foods with potassium and B6, such as bananas, which help produce melatonin.
- Lean proteins such as salmon, as well as healthy fats such as nuts, are high in the amino acid tryptophan, which increases serotonin. (11,12)

Food for thought:

1. What are some habits that may be hindering your sleep?

2. What are some things you can do to improve your sleep?

Journal your thoughts.

Week 3

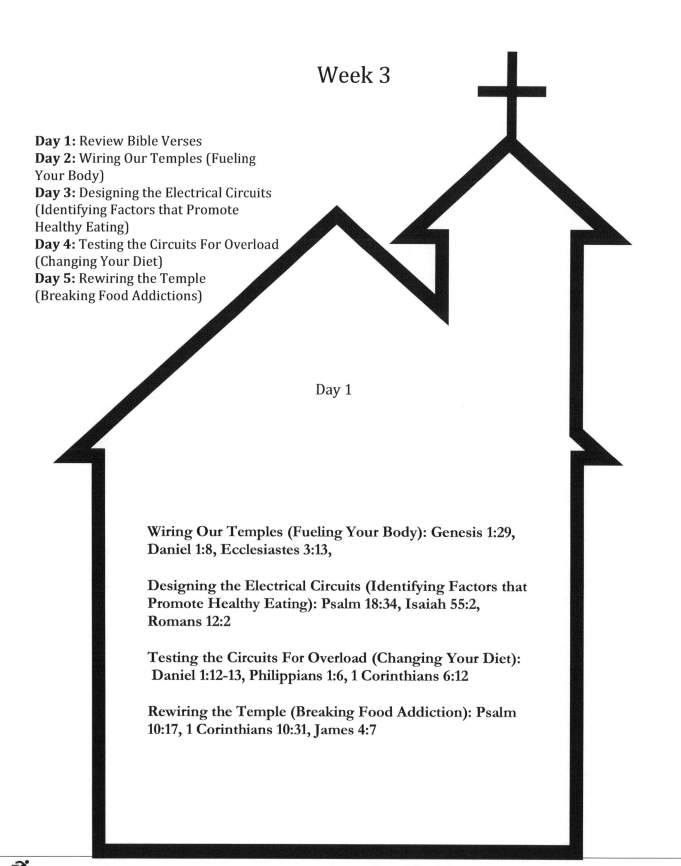

Day 1: Review Bible Verses
Day 2: Wiring Our Temples (Fueling Your Body)
Day 3: Designing the Electrical Circuits (Identifying Factors that Promote Healthy Eating)
Day 4: Testing the Circuits For Overload (Changing Your Diet)
Day 5: Rewiring the Temple (Breaking Food Addictions)

Day 1

Wiring Our Temples (Fueling Your Body): Genesis 1:29, Daniel 1:8, Ecclesiastes 3:13,

Designing the Electrical Circuits (Identifying Factors that Promote Healthy Eating): Psalm 18:34, Isaiah 55:2, Romans 12:2

Testing the Circuits For Overload (Changing Your Diet): Daniel 1:12-13, Philippians 1:6, 1 Corinthians 6:12

Rewiring the Temple (Breaking Food Addiction): Psalm 10:17, 1 Corinthians 10:31, James 4:7

Weekly exercise: The assignment this week is twofold. Spend this week reading the scriptures and learning to use them to fight off temptations. Take time to compare the food God has provided for you to the processed food you like to eat. Look at 2 foods. Examine the colors, notice the shapes, feel the texture, smell the aromas, and taste the two types of food. Take the time to savor the taste of each. Do this with a variety of foods and report to your group what you experienced.

WIRING THE TEMPLE
(FUELING YOUR BODY)

Electricity provides the temple with power to give it warmth, energy, and lighting.

Nugget of the day: Why spend your money on food that does not give you strength? Why pay for food that does you no good? Listen to me, and you will eat what is good. You will enjoy the finest food (Isaiah 55:2).

We spend a lot of money and energy on things that hinder our well-being rather than on what nourishes us. God knew what He was doing when He created the earth. He provided us with all the essentials to live healthy and fulfilling lives. Man, through science, has been trying to improve on what God provided for us. Mankind also created a belief system that did not include God and called it faith. Then he changed the rules to make them fit his wants and needs. In the world today, there is so much sickness and diseases such as diabetes, heart disease, obesity, and cancer. We need to get back to the basics and realize God will feed us, not only physically but also spiritually. God, our Creator, knows what we need to live healthy lives. God gave us everything we need.

My prayer is that you listen to God. The Bible has all the information you need to live a healthy life. Unlike people, who have ulterior motives, God has your best interest at heart. You honor God when you eat His vegetables and fruits. You give Him glory and honor when you follow His teachings. You are the one that truly benefits from being fed by God. Your life becomes more fulfilled and meaningful. You have a sense of peace in your soul, are healthier, and you enjoy life much more. So get back to the basics and let God feed you in every aspect of your life. You will be fulfilled when you accept God's plan for your nourishment.

****

The temple utilizes electricity as its energy source to power the temple. Without electricity, the temple will be cold, dark, and lifeless. To provide electricity to the building it must be properly wired. The electrician cannot begin to wire the building until he runs wires from the main power source, which is the utility company, to the building. The power running to the house is unlimited and can power the whole home. However, for the energy to be utilized in the home, it has first to be brought into the main panel where circuit breakers can funnel the power correctly through various circuits throughout the home.

We too, need an energy source to nourish our bodies. When we provide our bodies with the correct energy source, we can function much more efficiently. The fuel we receive from our food can either give or deplete our bodies of energy. It is our choice as to how we power our temples. Tapping into God (our external source) provides us with the correct food to fuel our bodies and is sufficient to give us the energy to get through our day and accomplish our goals. Our bodies need a variety of nutrients to function at their optimal potential. Eating a variety of vegetables and fruits will fuel all the organs and tissues so that our bodies can be well maintained.

If God did not see the diet as necessary, He would not have included information about nutrition in the Bible. God, in His infinite wisdom, would not address any issues unless they help us grow in faith, improve our lives, and bring us closer to Him. The Bible is the greatest self-help book ever written and is packed with ways for us to live healthier and more fulfilling lives. The Bible provides essential instructions on how to live each day. So, when are we going to start listening and stop trying to make it on our own?

Take some time to review Daniel 1:6-16. What were the benefits Daniel and his men received from eating vegetables and water?

Daniel knew the benefits of a healthy diet, so he chose to adhere to his beliefs even when others pressured him. Upholding his convictions took a lot of strength for Daniel to do what did because he had to stand up to people who could not only destroy him but also destroy his friends who followed his lead. Daniel was able to convince others to eat healthily and improve their lives because he stood up for what he knew was right. We often face this same dilemma when we choose to maintain healthy lifestyles. Well-meaning friends and family try to convince us that we need to go off our diets, whether it is at home, in a restaurant, or at a party. We are often pressured to "just try this" or may give in so as not to hurt their feelings. We quickly discover that it takes willpower to eat the right way. When we set an example, others will see the real benefits of a clean diet and may want to change theirs, but if we give in to please others, we cannot lead by example.

Is it hard for you to eat healthy around your friends and family?

What are some of the ways family and friends pressure you into eating the way they do?

How can you prepare yourself so that the next time you are pressured, you can remain strong and eat the way you know you should?

At the end of ten days, Daniel and his three friends had proven that their eating healthy food made them more robust than those who were eating the rich diet provided by the king. Are you willing to take Daniel's ten-day challenge (If you are not ready to make drastic changes, can you make some small changes and maintain it for ten days)?

What are some obstacles that prevent you from doing this for ten days?

Daniel lived his life to honor God, and God rewarded him for remaining faithful. Daniel knew that God was the only One who could guide him in this world. He knew God was his strength, and so he spent much time in prayer. *But when Daniel learned that the law had been signed, he went home and knelt down as usual in his upstairs room, with its windows open toward Jerusalem. He prayed three times a day, just as he had always done, giving thanks to his God (Daniel 6:10 NIV).*

How often do you pray for God to give you the strength to live a healthy lifestyle?

How can you include God more frequently in your daily life so that He can give you strength when you are weak, or you are feeling pressure from others to go off your diet?

The following Bible verses speak of God's ability to give us willpower when we are weak. How do these verses speak to you?

Romans 13:14

Jeremiah 32:27

1 Corinthians 9:24-25

Colossians 3:17

God can give you strength and willpower to overcome any obstacle in your life. However, you have to be willing to go before Him and ask for this strength and then lean into Him for support. When you veer from God and His Word, you will feel weak. One way you can choose God over food is to ask yourself these questions: Is this candy bar, french fries, cinnamon roll, etc. more important than God's plan for my health and wellness? Will eating this food restore my temple or tear it down? Memorizing and using Bible verses to ward off temptation and to give you strength will help you succeed.

How important is your diet in God's eyes? You don't have to look any further than the first book of Genesis. It is here God gives you your first lesson. *Then God said, "Look! I have given you every seed-bearing plant throughout the earth and all the fruit trees for your food (Genesis 1:29).* Travel a little further to Deuteronomy 32:13-14 and you will receive more dietary tips. *He made him ride on the heights of the land and fed him with the fruit of the fields. He nourished him with honey from the rock, and with oil from the flinty crag, with curds and milk from herd and flock and with fattened lambs and goats, with choice rams of Bashan and the finest kernels of wheat. You drank the foaming blood of the grape (NIV).* God made perfect food that would nourish our bodies, and man thought he could improve upon it. The arrogance of man has led us to believe that we could improve on God's great works and His perfectly orchestrated world. In doing so, we have created a mess, which has caused us to compromise our health and well-being. Man has also created shortcuts in food production, compromising the nutritional value of our food. By taking matters into our own hands, we now have GMOs (genetically modified organisms) that, in my opinion, threaten our health. GMOs are the result of transplanting the genes from the DNA of one species into the genes of an unrelated plant. They extract these genes from bacteria, viruses, insects, animals or humans.

When we return to the basics, we allow God to once again be in control of our food. We need to understand that only God can produce food that can truly nourish us. He has provided us with the proper vitamins and minerals to fuel our bodies. God knows not only the importance of eating this way on earth but also in Heaven. In the book of Revelation, God has shown us that He will provide the perfect diet in Heaven. *Then the angel showed me the river of the water of life, as clear as crystal, flowing from the throne of God and of the Lamb down the middle of the great street of the city. On each side of the river stood the tree of life, bearing twelve crops of fruit, yielding its fruit every month. And the leaves of the tree are for the healing of the nations (Revelation 22:1-2 NIV).* Not only does the first chapter of the Bible tell us that God has provided us with healthy food to eat, but the last chapter of the Bible also refers to God providing us with water and fruit to nourish us.

Since God will provide us with healthy food in Heaven, wouldn't He want the same for us here?

I often hear people speak of Heaven and how they are going to be able to enjoy all the foods that they are not supposed to eat on earth. I cannot imagine that God would allow man-made foods or chemicals in Heaven when He knows they are harmful to His children. God's food will not only satisfy us but will also be pleasing to our palate. In truth, when we are in the presence of our loving Father, we will realize that He did know what was best for His children. We will no longer desire food that is unhealthy or impure. Instead, we will enjoy food that genuinely satisfies us. In Luke's Gospel, Jesus talks about us eating at His table. *So that you may eat and drink at my table in my kingdom and sit on thrones, judging the twelve tribes of Israel (Luke 22:30 NIV).* Can you even imagine what this will be like in Heaven? I can assure you that when we walk away from the Lord's Table, we will be well fed both nutritionally and spiritually. There will be no heartburn or indigestion.

At the end of the ten days, Daniel and his three friends looked healthier and better nourished than the young men who had been eating the food assigned by the king (Daniel 1:15). Sometimes I have to stop and marvel at all the thought that God put into His creation. Everything He has placed on this earth has a specific purpose. Every type of food has a particular role in nourishing our bodies. Each fruit or vegetable has a specific combination of vitamins and minerals that give us energy, keep our bodies healthy, and provide healing. He gave us such a variety of produce that we can enjoy many combinations of food.

Along with nourishment, we can use food to bring families together to share a meal and make eating a joyful experience. When I take the time to study His creation of food, not only does it amaze me as to how it provides me with nourishment, but also how beautiful and appealing it is to my other senses. The colors are vibrant, and the shapes are unique. The smells of these foods have a variety of effects on us. They can be calming, stimulating, and mood enhancing. All these characteristics help add to the experience of enjoying the taste of our food. The tastes vary from sweet to sour, bland to bursting with flavor. Unfortunately, some people's palates have become accustomed to the taste of processed food and have lost their desire for the healthy foods God has given us. We may need to retrain our palates and change how we think about healthy eating. There is no excuse for people to say they do not like fruits and vegetables. There are so many from which to choose. If you have not found vegetables or fruit you like, take time to explore the many varieties and options God has provided us with on this great earth.

Have you ever taken the time to think about and appreciate how much effort God put into creating such amazing foods for us to enjoy and receive nourishment?

What are some thoughts you have as you contemplate this?

Compare your favorite processed food with one of God's creation. Look at how much more appealing it is to your sense of sight and smell. What are the differences?

After comparing the two, can you see how God's foods are more beneficial to your diet?

If you are not already living a healthy lifestyle, you can begin by starting with the basics. Living by the I AM F.E.D. (faith, exercise, diet) model is an excellent example to follow. You need to trust God and know that He is the Great I AM and our loving Father who is providing for His children. God will not steer you wrong. His food will fuel your temple and provide you with the energy you need to answer your callings. Exercise is essential to help you reduce stress, improve sleep, increase your metabolic rate to burn more calories, and help with weight loss.

Over the next three weeks, I am going to discuss many ways in which you can enhance your diet. I understand that many people are not ready to make drastic changes to their diets at this time. Some of you need to make small changes, and when you become comfortable with these changes, you can progress and address another dietary need. There is no right or wrong way to make changes to improve your eating habits. There are many factors that play into how you purchase and prepare your food. You need to proceed at a pace at which you are comfortable and will not overwhelm you.

I want you to be well informed as to what foods are good for you, and which foods can cause health issues. People cannot make changes until they know what is available and understand the reason as to why they should or should not eat a particular food. Becoming more aware of the foods you are purchasing and consuming as well as their nutritional value is the first step in making changes. Remember, small changes are better than no changes. Do not let these next few weeks of homework inundate you. My goal is to empower you by giving you the knowledge to make informed decisions about your diet so you can be successful and receive the benefits of eating healthy.

Food for thought:

1. How does it make you feel that God has provided for all your needs and wants you to live a healthy life?

2. What are some concerns you have at this time as to whether or not you can live this healthy lifestyle?

3. Are there people in your life that are hindering you from making changes?

4. Come up with a game plan so that the next time people tempt you, you will have the strength to stand firm.

Below are some Bible verses that can help you on your journey.

When your mind says, "I can eat what I want."

God says, *"You say, 'I am allowed to do anything'—but not everything is good for you. And even though "I am allowed to do anything," I must not become a slave to anything"* (1 Corinthians 6:12).

When your mind says, "This is too hard!"

God says, *"For I can do everything through Christ, who gives me strength"* (Philippians 4:13).

When your mind says, "Why does it matter what I eat?"

God says, *"Don't you realize that your body is the temple of the Holy Spirit, who lives in you and was given to you by God? You do not belong to yourself, for God bought you with a high price. So you must honor God with your body"* (1 Corinthians 6:19-20).

When your mind says, "This is not working."

God says, *"The Lord is my strength and shield. I trust him with all my heart. He helps me, and my heart is filled with joy. I burst out in songs of thanksgiving* (Psalm 28:7).

When your mind says, "What is wrong with going off my diet for a day?"

God says, *"Instead, clothe yourself with the presence of the Lord Jesus Christ. And don't let yourself think about ways to indulge your evil desires* (Romans 13:14).

When your mind says, "I have no willpower."

God says, *"He gives power to the weak and strength to the powerless* (Isaiah 40:29).

When your mind says, "Go ahead, everyone else is eating what they want."

God says, *"Don't copy the behavior and customs of this world, but let God transform you into a new person by changing the way you think. Then you will learn to know God's will for you, which is good and pleasing and perfect"* (Romans 12:2).

When your mind says, "no one else cares what I do with my life. "

God says, *"And so, dear brothers and sisters, I plead with you to give your bodies to God because of all he has done for you. Let them be a living and holy sacrifice—the kind he will find acceptable. This is truly the way to worship him* (Romans 12:1).

Add your own self-defeating thoughts and let God answer them.

When your mind says, _____

God says, _____

When your mind says, _____

God says, _____

God always has an answer for all of your questions, doesn't He?

Journal your thoughts.

51

DESIGNING THE ELECTRIC CIRCUITS
(IDENTIFYING FACTORS THAT PROMOTE HEALTHY EATING)

Many things in our temple require power. Therefore, they design a plan that uses the energy efficiently. Developing this plan takes time and patience.

Nugget of the day: If you need wisdom, ask our generous God, and he will give it to you. He will not rebuke you for asking *(James 1:5)*.

God does not expect us to be perfect. When we accept that we do not have to be perfect in this world, it takes a lot of pressure off of us. We do not have to put undue expectations on ourselves. Relieving this stress frees us up to enjoy a better life, and it gives us the ability to try new things without fear of failure. As we begin to make changes in our diet, we will make mistakes and will have to make corrections. When we pray to God, He can give us the insight to make these changes. We also have to be willing to be patient with ourselves. Changing our lifestyle is a learning process. When we trust God, He will lead us and help us to make changes so we can live the lives He has planned for us. The Bible is packed with information as to the changes we need to make and how to do it. When we utilize this information, we increase our chance of being successful.

My prayer is that you realize you do not have to be perfect in this world to make a difference. God uses you right where you are. I pray that you learn to trust God and know that He is faithful. He has given you the desire to make changes in your life. When you trust God, He will guide you and provide you with the knowledge, wisdom, and resources to accomplish this goal. You are capable of doing many things that you may not even be aware of at this time. When you turn your life over to God and trust Him, He works in mighty and mysterious ways. Spend some time offering God your life and asking Him to lead you on this journey. Thank Him in advance for the good works He will perform in your life and the journey He will share with you.

****

Before the electrician begins putting the wiring into the temple, he must know how he is going to wire the building to make sure that the circuits will not be overloaded. The circuit consists of all the outlets and appliances that will connect to one circuit breaker. Some appliances, such as a refrigerator or furnace, will draw more energy so they may need to be put on their own circuit. He has to know what appliances will be using the various outlets so that he can design the circuit. If the circuit draws to much power from various appliances and equipment, the circuit breaker will trip, and all the power will be cut off to the circuit.

Our bodies need nutrients from vegetables and fruits. When we try to replace these nutrients with processed foods that contain chemicals and artificial additives, we can easily "trip our circuit breakers" and cut off our power supply. There is a lot to learn as you establish a new diet to avoid the obstacles that can cause health issues, deplete your energy, and affect your mood. We want our bodies to be as efficient as possible, so we need to try and identify these obstacles, so they do not hinder our success. After we identify the obstacles, we can come up with a plan to help us be successful in changing our lifestyles.

Trying to make improvements in your life is not always easy, especially when just starting. There are so many pressures, false advertisements, and misleading sources of information that influence our perception as to what is healthy living. People will try to pressure you into eating their way, give you bad advice, or make you feel guilty for choosing to eat healthily. We can relieve ourselves from these pressures and live our lives the Biblical way. When we use the Bible as our guide, we find that living a healthy lifestyle pleases God. Honoring God should be our number one priority. We will accomplish much more than when we try and improve our lifestyles on our own. I genuinely believe failure to enlist God's help and trusting Him is why so many people fail when trying to change. We cannot do anything without God supporting us and providing us with the strength to make permanent changes. We may be able to change temporarily, but God is the One who gives us the willpower to stay strong. There are many instances where people attempt to do this on their own and fail. People are continually joining weight loss programs and are successful for a short period only to gain all the weight back at a later time.

Taking care of our bodies requires us to understand that our bodies are worth the effort. We have to accept the truth that God loves us and that He created us to be the person we are right now, which is why sturdy external walls are essential to help us see our self worth so that we can make changes. We have to realize that God did not make a mistake when He created us. To be able to treat our bodies with respect, we need to remember that our bodies are His temple and treat them as such. We need to release unrealistic social norms that predetermine what weight and body types are considered to be "beautiful." These ideals can cloud our minds. Then we feel as if we have let ourselves, and possibly others down when we do not reach or maintain these goals. With this being said, we should strive to try and maintain healthy body weight and keep our bodies in good physical shape, so we can participate more fully in life and fulfill our callings. We are often harder on ourselves than others are on us. When we set goals that are unrealistic, not attainable or unsustainable, we become discouraged and give up. It is best to set small, short-term goals and adjust them to our own needs as we go along. Each person is different. Just as our food choices will be different, so will our results. Know that you will make mistakes, you will have temptation, and struggles, and that's okay. Rather than be upset, forgive yourself and move on!

Do you see your body as a temple for God?   Why or why not?

If your body is a temple for God, don't you owe Him the respect of taking care of it?

In what ways does food control your life?

"No one can serve two masters. For you will hate one and love the other; you will be devoted to one and despise the other. You cannot serve God and be enslaved to money. "That is why I tell you not to worry about everyday life—whether you have enough food and drink, or enough clothes to wear. Isn't life more than food, and your body more than clothing? Look at the birds. They don't plant or harvest or store food in barns, for your heavenly Father feeds them. And aren't you far more valuable to him than they are? [27] *Can all your worries add a single moment to your life* (Matthew 6:24-27)? False idols are more than money and material goods. They are anything that comes between our Heavenly Father and us. These gods become a distraction. We can only see as far as the next meal, gadget, or activity. Rather than being secure in who we are in Christ, we become secure in who we are in our earthly pleasures. Take some time to read this verse. Let it sink deep into your heart and let it become ingrained in your life. You must choose: Do you worship God or the food you eat?

Which do you choose to worship?

Let's be realistic for a moment. We all know what types of food we need to eat to maintain healthy lifestyles. Everyone knows that fruits and vegetables must be an essential staple in our diet. We all know that maintaining a diet consisting of mostly junk food makes us unhealthy and often overweight. Healthy eating is not rocket science. There are many things we can learn as we embark on this new journey. If we live our lives based on the fundamentals of healthy eating, we will all be in much better shape. What holds us back from eating healthy is not that we don't know what we should eat. It is all the distractions of this world and our internal struggles. Until we completely surrender our lives to God, we will continue to battle.

What do you need to surrender to God?

The line in the following Bible verse is for your name. God speaks through the Bible to each one of us. The Bible will become more personal and alive in our lives if we insert our name into some of the verses.
But he said to_____, "My grace is sufficient for you, for my power is made perfect in

weakness." Therefore I will boast all the more gladly about my weaknesses, so that Christ's power may rest on me. That is why, for Christ's sake, I delight in weaknesses, in insults, in hardships, in persecutions, in difficulties. For when I am weak, then I am strong (2 Corinthians 12:9-10 NIV).

What is God saying to you with these verses?

If you honestly and wholeheartedly want to make a lifestyle change, trust God with your life. Accept that when you seek Him in your moments of weakness, He will give you strength and empower you to overcome your food addictions.

Before starting a new diet, take some time to pray and ask God to guide you on this journey.

Dear God,
Please give me strength as I embark on this new journey. I want to restore my body so that it is a temple that honors You. You know my weaknesses; please help me when tempted by the foods that are harming my body. Help me find nourishing foods as a replacement so that I may enjoy and find pleasure when I eat. Help me to find my strength in You, oh Lord, because I know that with You all things are possible. You have provided me with many delicious foods that give me energy. Please change my taste buds so that these are the foods I crave. I can do all things through You, and I relinquish control to You. Guide me and lead me to a healthy lifestyle. Show me your glory throughout this journey. In Jesus name, I pray. Amen

Remember that as you embark on this new journey, you will receive pressure from many sources to continue living an unhealthy lifestyle. One of your biggest distractions comes from the enemy. He is ruthless in his attack because he knows that a healthier person is a threat to his world. When you improve your lifestyle, you will have more energy and motivation to answer the calling God has placed in your heart. The devil knows that you will be able to share your love for God and the Good News of Jesus Christ with more people when you are healthy. He knows that if your lifestyle improves because of your faith and you become more secure in Christ, others will witness God's glory. The enemy will try to do whatever it takes to destroy you and keep you from becoming a good and faithful servant. He loves to tell you that you are not worthy, no one cares about you, or you are a failure (only a few of his many lies). Remember, these are <u>his</u> words, not God's Words. God does not see any of His children as worthless or unworthy of love.

What lies does the devil tell you that keep you from changing your lifestyle?

What are some of God's Words that can replace these lies?

Most likely, you will get pressure from well-meaning family members, friends, and coworkers who will try to discourage you from making these changes. At times, family members will tease you or make negative comments about your diet. You need to remember this often occurs because they need to justify their eating habits. I regularly have people telling me it is not worth all the trouble. They do not want to give up their lifestyles, and they enjoy eating whatever they like too much to give it up. These same people have health issues of their own, and some are limited in participating in physical activity. It will take an effort to stand up to people you care about and respect.

What pressures do you face from family members or friends that cause you to struggle on your diet?

Many people we will encounter are uneducated on the importance of diet. The only information they hear is from advertisements and magazine articles. This information is biased toward the product being sold or reviewed. Try to counterbalance these negative influences by talking with people you know who have opted for a healthy lifestyle. Ask them questions and get tips from them as to how they were able to change their lives. Go to dinner with them or go to their home for a meal to see that you can enjoy yourself while eating well.

At times, the medical field downplays the importance of diet both for prevention of illnesses and as a way to naturally heal our bodies. When I consulted with the hospital dietician after my surgery, she told me it was okay to eat anything and not to change my diet while undergoing treatment for cancer. I absolutely believe diet played an essential role in my recovery and allowed me to maintain my lifestyle while receiving chemotherapy and radiation. My body needed to have the proper nutrients to keep my healthy cells from being destroyed by the chemotherapy. Because chemotherapy tends to tire out a body, it was imperative that I provided it with the proper fuel to restore energy. Junk food drains the body, making it sluggish and slow. People in the medical field have their strengths and weaknesses. Just because they are in these professions does not mean they understand all the ramifications of healthy eating. They know what they know based on their education and advanced medical training. Many have not received training in nutrition. It is not that we should distrust our doctors, but we should be educated advocates for ourselves. Each one of us should take responsibility for our health. No matter whose advice you seek, you should always do your research and do not be afraid to ask them questions about their choice for your plan of care. You alone have your best interest at heart.

Do you put so much confidence in the medical profession that you fail to do your research when it comes to caring for your body?

Drug companies are promoting their products. They want the consumer to buy their drugs, so they run commercials that can be misleading. They downplay all the side effects. These ads quickly report the adverse side effects while showing healthy people happily enjoying life. The fine print is often hard to read and goes unnoticed.

At times, medication is necessary. However, quite often, nutrition can enhance or provide a better alternative. Make sure you do your research or talk with doctors who can help you make the changes necessary to decrease or eliminate medications that may be causing adverse effects on your body.

Are there any changes that you can make in your life that would help to eliminate the need for medication?

Just as drug companies can make everything sound so wonderful, you must also be aware of food advertisements. They can be very misleading. Commercials are written to convince people to buy products. You need to be a well-educated consumer and not take an advertisers word for the truth. Many ads use keywords that make their product sound healthy even though there is no real nutritional value in their food. You need to evaluate each product for yourself to make sure the food is worth eating.

What food advertisements have you found to be misleading?

Take some time to ponder these questions:

- Do you eat to live or live to eat?
- What foods do you include most in your diet?
- Are you addicted to food?
- Do you reward yourself by eating?
- Do you eat fast food?
- Do you eat junk food?
- Do you eat processed foods?

- Do you know what you are really eating?
- Do you read the packages, or do you take the manufacturers' word?
- Do you eat large portions?
- Do you drink a lot of water, or do you drink soda and sugary beverages?
- Do you feel you can eat anything you want because some medicines and surgeries can heal you?

One of the first questions to address is: **Do you eat to live or live to eat?** There is a difference. This question is important because the answer can determine how you value food, how you live your life and how well you maintain your body. The answer to this question determines whether or not you are invested in a healthy lifestyle.

How would you answer this question right now?

Eating to live: Food is essential to life. A well-balanced diet maintains your body, provides it with fuel, and allows you to lead a productive life. Healthy food helps you maintain a robust immune system and can also enable you to resist germs and fight infections. It can allow the body to heal when it is sick. The proper nutrients can help the body to develop, replace, and repair cells and tissues. A person must consciously eat the right foods and make sure they have a balanced diet for the body to function at its maximum capacity.

Living to eat: When a person lives their life to eat, much of their daily activity and routines are driven by their next meal, what they can snack on or where to get a sugar fix. Too often, a person consumes all the wrong foods.

Watching people at parties is fascinating. People will gather around the snack table, pull up a chair, and sit there all night consuming an enormous amount of food. Much of this food has little or no nutritional value. They wait for the next food item to be put on the table. People spend more time eating rather than enjoying each other's company. I used to do this as well. Then I would leave feeling sluggish, bloated, and have a food hangover the next day. Now that I am on a strict diet, I go to parties, and I sit away from the food table. I eat before I go so that my body gets the nourishment it needs. Parties are now more enjoyable because instead of focusing on the food, I get to enjoy good conversations with people. I have noticed the same occurs in restaurants. People are so focused on the food on the menu or what others have ordered that they lose the purpose of eating together: sharing good conversation while nourishing their bodies. There is nothing wrong with enjoying the food you consume. However, you need to consume the right food. Over time you will come to appreciate a healthy diet.

Food for thought:

1. Become more aware of how advertisements and other people influence your way of eating.

2. When you change your thinking so that you realize you are eating to live and not living to eat, does it change the way you see food?

Journal your thoughts.

TESTING THE CIRCUITS FOR OVERLOAD
(CHANGING YOUR DIET)

There are many circuits necessary to provide the power for the temple. These circuits have to be designed so to distribute the power evenly, or the wires will become overheated causing a fire.

Nugget of the day: Suddenly, they saw the fingers of a human handwriting on the plaster wall of the king's palace, near the lampstand. The king himself saw the hand as it wrote, and his face turned pale with fright. His knees knocked together in fear and his legs gave way beneath him (Daniel 5:5-6).

Have you ever thought about the phrase "the handwriting is on the wall" and wondered where it evolved? It is a phrase often used in conversations. How often does God put the handwriting on the wall for us and we miss it? It may not be literally on the wall, but He definitely gives us signs. It may be in the form of a Bible verse, a comment from a stranger, or that small voice inside us. God uses many sources to get His point across. We need to keep our eyes and ears open and trust our Dad to guide us through life. God has put the handwriting in the Bible. It tells us the importance of eating healthy diets and living healthy lifestyles. Take the time to read the writing.

My prayer is that you heed the "writing on the wall." Take our Father's advice and make good decisions. We all know our Father gives us this handwriting not to torment us, but to make our lives better and more fulfilling. When you follow God's advice, you will find your life becoming more productive. You will be able to live your life with less stress and find peace and joy that only God can give you. So spend some time reading the Word God has given us because it was written to help you, not hinder you.
****

Even after an electrician has planned out how to run the circuits throughout the home efficiently, there may be problems that arise. The owner may choose to plug in additional items into the circuit, or they are using faulty equipment, causing the breakers to trip. When this occurs, the electrician needs to check to see what is being powered on each outlet that feeds into that particular circuit breaker.

We too have to may have to take the time to evaluate and reassess our diets periodically. It is easy to fall back into old eating patterns when stressed or overworked. We can give in to food cravings, and then the food becomes a regular in our diet again, or we let peer pressure guilt us into eating foods we know we should not eat. Take the time and review what might hinder your ability to get into the practice of eating a healthy diet. You are responsible for your eating habits and making sure you do not overload your body with excessive food or poor food choices.

Food is a comfort for many of us. It may not be the taste of the food that is addicting as much as what it represents. Think about your comfort foods. Cookies may symbolize the joy of Christmas, fried chicken remind us of Sunday meals as a child, and hot chocolate warms us on a cold evening. Popcorn made in oil and coated with butter is what we ate at the theatre. One of the keys to eating and enjoying the new diet is finding new comfort foods. To do this, you might need to retrain your taste buds.

What foods give you comfort, and why?

What are some healthy foods you enjoy and might become new comfort foods for you?

Become aware of how you address your food. Become mindful as to how you talk to yourself subconsciously. When you talk about needing a sugar fix, chocolate, or a diet soda, you convince yourself you need this food in your life to please you or to help you survive. Work on changing your way of thinking, so you focus on how these foods are a detriment to your health. I often refer to junk food as "crap." One day while speaking to a group about my diet, I realized that when I call junk food crap, it gives it a negative connotation. It turns me off to eating something that I once enjoyed. After all, who wants to eat crap? My mouth no longer waters when I hear someone talk about cookies or candy. It is a different story if you speak to me about a tasty salad or a healthy snack.

What are some of the terms you use to address your unhealthy food and give it a place of honor in your life?

How do you address healthy food?

What are some terms you can use for healthy food to give you the same satisfaction?

Nutritious food is worth the cost. Many people complain that it costs too much to eat nutritiously. However, it is more expensive to treat cancer or other diseases than it is to eat healthily. Americans spend a lot of money on cars and homes. Every 4 to 5 years, many of us will sell our cars and get new ones. People will continually make home improvements and at some point will likely sell their house and buy a new one. We have to live in our bodies our entire lives, and they are our primary mode of transportation. Therefore, we should choose to live in a body that is at its optimum, as it needs proper exercise and nutrition.

Now you have a decision to make. Do you choose to live in a body that can be pain-free and disease free? Or will you live in a body that limits your activity with below-average performance?

There is research that has shown that people who consume mainly vegetables and fruits are not as likely to develop cancer or some other diseases. Many scientists believe that at least 30 percent of all cancers are directly related to diet. Some of these scientists believe the percentage is closer to 70 percent. [1] Cardiovascular disease, diabetes, and arthritis are just a few other diseases that are caused or worsened by eating a poor diet. People often spend a lot of money on food that does not nourish the body. Because much of the money may be spent at fast food restaurants or getting drinks and snacks at a convenience store, people do not realize how much money they waste on junk food.

List some of your unhealthy expenses this past week:

Educate yourself about what you are eating. Our bodies were not designed to eat chemicals. When God created us, He created us to be hunters and gatherers. We were meant to survive on diets rich with fruits, vegetables, whole grains, nuts, seeds, and lean meats. These foods give our bodies nourishment while they satiate our appetite. God provides us with all the nourishment we need. We were not meant to eat genetically altered food or food processed in a factory with chemicals. God designed produce to nourish our bodies. Altering the Review the book of Daniel. Daniel knew His God provided for him. He chose to listen and ate only vegetables and fruit. The results proved Daniel made the right diet choice.

Have you ever thought about the strength it took for Daniel to stand up to the chief official and refuse to eat unhealthy food?

The result was that all the men benefitted from eating Daniel's way. If it were not for his courage, others would have suffered the effects of poor eating. How can you be the strength for your family and friends?

Have you thought about how important it is for others to see you eating a healthy diet?
Your example may be just the one to help them change their eating habits.

Who do you care about that needs help in changing their lifestyle?

Spend some time in prayer, asking God to help you accept Daniel's challenge. Ask God to release the strongholds that are preventing you from accepting this challenge.

There is no perfect diet. Research has shown there is an alarming number of people in the United States who are overweight (68.5 percent) with 34.9 percent of those being obese. (2) This weight issue arises not only because of the amount of food people consume, but the type of food they consume. There are many diets out on the market. No one diet is the perfect diet. Every person you talk to will have a variation of the ideal diet. Each person believes his or her way is right. Each person responds to various foods differently to be at our best. Some people do best with little or no meat; others need some meat to be the most productive. Do your research. Understand the foods and what they offer to your diet. Then make an educated decision as to how you are going to eat. Know that you will have to make adjustments as your knowledge grows. I still tweak my diet and remove things I find I should not eat and add new foods I find that will enhance my diet. Again, pray in this area. Our loving Father gave us food to nourish our bodies. He knows what we need to live healthy lifestyles. Beware of fad diets or diets and foods that promise miraculous weight loss while still eating junk or processed food. Even if you lose weight on these diets, you are still getting empty calories, and you may be thinner, but not necessarily healthier.

Eat plant-based foods whenever possible. Plant-based foods are vital in your diet. These foods are vegetables, fruit, nuts, grains, and beans. They are usually best prepared raw or minimally cooked. Plants provide us with the essential vitamins and minerals that our bodies need to be healthy and fight disease. They contain fiber. Fiber is necessary in your diet because it aids in the elimination of waste products. As fiber passes through the digestive system, it removes waste, which can be disease-causing when not eliminated regularly. Fiber is often referred to as roughage or bulk. (3) Some good examples are brown rice (not instant), whole grains, oatmeal, popcorn, fresh fruit such as pears, bananas or apples, potatoes with skin, carrots, celery, bell peppers, and beans.

Keep cancer-fighting foods in your diet. Diets need to include antioxidants because they are crucial to your health. The antioxidants are potent vitamins, which help protect the cells in your body. The best sources of antioxidants are from foods that contain beta-carotene, lycopene, vitamins C and E, and selenium. (4) It is best to include an array of colorful vegetables in your diet since the different colored produce contains different phytochemicals, which will improve your immune system. (5) Use spices and herbs when cooking. They can help boost the immune system. Some of these are turmeric, rosemary, basil, and coriander.

Drink plenty of water: Our bodies consist of 60-75 percent of water. Water helps regulate body temperature, remove waste and toxins, and aids in the transporting of nutrients throughout the body. Water works as a shock absorber and helps improve nerve cell function. (6) These are just some of the reasons water is essential to our bodies.

Prepare food properly. When buying healthy food, protect your investment by preparing and storing it correctly. Wash all the fruits and vegetables to get rid of the pesticides. Steam vegetables until tender since overcooking removes the nutrients. When using oil for cooking, use only healthy oils. Burning or charring food creates carcinogens in food. Microwaving food decreases the nutritional value. If you choose to use a microwave, never use plastic containers as they release chemicals into your food.

Exercise Regularly: For some people, weight can be a problem and affect their overall health. Although a proper diet is essential to losing unwanted fat and then to continue to maintain your body weight, exercise is an added component, which will help to enhance the benefits you receive from eating a healthy diet. (7) Inactivity can cause you to gain weight. Both aerobic and anaerobic exercises play a critical role in maintaining healthy body weight. Cardio exercises (aerobic) have been shown to burn fat, especially the belly fat that people find hard to lose. When a person tries to lose weight by diet alone, they can lose muscle mass rather than fat. By performing resistive training exercises, they can maintain or build muscle mass. Although their weight may not decrease, and in some instances, it increases, it is because the person is adding healthy muscle mass. The higher muscle mass increases the body's metabolism helping a person burn more calories and maintain their new weight.

Be a well-informed consumer. Diet plays a significant role in how healthy you are and how you feel. Consumers must educate themselves about what types of foods their bodies need and how to read labels to avoid ingredients that negatively affect them. Just because a label says it is healthy or natural does not mean it is good for you. The government has very loose requirements regarding what companies can or cannot put on labels. Many of the foods labeled "natural" contain genetically modified organisms (GMOs). Processed food labeled organic can still have unhealthy ingredients added. The best foods to consume are non-processed foods, which include fruits, vegetables, grains, and lean meat. It is also important to buy organic and local whenever possible.
(Which foods should be organic will be addressed in a later chapter.)

Food for thought:

1. What steps can you take to become a well-informed consumer?

2. What have you learned in today's session that you can use to improve your lifestyle?

3. How has your frame of mind affected how you eat?

4. How can you change your thinking?

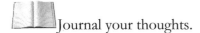Journal your thoughts.

Day 5

REWIRING THE TEMPLE
(BREAKING FOOD ADDICTIONS)

There are times after the electrician checks the circuits; he may need to adjust his work. When the temple owner uses the lights or outlets, he does not want to trip the circuit breaker.

Nugget of the day: Keep watch and pray, so that you will not give in to temptation. For the spirit is willing, but the body is weak" *(Mark 14:38).*

Take some time to study this verse. This verse is in the Bible to teach us a valuable lesson that takes years to grasp. What did Jesus do when His disciples were unable to keep watch for Him and fell asleep? Did He rant and rave at them, or give up on them? No, Jesus used the moment to teach them. Jesus knows we are not perfect, and He knows that no matter how hard we try, there will be times we will fail. He knows that there will be temptations in this world and we will, at times, succumb to them. Jesus wants us to know there is help. God will give us strength, and He will pick us up when we fail. He can break addictions and help us overcome temptations. We need to accept that we will have battles in this world, and we need to seek the guidance of our loving Father to overcome them.

My prayer is that you realize you are human, and with this humanness comes imperfections and struggles. Be patient with yourself and know it will take time to improve your diet and change habits. I pray that you learn to lean on God. His strength will sustain you when you feel as if the pressures of this world are too much to handle. If Jesus, the perfect One, can be patient with His disciples when they fail, you need to be patient with yourself. Rather than get down when you struggle, use the opportunity to grow in faith and learn to put your trust in the One who can help. He will break your addictions and the chains that bind you in this world. I also pray that you learn by Jesus' example and that you too are patient with others. Rather than getting upset with them when they fail, you need to gently point them to the One who can change their lives.

****

When a circuit is overloaded, there are warning signs that may occur. For example, the lights may dim, especially when turning on an appliance or using an outlet. The switch covers may be warm to touch, or you may hear a buzzing from the outlet or switch. You may notice there is insufficient power to use electronics, appliances, or power tools. Eventually, the circuit will trip, and no more power will go to the switches or outlets. The tripping of a breaker prevents the wires from overheating and causing a fire.

Our bodies also give us warning signs when we are not nourishing our bodies with the right nutrients or that the food we are eating is causing damage. Food can be addicting. Some of the warning signs are feeling guilty after eating foods we know we should not, eating even after we are full and feeling discomfort, feeling sluggish or sleepy after eating, or weight problems.

Food has always been part of our lives. When we were young children, our parents were responsible for providing us with a healthy diet so that we grew big and strong. It is now our responsibility to provide the proper nourishment for our bodies. We may have to rewire our brains as to how we view the food we eat or to break food addictions.

Junk food can be very addicting and can consume most of a person's thoughts. Therefore, we need to address this issue before attempting to change our diet. For many, a food addiction can be harder to break than a cigarette or alcohol addiction. Some research shows that sugar can be as addictive as cocaine. [1] The brain gets used to the sensation it receives from the junk food we take in, and it will continue to need more junk food to sustain that feeling. [2] People need to understand that eating a small portion of unhealthy food can lead them right back to their food addiction. You need to watch what foods you eat and understand what foods are addictive to you. For many people, the most addictive foods contain sugar, wheat, or dairy. [3]

Answer the following questions honestly to determine if you have a food addiction. Becoming aware of the problem is the first step to breaking the habit of poor eating.

- Do you continue to eat even when you have just finished a nutritious meal and are full?
- Once you start eating junk food, can you stop?
- Are there specific foods or drinks you feel you cannot give up?
- Will you keep eating even when you feel sick?
- Do you have physical withdrawals when removing certain foods from your diet?
- Do you feel tired or sluggish after eating?
- Does consuming the same amount or type of food not produce the same amount of pleasure as it once did?
- Do you use food to change your emotions (combat a lousy day or relieve your stress)?
- Do you feel guilty after you binge?
- Do you always think of food or drink, wondering when you can eat or drink it again?
- Does food take precedence over other areas of your life?
- Is food more important to you than having a healthy body or being physically active?

Food addictions are hard to break. However, if you are going to take charge of your diet and health, you are going to need to cut these emotional and physical attachments to certain foods and drinks.

When dealing with an addiction, realize that no matter what the habit is, it distracts you and it prevents you from honoring God in the way you should. Satan loves to feed into your addictions because it keeps you from doing God's work to your fullest potential. When you are overweight, not properly fed, or both, you have decreased energy and ambition. It limits your ability to do God's work. Realize that Satan is trying his best to pull you down and you need to go to the One who lifts you up. *The temptations in your life are no different from what others experience. And God is faithful. He will not allow the temptation to be more than you can stand. When you are tempted, he will show you a way out so that you can endure. So, my dear friends, flee from the worship of idols* (1 Corinthians 10:13-14).

What does God want to provide for you?

How have you seen God hold true to His promises?

Let us draw near to God with a sincere heart and with the full assurance that faith brings, having our hearts sprinkled to cleanse us from a guilty conscience and having our bodies washed with pure water. Let us hold unswervingly to the hope we profess, for he who promised is faithful (Hebrews 10:22-23 NIV). Too often the reason we do not see God's faithfulness is that we give up on Him. We pray, and when He does not answer our prayers on our timeline or exactly how we expect, we give up hope or we stop praying and seeking God's guidance.

What lies does the enemy tell you that hold you back from trusting in God that He can break your addictions?

How can you hold onto the promises of God?

Here are some suggestions for curbing your addiction to food.

Pray. Ask God to help you overcome your food addiction. Every time you have an urge to eat or drink something you know you shouldn't, immediately turn to the One who can give you strength when you are weak. *"Keep watch and pray, so that you will not give in to temptation. For the spirit is willing, but the body is weak"*(Mark 14:38 NLT).

What did Jesus do when He realized His disciples could not stay awake?

Restock your pantry and refrigerator. Remove foods that are unhealthy and addicting that may cause you to binge and replace with food that has good nutritional value. Stock your pantry with herbs and spices that can be used to enhance the flavor of your food.

Change your shopping habits. Plan your menus and only buy the ingredients needed to make healthy meals and snacks. Shop after you have eaten so as not to buy on impulse.

Put snack foods in small containers. This way, you will only eat a little at a time, and help you not binge on everything at once.

Avoid temptations. When going out to eat, make sure to look at the menu ahead of time. Choose your entrée even before entering the restaurant so you can make a healthy choice. Stay away from all-you-can-eat buffets or restaurants that offer you no healthy options.

Educate yourself about nutrition. It is much easier to stay on a healthy diet when you know why you are eating this way and how it affects your body.

Replace your old comfort foods with new comfort foods. Find a way to associate healthy foods with pleasure.
Only eat when hungry and control your portion size. It is okay to enjoy your food, but watch how much

food you consume at a sitting. Learning how much food to eat and how to portion your food sets you up for success. After each bite put the fork down, chew thoroughly and savor every mouthful.

Exercise regularly: Exercise not only helps you control your weight and improve your fitness, but it also raises the dopamine levels in your brain. Exercise helps control your brain's reward center.

Address your emotional needs: If you are struggling emotionally, it is much harder to watch the food you eat. You need to address the issues that are prohibiting you from being successful. If you need professional help, seek a Christian counselor.

Food for thought:

1. What foods are the most addicting for you?

2. What type of changes can you make in your diet?

3. What is holding you back from improving your diet?

4. Who can you look to for advice and support as you make changes in your diet?

5. Write a prayer asking God to help you improve your diet and to give you the motivation necessary to accomplish this.

6. Keep a log of your daily food intake, including all snacks. This diary will help you get a grasp on which foods you are eating and how much you are consuming.

Journal your thoughts.

Week 4

Day 1: Review Bible Verses
Day 2: Conserving Your Energy Supply (Buying Food)
Cleaning, Storing, and Preparing Food
Day 3: Using the Right Gauge Wire (GMOs and Organic Produce and Cooking with Oil)
Day 4: Quality Control (Food Substitutes)
Day 5: Juicing and Smoothies
The Dangers of Sugar

Day 1

When we try and give up foods that we have become addicted to or crave we need God's Word to get us through these times. Making changes can be difficult, but God can give us the strength to keep trying to improve our temples so they honor Him in every way. Food can become our idol.

Conserving Your Energy Supply (Buying Food): Psalm 136:25, Isaiah 1:19, 1 Timothy 4:4

Conserving Your Energy Supply (Cleaning, Storing, and Preparing Food): Nehemiah 8:10, Matthew 6:11, 1 Timothy 4:5

Using the Right Gauge Wire (GMOs, Organic Produce, and Cooking With Oil): Galatians 5:22-23, 1 Corinthians 10:23, Titus 2:12

Quality Control (Food Substitutes): Isaiah 33:2, Philippians 2:13-15, 1 John 2:16

Juicing and Smoothies, Dangers of Sugar: Matthew 6:13, 2 Corinthians 10:5, James 4:17

Weekly exercise: Try one of the food substitutes suggested on day 4 and report to the group what you tried

CONSERVING YOUR ENERGY SUPPLY
(BUYING FOOD)

To make the temple energy efficient, many factors need to be considered so that the builder installs appliances and systems that utilize the least amount of energy and ensure the temple is warm and inviting.

Nugget of the Day: You can make many plans, but the Lord's purpose will prevail (Proverbs 19:21).

Don't we all love to be in control? We like to be in charge and make our own decisions. The world teaches us that independence is a good thing and that we should not rely on anyone. God teaches just the opposite. He wants us to give up control and trust in Him. God wants to guide us through life, knows our true heart, and understands what is best for us. God knows what we were created to do in this world and how we can make a difference. When we try to make it on our own, we meet resistance and life often becomes a struggle. We encounter closed doors and have to take many detours. God can open these doors we need to pass through. There is only one requirement: We must relinquish control, letting God be in charge.

My prayer is that you realize God is a much better commander of your life than you. When you give Him complete control, you will be amazed at just how much easier life can be. You will find peace and joy that only God can give. It will replace the fear of going into unknown territory. We will stand in awe as we see what we are truly capable of accomplishing. We will find we can do things we never thought possible. Go ahead, turn over the wheel to God. At first, it is difficult, but soon it is nice to sit in the passenger seat. Enjoy the ride.
****

Much detail goes into choosing the appliances and heating and cooling system that will be installed to make the temple energy efficient. The architect also looks at other variables such as insulation, window and door seals, so that the heat in winter and cool air in the summer does not escape thus keeping the energy use and cost as low as possible. The initial cost of putting in quality equipment and materials may be higher but will produce lower energy bills. A good architect strives to design the temple to meet the people's needs, be a welcoming environment, and preserve our resources, while planning to keep the temple's operational costs as low as possible so the church funds can be used to help others and further God's Kingdom.

Eating healthy food is an investment in our lives, and we should take care of our resources. There are many things we can do to help ensure we purchase healthy, nutritious food. Conserving our energy supply (food) is essential to being able to nourish our bodies the right way. When we buy nutritious food, the body needs less quantity because it is getting quality. Eating healthy also requires us to store and prepare food correctly so it doe not spoil as there are no chemical preservatives to make it last longer than it should last. The cost of eating quality food may be higher initially, but it may lower our cost for medical care and improve our quality of life.

In their hearts humans plan their course, but the Lord establishes their steps (Proverbs 16:9 NIV). We need to learn to rely on God in every aspect of our lives, and this includes buying and preparing our food, especially as we begin this new journey. When we first start, going to the store can be a challenge because we will have to walk past the foods that once gave us comfort and our taste buds still long for. Before we even step foot in the grocery store, try praying. Pray that God gives us the strength to walk past the foods we are addicted to and that He helps us find pleasure in the new foods. We will be much more successful on this journey if we invite God to shop and prepare our food with us.

When you change your diet and eat food that is nourishing for your body, your food bill will most likely go up initially because you will have to restock your pantry and refrigerator with food that is healthy and clean. After you have made the initial investment, the food bill should not be that much different if you are cautious with what you buy. One of the biggest mistakes people make is buying too much food at one time. When the food is not laden with chemicals and preservatives, it will go bad much more quickly.

There are things you can do to lower your food bills and make sure you are getting the quality food your body needs. Here are some tips for buying food:

Prepare before you go to the store. Plan out meals and compile a shopping list. Do not add extra items to the cart. It is easy to want to buy extra fruit and vegetables, but if you are not going to use these in a timely manner, they will spoil.

Buy locally. Whenever possible, buy your food locally. Because the food is not transported long distances, it will be fresher, and it will last longer. Freshness accompanies an increase in nutritional value. Many cities have farmer's markets where people can go to buy a variety of fruits and vegetables. These local markets will carry the foods that are in season for your region.

Buy what is in season. The body responds best to eating the fruits and vegetables that are in season. When in season, the produce is usually more flavorful. During the different seasons, the body has different nutritional needs. [1,2] Some foods are good for more than one season.

- Spring: This is a season of new growth. Therefore, the foods you eat should represent this time. Leafy greens are ideal in the spring. Some of these vegetables include Swiss chard, romaine lettuce, spinach, basil, asparagus, broccoli, cauliflower strawberries, and honeydew.

- Summer: The body needs food that acts as a coolant and will help replace fluids lost from sweating. Summer foods include strawberries, watermelon, apples, pears, plums, arugula, eggplant, summer squash, tomatoes, zucchini, broccoli, cilantro, and peppermint.

- Fall: This is a time to prepare the body for winter. The body does best with warming autumn food. Foods to consume during this time are carrots, squash, brussel sprouts, hot peppers, pumpkin, grapes, pears, sweet potatoes, garlic, onion, ginger, and peppercorn.

- Winter: The body continues to need warming foods. Root vegetables are a good choice. Winter foods include carrots, potatoes, onions, winter squash, nuts, dates, kale, butternut squash, and brussel sprouts. Meats to eat during this season are beef and chicken.

"Natural" does not mean the same thing as "organic." Labels that say "natural" do not necessarily mean the food is healthy. There are minimal regulations as to what is required to put "natural" on the label. Therefore, the buyer must **BE AWARE**. The USDA states natural meat, eggs, and poultry must be minimally processed and contain no artificial ingredients. Since "natural" is not well defined, they can produce food with GMOs, pesticides, antibiotics, or preservatives. Often there are chemicals and sugars added to these products. [3]

Read the ingredients on all labels. Products you think may only have one or two ingredients can be deceiving. They may contain artificial colorings and flavorings. Many products contain high fructose corn syrup. Some manufacturers and stores that advertise they are health conscious can fool you. Many of these products offered might have ingredients you do not want to put into your body. You still need to read all product labels so that when you get the item home you have not wasted your money on a product you will not use.

Buy Non-GMO and organic products whenever possible. GMO stands for a genetically modified organism. The produce that can be GMOs includes corn, Hawaiian papaya, edamame (soybeans), zucchini, and yellow summer squash. Stores that sell the non-GMO product will have them marked as USDA certified organic or have a seal on them that they are verified by a third party not to be a GMO product. Unfortunately, many processed foods use GMO produce. Because of this, you should check the ingredients before purchasing processed foods. Dairy and meat products can also be affected when the animals have been fed GMO feed. Again, you should check the meat and dairy labels to verify GMO products have not been used. [4]
Organic refers to how the product is farmed and processed. Organic farming does not allow farmers to use

synthetic fertilizers, most pesticides, antibiotics, or growth hormones for livestock. It also excludes GMO products. Overall, organic produce is better for you to consume. Some produce does not have to be organic due to fruit or vegetables having thick exterior skin or shell preventing the edible part from being exposed to all the pesticides and chemicals. It is important to know which products should be organic and which do not have to be. (This is addressed tomorrow.)

Buy fresh, organic foods in small quantities. These products tend to spoil more quickly. It is better to go to the market several times a week rather than buying all the groceries at one time.

Frozen organic foods last longer and may be cheaper. These products are often frozen at the peak of their ripeness, so if you are on a tight budget, this may be a way to save money. Frozen vegetables and fruits can be bought in larger quantities because they last longer. It is best not to buy frozen foods that have been chopped, peeled, or crushed, because this may deplete some of the nutrition. [5]

Purchase grass-fed beef. Be cautious when determining that what you are buying is actually grass-fed beef. Some farmers use grain at the end of the animal's life so they can fatten them up. Some farmers give the cattle the option of grain. The cattle will choose the grain, and this ruins the nutritional value of the meat. The label needs to read one hundred percent grass fed. Grass-fed beef provides omega 3 fatty acids, which are important for brain and heart health. It also provides a higher level of vitamins and helps to decrease our cancer risks. [6]

Avoid canned food when possible. The linings of most canned foods contain BPA, which can interfere with the estrogen in your body.

Buy healthy seafood. Wild-caught Alaskan salmon and Sockeye salmon are the healthiest. Farm-raised fish can present with many of the same problems of land-raised animals. They have a decreased nutritional value, may be fed GMO products, and have diseases. [7] When eating fish, we want the omega-3's, but Dr. Mercola reports that farmed fish being fed grain can have up to fifty percent less omega 3s. [8]

Avoid buying products in plastic whenever possible: Plastic is not healthy to store our food in so try and buy products in glass jars or transfer the food to glass containers when you get the product home.

Food for thought:

1. Can you see that reading the product labels can be beneficial and can help you eat healthier?

2. How can you alter your shopping habits to improve your diet and still eat within your budget?

3. Which of these tips can you implement in your life now to improve your eating habits?

Journal your thoughts.

CLEANING, STORING, AND PREPARING FOOD

Choosing to eat healthily is an investment in your body. Therefore, you want to conserve the food you buy rather than waste it. Here are some suggestions to help with preserving the food.

Clean the produce. When you bring your produce home from the store, before putting it away soak it in water and vinegar to remove the pesticide and chemicals. Then place it in glass bowls with lids. Not only will this make it easier to grab healthy snacks on the run, but it also helps preserve the produce for an extended period.

Storage: Storing fruits and vegetables correctly helps to keep them fresh longer. Below are a few helpful tips.

Tomatoes are best stored on the counter to prevent them from losing their flavor. If you do put them in the refrigerator, leave them out on the counter for twenty-four hours before eating to restore some of the flavor.

Store potatoes in a cool dark place. Keep them away from onions to give them a longer life. Storing potatoes with apples will keep them from sprouting as quickly.

Greens are affected by heat. When I get them home from the store, I pour cold water over them and then dry in a salad spinner. Keeping the greens moist will cause them to spoil more quickly. Salad greens can also be kept in a salad bowl with a paper towel on top to absorb the moisture and then covered with a lid. Keeping the lettuce leaves dry is also important when serving in a salad. Since salad dressings are made with oils, the oil will be repelled from the wet leaves, making them less flavorful.

Avoid plastic and Styrofoam™ storage containers. Plastic and Styrofoam are common materials used to store and serve our food. Plastic water bottles are a convenience. Some studies show that these items can be detrimental to our health. When plastic is heated or made cold, it can be even more toxic. There are many chemicals in addition to BPA in the plastic that can wreak havoc on our bodies. Phthalates have been found to be toxic to the reproductive system. [1] Subjecting plastic to high heats such as a dishwasher or boiling water can cause the plastic to leach toxic chemicals into our foods. [2] Plastic is much harder to clean and can have grooves and lips that can allow bacteria to grow and contaminate our food. Therefore, it is best to use glass, ceramic, or stainless steel to store and serve your food.

Use glass containers. When possible, store food in glass containers. Glass containers will not leach chemicals into your food, and they are much more sanitary. They are easy to clean. Stock your cabinets with a variety of sizes of glass dishes with lids, making it is easy to store leftovers and to make healthy lunches to take to work. Glass is also suitable for keeping some of the fruits and vegetables in after they are cut up. Mason jars also make great containers. I store all my seeds, beans, nuts, and dry goods in glass canisters in the panty. By storing leftovers in glass dishes, it makes it more convenient to heat the food in the oven.

Choose cookware with care. We are working hard to keep chemicals out of our bodies, and yet many people cook with Teflon™-coated cookware to save time and make cleanup easier. Teflon is made with the chemical perfluorooctanoic acid (PFOA) and is a carcinogen. The pans, when heated to temperatures over 400 degrees, can expose you to fumes that cause flu-like symptoms in humans. It is called polymer fume fever. These vapors are also toxic to birds and kill hundreds of them a year. [3] When these pots and pans get scratched or start to flake, even more toxins are released into the food. [4] The best types of cookware to use to ensure our safety are glass, stainless steel, cast iron, ceramic, or clay cookware.

Aluminum has been associated with Alzheimer's disease. It is best to be safe with your health and avoid using aluminum pots and pans as well as aluminum foil. The stainless-steel cookware will have aluminum encapsulated in the stainless steel so that it does not touch the food. When baking foods, use glass dishes. Many safe baking dishes have lids that can be heated up to avoid using aluminum foil. Your health is worth the extra effort it may take to clean up after preparing your food.

Freeze food. Freezing fresh fruit and vegetables can help preserve them. Buying the fruit and vegetables while at their peak of freshness makes for better freezing. The best way to seal in the freshness is to freeze them as soon as they are brought home from the store. The key to keeping the food fresh is making sure the food is wrapped as tightly as possible to keep the air out of the produce. Maintain the freezer temperature at 0 degrees and do not overfill it. Overfilling the freezer prevents the air from circulating, and damage to the food will occur.

Buy fresh vegetables and place them in small containers so when you want some for dinner, you have a variety from which to choose. Then you have vegetables that are ready to prepare by steaming or in a stir-fry. I often put beans, onions, cauliflower, carrots, and broccoli together for a good vegetable medley.

Work ahead on food preparation. It can be hard to find time to cook or prepare healthy foods for lunches and dinners during the week. I have come up with an easy way to make meals for the whole week in a short period. Preparing ahead of time allows me to have a variety of foods available during the week. I steam most of my vegetables on Sunday. I prepare enough salad for several days, keeping ingredients that will make the salad soggy in separate containers so that I can add them quickly when packing my lunch. At this time, I also make any recipes that I want to use with my meals during the week. I put the food in small glass bowls, which makes it easy to grab them during the week for lunch. Mixing and matching the food allows me to have a variety of options for lunch and dinner. I am guaranteed to have a healthy meal even when I have to eat and run. Cutting up fresh fruit and vegetables and storing them in glass bowls in the refrigerator makes for grabbing a quick, healthy snack.

Prepare emergency packs of food. We all know that when we are hungry, it is easy to be tempted to go off our diets. You need to prepare for hunger emergencies. When at work, there is often tempting food in vending machines and laid out in lunchrooms. When driving, fast food is easily accessible and cheap to purchase. One of the keys to eating healthy is to have good, nutritious food available for just this purpose. You can make emergency kits to store in desk drawers, purses, and glove compartments of your car. Make packets of nuts, seeds, and dried fruits (without added sugars) to keep on hand. Preparing ahead of time can prevent you from breaking down and eating foods not nourishing to your body.

Food for thought:

1. How can some of these ideas help you to make more conscious, healthier choices?

2. How can you incorporate some of these ideas in your daily life?

3. Are you willing to forgo some of the conveniences to maintain or improve your health?

4. Are you more aware of some healthy food prepping or storing habits that can help you preserve your food and reduce health risks?

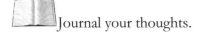Journal your thoughts.

USING THE RIGHT GAUGE WIRE
(GMOs and Organic Produce)

When the electrician wires the temple, he must make sure he uses the right gauge wire for the circuit.

Nugget of the day: Jesus told him, "I am the way, the truth, and the life. No one can come to the Father except through me *(John 14:6).*

There should be flashing lights and warning signs in this section of the Bible. People not only need to read this verse but also understand it and take it to heart. The Bible is the truth. It is our owner's manual for life. How often do people say if only life came with instructions it would be much easier? Well, it does; the Bible is a comprehensive and exact manual. The problem is, we humans do not like to be told what to do. God created this owner's manual for our benefit. Who better to create this manual than the Creator Himself? He knows exactly what we need. He knows how important every aspect of our life is and how we must care for our bodies, minds, and souls. People need to read it and understand it. How many of us buy a product and try to assemble it without reading the instructions? When completed, it often is missing parts, is unstable or needs to be redone because we think we can do it on our own. God knew we could not, and so He sent His beloved Son.

Jesus taught us how God wants us to live. However, we have preachers, teachers, and parents teaching us that we can live life however we want. We have health professionals telling us diet does not matter, and yet people have ailments they cannot heal. People tell us God is whomever we make Him. I have had people tell me eternity is what we make it; it will not be the same for everyone. God and Jesus do not change to fit our needs and desires. They are the one constant in our ever-changing world, and we always know what to expect from the Trinity.

My prayer is that you read your owner's manual thoroughly and live by its principles and laws. Not only trust what it teaches about faith but also how to live healthy lives and how to take care of yourself. I pray that you accept God and Jesus for who they are and do not make them who you want them to be. I pray all my nugget buddies accept Jesus as their personal Savior and do not veer from His teachings. God has not changed the rules of healthy eating. Our bodies have not evolved to thrive on processed or chemically laden foods. I also pray we raise our children to believe the truth and know how to live full and satisfying lives in Christ. After all, we want them to spend eternity with us.

****

The electrical wire transfers the current from the circuit breakers to the temple. The wire's purpose is to transfer the energy with the least amount of resistance. There are various gauges of wire depending on the amperage of the circuit breaker. If the wire is too small, the electricity can melt the wire and be a fire hazard or overload the circuit and cause the circuit to trip. Ground fault outlets need to be used near water sources to prevent electrocution.

Eating fruits and vegetables provides us with the nutrients our bodies need to operate efficiently. If the quality of the produce is altered, it can cause health issues. It is essential to know what is in the food we are purchasing.

Then God said, "Look! I have given you every seed-bearing plant throughout the earth and all the fruit trees for your food (Genesis 1:29). Notice who gave us our produce? God did, and He does not make mistakes, nor do His creations need improvement. God knew how to create each type of crop so that it would nourish our bodies. Humans often think they can do better than God, and therefore, they have tried to alter what God perfected. The results: making a product that is far less than perfect. Let's face it; we cannot do better than God. Once we realize God does know what He is doing, our world will be a much better and healthier place to live. We need to use the right foods to nourish our bodies.

GMOs are genetically modified organisms, which means that the genetic makeup of the plant is altered with

DNA from another source such as bacteria, viruses, or other living organisms. The genetic alteration of the seeds can be from a source not even in the plant kingdom. These crops have been modified to have an increased tolerance to pesticides. Thus, farmers use even more pesticides on these plants. Since these plants are designed to tolerate being sprayed with glyphosate herbicides, the weeds the farmers were trying to control have now become resistant to this chemical. In turn, more spray is needed, causing consumers to ingest higher levels of this dangerous chemical. Some farmers are even reverting to using older, more toxic herbicides to try and control their weed problem. (1) Glyphosate is destroying the nutrients in the soil. Therefore, the plants are becoming nutrient deficient.

The American Academy of Environmental Medicine has issued a warning to doctors. It reads as follows: "With the precautionary principle in mind, because GM foods have not been properly tested for human consumption, and because there is ample evidence of probable harm, the AAEM asks: Physicians to educate their patients, the medical community, and the public to avoid GM foods when possible and provide educational materials concerning GM foods and health risks." (2) Studies have shown that GMO products can have an impact on our health. After the introduction of GMOs in 1996, Americans have experienced more health problems. More Americans are presenting with three or more chronic illnesses. They also have more food allergies and reproductive and digestive issues. Autism, as well, is on the rise. Although there is not sufficient research to confirm that GMOs are a contributing factor, doctors groups such as the AAEM tell us not to wait before we start protecting ourselves, and especially our children who are most at risk. (3)

The crops that can be genetically modified are as follows:
- Corn
- Soybeans
- Cotton
- Canola
- Sugar Beets
- Alfalfa
- Papaya
- Zucchini and yellow squash
- Potatoes
- Apples

Not only do we consume these products, but many farm animals also consume grains that are GMO products. This is why we must be cautious as to what type of meat we consume.

Organic produce can be expensive but worth the added cost when buying certain fruits and vegetables. The produce cannot be a GMO product since farmers cannot plant GMO seeds. Pesticides harm our health and have been shown to have some adverse effects on fetal and childhood development. One study has shown that eating organic produce not only reduces our exposure to pesticides but also improves the food's nutritional value. Organic foods help with healthy growth and development during early childhood. It has also been shown to reduce our risks to certain diseases, including cancer. (4) Another benefit to eating organic fruits and vegetables is that the antioxidants in the produce are significantly higher. (5) We know that antioxidants are crucial to ridding our bodies of free radicals, which can harm our bodies. (This is in week 5, day 4)

Some fruits and vegetables are more affected by pesticides, and so if you are on a limited budget, these 15 foods should be purchased organically or homegrown:
- **Apples***
- **Strawberries***
- **Grapes**
- **Celery***
- **Peaches***
- **Spinach**
- **Sweet bell peppers**

71

- **Nectarines**
- **Potatoes***
- **Tomatoes**
- **Hot peppers**
- **Kale**
- **Summer squash**
- **Collard greens**
- **Cherries**

> * These foods have the highest concentration or pesticide counts, with potatoes being the highest. Apple peels retain pesticides, and although they can be peeled, the skin is the healthiest part. The skin contains phytochemicals to reduce cancer risks and heart disease. Some foods may be healthier when they are organic. For example, research has shown the antioxidant levels in organic strawberries are 19 percent higher.

The produce that does not have to be organic is as follows:
- Onions
- Sweet corn (Make sure it is not a GMO.)
- Pineapples
- Avocados
- Cabbage
- Sweet peas
- Asparagus
- Mangoes
- Eggplant
- Kiwi
- Cantaloupe (domestic)
- Sweet potatoes
- Grapefruit
- Papayas (make sure it is not a GMO.)
- Mushrooms

Remember that it is important to include vegetables and fruits in your diet, so do not eliminate them if you cannot afford to buy organic produce. Properly clean your produce to remove some of the pesticides. The above lists can change as new GMO products are developed or the use of pesticides on produce changes. As an educated consumer it is good to periodically check on the changes to these lists.

COOKING WITH OIL

For the Lord your God is bringing you into a good land—a land with brooks, streams, and deep springs gushing out into the valleys and hills; a land with wheat and barley, vines and fig trees, pomegranates, olive oil and honey; a land where bread will not be scarce and you will lack nothing; a land where the rocks are iron and you can dig copper out of the hills (Deuteronomy 8:7-10 NIV). God gave man pure oil from plants that He knew would nourish our bodies. Once again, humans have decided that they could make oils that were better to use. They found they could manufacture cooking oils more cheaply, allowing them to make a more substantial profit. We need to be informed consumers and use only the oils that will nourish us and not harm our bodies.

Some of the oils that we use to cook with have adverse effects on our bodies. There are health benefits when using certain oils on uncooked dishes, but when heated, they are damaged, thus making them harmful to consume. If we are going to make a conscious effort to eat healthy food, we must also make a conscious effort to prepare our foods so as not to damage the nutrients or poison the body.

The most important thing to consider when cooking with oil is whether or not it is stable when heated up. Many oils will oxidize when heated. One of the indicators for how well the oil responds to heat is its smoke point. A smoke point occurs when the oil is heated to a certain temperature, causing the oil to break down and release free radicals. This breakdown lets off small lines of smoke. Few oils can withstand heat without losing their stability. When cooking with oil, it is essential to know its smoke point temperature. When the nutrition world started to research cooking oils, they learned that canola, vegetable, and seed oils were linked to many health conditions. People then turned to olive oil. Although olive oil has many health benefits, these are better obtained when the oil is not heated.

The best oil of choice for cooking, in my opinion, is coconut oil. It offers many health benefits both when heated and when used in foods that are not cooked.

Coconut oil: Over 90 percent of the fatty acids in this oil are saturated, which makes coconut oil stable enough to be resistant to heat-induced damage. [1] The smoke point is 350 degrees for unrefined oil and 400 degrees Fahrenheit for refined coconut oil. [2] Therefore, it should not be heated to higher temperatures. Use coconut oil for cooking, consuming as is, and as a substitute for other oils in recipes. Studies have shown that coconut oil has many benefits. It strengthens our immune systems, improves brain and heart function, increases energy, and is good for the hair. [3] Dr. Axe reports that coconut oil may also help prevent and treat cancer, reduce inflammation, reduce arthritis, cure urinary tract and kidney infections, improve digestion, prevent gum disease, prevent tooth decay, and improve skin issues. [4]

Coconut oil is a healthy saturated fat, and we need saturated fats for cell function and growth. This oil has rich antioxidant properties. These antioxidant properties inhibit the oxidation of other molecules. Oxidation can produce free radicals that cause damage to our cells. Coconut oil is high in medium and short chain fatty acids so that the body can easily digest it, and it is sent immediately to the liver to help with energy production. [5] It can also help improve blood cholesterol levels. [6] Studies have shown that coconut oil improves the HDL (good cholesterol) and it lowers the LDL (bad cholesterol) and triglycerides. [7]

Over 40 percent of this oil is composed of lauric acid, making it the richest natural source available. Only breast milk has higher levels of lauric acid. Research has found that lauric acid helps in fighting viruses and disease and improving the immune system. [8] Lauric acid has also been shown to work as a preventative against some cancers. [5] It has also been found to help boost metabolism, which may help with weight loss. Other possible benefits of this oil are that it can improve thyroid health, help promote bone strength by allowing better absorption of calcium, vitamin D, and minerals, and helps improve the way the body handles blood sugars since it can improve insulin use within the body. Coconut oil can also improve the immune system and brain function. Some research shows it helps reduce the symptoms of patients with Alzheimer's. Add coconut oil to smoothies, tea, salads, oatmeal, or other foods.

Oil pulling is another effective way to use coconut oil, as it is an excellent way to remove bacteria in your mouth. It is also believed to help eliminate toxins in your body. The benefits are that it kills bad breath, heals bleeding gums, and decreases inflammation. It also soothes a sore throat, prevents cavities and whitens teeth. [9] When I went through chemotherapy, it helped prevent the metal taste most people get as a side effect. Technique: Do oil pulling the first thing in the morning, possibly while in the shower. Use 1-2 tablespoons of coconut oil and swish it around in your mouth 10-15 minutes. When finished, spit it out in the toilet and rinse your mouth with warm water, spit out the water and then brush your teeth.

The two types of coconut oil to be familiar with are:
1. **Unrefined coconut oil** may also be referred to as virgin or pure. This form has more of a coconut flavor and retains more of its nutritional value when being processed. Virgin and extra virgin coconut oil are the same,

unlike olive oil, which has different amounts of fatty acids.

2. **Refined coconut oil** is more processed than unrefined. When refined, most people notice less of the coconut taste. This form also has a higher smoke point when used for cooking. If the oil is refined, make sure that is done by a chemical-free method (expressed pressed).

Olive oil: Olive oil is a healthy oil when not heated. [10] When heated, the oil is prone to oxidative damage. It is best used when added to cold foods such as salads or drizzled on vegetables. It is also beneficial for applying to the skin. There are two types: virgin and extra virgin olive oil. Extra virgin oil has many more health benefits.

Olive oil is primarily composed of monounsaturated fat called oleic acid, which is an antioxidant. It also contains omega 3 and 6 fatty acids. [11] Fatty acids are essential to improving our brain health, sharpening our focus and memory. Due to its antioxidant properties, olive oil may help slow the aging process. [10] This oil has also been shown to assist in the prevention of cardiovascular disease, arteriosclerosis, and certain types of cancers. [12] Olive oil contains polyphenols that strengthen the cell walls and improve the elasticity of the arterial wall. [13] Other studies have shown olive oil to be effective in weight loss and help with depression and mood disorders. The healthy fats in olive oil help to balance hormones when dealing with PMS and menopause.

Olive oil will hold its nutritional value longer when stored in a cool, dark place. As soon as you use the oil, replace the lid. It is best to buy smaller containers so that it does not expire before it is all used. Be cautious when purchasing olive oil since many of the brands contain GMO canola oil or other additives. Research the brand to know where it is from and who is bottling the olive oil to ascertain its purity.

Vegetable oil: These oils include corn, soy, sunflower, safflower, or canola oils. These oils are composed of polyunsaturated fats referred to as omega 6s, which in large amounts are harmful to the body. The body needs to keep a ratio of 4:1 between the Omega 3s and 6s in our system. When these are unbalanced, and the omega 6's outnumber the omega 3's in our cells, complications arise. [14] This imbalance has been linked to heart disease, type 2 diabetes, irritable bowel syndrome, inflammatory bowel syndrome, asthma, and cancer. [15] Over ninety percent of canola oil is a refined oil that is genetically modified. To improve the stability of the oil, it is partially hydrogenated. This partial hydrogenation can have adverse effects on our health. [16,17]

Hydrogenated oils: These are called trans fats and are made when hydrogen is added to vegetable oil, causing it to solidify when it is at room temperature. This oil has been shown to raise the bad cholesterol, lower good cholesterol, and increase our risk of heart disease. Manufacturers use it in their food products because it has a longer shelf life. Some restaurants choose to use this because they do not have to change their oils as frequently. Products that often contain trans fats are baked goods, potato, corn, and tortilla chips, fried foods, margarine, and creamers. In the United States, if there are less than five grams of trans fat per serving the label does not have to include this information. People often eat more than one serving at a time, thus increasing their total intake of trans fats. In turn, this will affect their health. Get in the habit of reading food labels before purchasing a product.

Food for thought:

1. What have you learned about using organic and non-GMO produce, and does this information affect how you will shop in the future?

2. What did you learn about cooking oils?

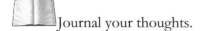Journal your thoughts.

QUALITY CONTROL
(FOOD SUBSTITUTES)

When building our temples, we only want to use the best quality materials so that the building does not collapse or need constant repairs.

Nugget of the day: He cuts off every branch of mine that doesn't produce fruit, and he prunes the branches that do bear fruit so they will produce even more *(John 15:2)*.

God most definitely knows His children. He knows us better than we know ourselves. God will watch over us. He will remove the obstacles that are detrimental to our living Christian lives if we allow Him. There may be things we do in this world that bring us pleasure while doing them but cause us much strife later because of the guilt and shame they inflict. There are also good things in our lives that bog us down and make us too weary to focus on our calling. God will help us to find our priorities and focus on what we need to do. We do not want to miss out on accomplishing our callings and let distractions rob us of this joy. The world makes us think that to be successful we need to be continuously busy. The devil also wants us to be distracted, so we do not achieve what God has planned for us. God knows we need to focus only on a few things, and we need quiet time to rest our bodies and minds as well as to find time to sit in our loving Father's presence.

My prayer is that we ask God to prune our lives. When we ask this of God, we must also listen to Him. Although we often want to do everything in this life, in reality, we cannot. Instead, when we remove the distractions in our lives, we will bear much fruit in this world. We will find that when we focus on what God is calling us to do, we will be successful. So let God expose any distractions in your life that need to be removed. Then get down to the business you are supposed to be doing. When you accept that God is in charge and allow Him to prune your life, you will not only find you have time to do His will but to also stay in the Word and recharge. Then you will live the life God has planned for you, and you will produce much fruit.
****

Using cheaper building supplies may save on the initial cost of constructing the temple, but the materials will not last as long and will require extra maintenance. Often, the appearance of the temple will also be altered so that it is not as appealing to look at and can appear to be run down. More importantly, the use of poor quality materials can cause the temple to collapse and cause personal injury or death to the congregants.

Why spend your money on food that does not give you strength? Why pay for food that does you no good? Listen to me, and you will eat what is good. You will enjoy the finest food (Isaiah 55:2). I feel very strongly that God is telling me to print this Bible verse in large print so that we do not miss what He is asking of us. God took the time to provide us with nourishing food so that we could live productive lives. He does not want us to waste our energy, time, or money on things that are detrimental to our health. Just as buildings need to be constructed with high-quality materials, we need to nourish our bodies with the right foods. Too often I witness friends and family members who miss out on all life has to offer by choosing to eat poorly. Their energy level is low, and they have so many aches and pains that they are limited in how much physical activity they can do in a day. They are missing out on not only fulfilling their calling God has for them but also on experiencing all the beauty and wonder God has given us in this vast world.

What about you? Are you able to live life to its fullest, or do you allow food to be a priority in your life, thus limiting what you can do?

Think about all the food you have consumed today. How much of it was healthy, nourishing food?

Were there things you missed out on today because you lacked energy or were physically limited?

Why should we consume food that is unhealthy for us when we have healthy alternatives? We should be informed consumers if we want to benefit from the food we eat. The guidelines for labeling food are very lax, and manufacturers use this to their advantage to get consumers to buy their products. We cannot let their sales tactics lure us into buying food that can harm our bodies or provide no nutritional value. When we do, we are wasting our hard earned money. Let's make sure we put our money into quality food so that we use the right food to fuel our bodies and keep us healthy.

We need to be healthy food advocates for our families and ourselves. The only way to do that is to be well educated as to what type of foods we should eat and what we need to avoid. When we choose to buy packaged food, we need to inspect each label as to what ingredients are in the product. Do not assume that a product is healthy for you. Even simple products can have chemical additives. The other day I bought balsamic vinegar from a health-conscious store, expecting it would be free of chemicals. Much to my surprise, later that day when I was preparing to make a salad, I checked the ingredients, and it had caramel coloring in it. Don't get caught buying products you will not use once you get home. Check each label before purchasing the product.

You can still use many of your favorite recipes when substituting for the ingredients that should not be in your diet. Avoid the following products and ingredients. I've included suggestions to use as a replacement:

Breadcrumbs: Instead, use almond meal, rolled oats, or ground flaxseed seasoned with herbs. My kids love almond meal baked chicken. I roll the chicken in organic eggs and then almond meal seasoned with many herbs. I place this in a glass baking dish with a small amount of coconut oil on the bottom and bake it at 350 degrees.

Canned tomatoes: Most canned tomatoes have BPA on the can's lining. Due to the high acidity of the tomatoes, the BPA leaches into the food. BPA is associated with an increased risk of breast and prostate cancers, reproductive abnormalities, heart disease, and neurological problems. [1] I often substitute organic tomato sauce or marinara to make homemade pizza, chili, or other recipes calling for canned tomatoes. Many companies now sell tomato sauce in jars, or you can make homemade tomato sauce.

Cereal or instant oatmeal: Steel cut oats or quinoa with berries and seeds make a good breakfast. I usually make enough oats to last for the week and put servings in small glass bowls so that they are easily accessible in the morning.

Chips or salty snacks: Replace chips with air-popped popcorn. Use organic butter and then sprinkle with Himalayan salt and cayenne pepper or cinnamon. You can also make zucchini or kale chips.

Chocolate: Use cacao nibs or powder in your recipes. Cold pressing unroasted cacao beans makes cacao a healthy form of chocolate. Cocoa is not healthy because they roast the cacao beans at a high temperature. This process destroys the antioxidants that are in the cacao bean. [2] If you must have chocolate, buy only organic dark chocolate bars with cacao count over 72 percent. Add cacao nibs to berries or other fruits. The sweetness of the fruit brings out more of the chocolate taste we are used to without getting the sugar and additives. One of my favorite treats is strawberries, blueberries, goji berries, and cherries topped with sunflower seeds, pumpkin seeds, ground flax seed, and cacao nibs.

Croutons: Substitute almonds, nuts, and seeds on a salad. I love to use pumpkin seeds, chia seeds, sunflower seeds, and goji berries to top my salad.

Dressing: It is easy to make your own dressing with healthy ingredients. Use ingredients such as lemon juice, olive oil, various kinds of vinegar, and herbs. I use balsamic vinegar and olive oil on my salads. Unhealthy salad dressing can take away some of the nutritional value of your salad and add unwanted calories. Many salad dressings that say they use olive oil also use other oils, so make sure to read the full list of ingredients.

Eggs: Some people want to keep eggs out of their diet. If this is the case, substitute chia seeds for eggs. Mix 1 tablespoon of seeds to 1 cup of water and let them sit on the counter for 15 minutes before adding to a recipe.

Energy bars: Most energy bars are loaded with sugar and other ingredients that are not of any nutritional value. If you choose to buy energy bars, make sure they use natural sweeteners such as dates, honey, or maple syrup. I make my energy balls by placing 2 cups pitted dates, ½ cup almonds, 2 cups raw cashews, 1 cup figs, ½ teaspoon of cinnamon, ½ cup raw coconut, and 1 tablespoon of vanilla extract in a blender and then adding 4 tablespoons of water. When it's well blended, add any other ingredient to enhance the flavor. I also like to add ½ cup cacao nibs and ½ cup oats. The mixture should be moist but not sticky. I then roll them into balls and place them in a glass container to store in my refrigerator. These make a great snack.

Fast food: Many fast foods have little nutritional value. Many restaurants serve more food than anyone should consume at any one meal. The average fast food meal contains 1,205 calories. One meal is over half of the recommended daily allowance of 2,000 calories, and most of these are empty calories. [3] There are often so many additives that we are not getting the nutrition we need in these meals. Research has shown that people who frequently eat fast food have more depression, heart problems, and weight issues. [4] When traveling, look up what restaurants are in the area beforehand so that you are prepared and do not make bad food choices. When I travel, I prepare food ahead of time and take it with me. I make salads and meals that do not need to be heated up. I make hard-boiled eggs that I can eat for breakfast and bring my smoothie maker. I also have a variety of nuts, seeds, fruits, and cut-up vegetables. It takes a little extra planning, but it is worth the effort. By eating a healthy diet when I travel, I have good energy and no digestive problems. Initially, this may seem like a lot of extra work, but when we get into the practice of eating healthy all the time, we will prefer to be prepared because we know how much better our bodies feel when they are well nourished.

Flour: Instead of using white or wheat flour when baking, use coconut flour or almond flour.

Fruit juice: Fruit juice contains high levels of fructose, a form of sugar, which is released rapidly into the bloodstream. When eating fruit, we get the benefit of fiber, phytonutrients, and antioxidants. The fiber helps to slow the absorption of sugar into the blood. Fruit juice, especially if processed, does not offer the same benefits as the fruit. [5] Making a homemade fruit smoothie can be an alternative to fruit juice, as can drinking filtered water with lemon, lime, or orange slices added. I have learned that many smoothies sold at restaurants and juice bars have extra sugar and additives, so you need to beware of this too. Always ask what ingredients are going into your smoothie or other food.

Hot chocolate: Every once in a while, on a cold night, we need something extra to comfort us. I find my hot cacao mixture to be a good substitute. I use 8 ounces organic milk or coconut milk, ½ teaspoon vanilla, 2 tablespoons cacao powder, ½ teaspoon cinnamon, and ½ teaspoon honey. The taste may be different than what we usually associate with hot chocolate, but I find it comforting and a special treat.

Ice cream: Ice cream is loaded with sugar, and the dairy can be difficult for the body to digest. I have purchased a machine that allows me to make fruit ice cream. I place my frozen fruit in the machine, and it makes it into a frozen swirl. I then can add toppings such as cacao nibs, raw coconut, or nuts for a delicious treat.

Instant rice: Use wild rice, brown rice, or quinoa. Quinoa is a whole grain that is a complete protein and can be used as an alternative to rice or pasta in most recipes.

Margarine: Replace this with organic butter or avocado puree.

Mayonnaise: A great substitute is mashed avocado or Greek yogurt.

Meat: If you do not want to use grass-fed beef or organic chicken, then you can substitute 1 ounce of meat with ¼ cup cooked beans or lentils. Grill large portabella mushroom caps in place of burgers. Instead of meat on a salad, you can use nuts or seeds. To boost the flavor of the nuts or seeds, you can toast them in a skillet.

Microwave popcorn: The bag itself is lined with perfluorooctanoic acid, which is the same toxic chemical used in Teflon cookware. Many of the companies that produce this product use trans fats. Microwave popcorn contains diacetyl, a chemical used as a butter substitute. This chemical has been known to cause "popcorn workers' lung" because the workers repeatedly inhaled this chemical. [6] This chemical is also linked to affecting your brain health. Many companies have gotten rid of this chemical but if you are going to eat microwave popcorn, check the ingredients. You can use air-popped popcorn and flavor it as you like. I like to add cayenne pepper and organic butter to season my popcorn. If you use salt, use Himalayan salt.

Non-organic potatoes: Use organic potatoes. Conventional potatoes are high in pesticides. The USDA Pesticide Data Program has identified 35 different pesticides on these potatoes. Six of these pesticides are known or probable carcinogens, 6 can be toxic to reproduction or development, 7 are neurotoxins, and 12 are suspected of disrupting hormones. [7,8] If you do not use organic potatoes, another substitute with more nutritional value is sweet potatoes, which can be used in any potato recipe. These potatoes nourish the body with many vitamins including vitamin A (beta-carotene), vitamin C, manganese, copper, pantothenic acid, and vitamin B6, potassium, dietary fiber, niacin, vitamin B1, vitamin B2, and phosphorus. Another alternative for mashed potatoes is mashed cauliflower.

Vegetable oils: Replace vegetable oils with coconut oil. Another alternative when making a stir-fry or vegetable dish is to use organic vegetable broth. You can use olive oil for recipes that are prepared at room temperature or on cold items.

Pasta: Use zucchini, cucumbers, or spaghetti squash in place of pasta. Cucumbers and zucchini can be shredded, or you can use a spiral kitchen appliance to make these veggies into noodle form. To use spaghetti squash, cook them just like any other winter squash. Scoop out the seeds and rub the inside with salt and olive oil, then roast in a 400° oven for 45 minutes until the flesh is completely tender. Use a fork to gently lift out the tender flesh in long, delicious strands. Quinoa can also be used as pasta.

Pizza crust: There are many recipes on the Internet on how to make a pizza crust out of cauliflower.

Soda, diet soda, and sports drinks: Most diet soda contains aspartame, which increases sugar cravings and can cause weight gain. Soda can contribute to kidney problems, heart disease, cancer risks, type 2 diabetes, belly fat, fatty liver disease, and dental decay. [9] The phosphoric acid has been shown to decrease bone density, increase acidity, and decrease the nutrients in the body. [10] Sports drinks often have large amounts of sugar. Instead of these drinks, use coconut water or filtered water with a splash of lemon, lime, or orange. Another alternative is unsweetened tea. When drinking tea, make sure the tea bags do not contain epichlorohydrin or are made of plastic.

Sour cream: Replace in recipes with Greek yogurt.

Sugar and sweeteners: Researchers at the University of California-San Francisco have shown that sugar is a contributing factor in approximately 35 million deaths around the world each year. [11] Sugar increases the risk of breast and ovarian cancers, feeds cancer cells, suppresses the immune system, decreases calcium and magnesium absorption, contributes to obesity, causes copper and chromium deficiencies, contributes to heart disease, causes hyperactivity, increases crankiness, impairs focus, and increases the risk of arthritis. Sugar is an inflammation-causing ingredient. [12]

It is best to limit any sweetener, but when a recipe calls for sweetener, you can substitute maple syrup or honey. Replace 1cup sugar with ¾ cup pure maple syrup or raw honey and reduce recipe liquid by 3-5 tablespoons. Unsweetened applesauce or dates made into a paste also works well in most recipes.

Aspartame and artificial sweeteners: These sweeteners have been linked to headaches, change in vision, sleep problems, memory loss, dizziness, hives, joint pain, diarrhea, change in moods, seizures, abdominal cramps and pain, fatigue, and weakness, as well as brain cancer. (13) The body cannot completely break down these sweeteners, so they are often stored in the body and can lead to weight gain. These sweeteners change the gut microbiome, which has been associated with diabetes. (14) The use of artificial sweeteners tricks the brain into thinking it is going to get something sweet. Since there are no accompanying calories, the body craves carbs, increasing your dietary intake. These sweeteners may be addicting. Some other names for artificial sweeteners include Splenda™, saccharin, acesulfame potassium, and sucralose.

Table salt: Table salt has been shown to increase hypertension. All of the natural minerals are stripped from this product and then replaced with potassium iodine in potentially toxic amounts. It is stabilized with dextrose, which turns it purple and then bleached white. (15) Himalayan salt is a healthy choice to use as a replacement. Himalayan salt has many benefits for our bodies. This salt contains all 84 elements found in the body, and it promotes bone strength, healthy ph balances, sinus health, blood sugar health, and vascular health. It also regulates water content in the body and prevents muscle cramps. (16) Another healthy alternative is Celtic sea salt.

Tortilla wraps: Use lettuce leaves as a substitute.

Veggie dips: Hummus, avocado dip, or homemade salsa make nice vegetable dips.

White bread and food made out of white flour and refined flour: White bread provides empty calories and may contain bromide. Potassium bromate is a dough conditioner that many commercial bakers use. Bromide can disrupt the function of our thyroid gland. Bromide causes the body to have lower levels of iodine. Iodine is needed in our body to fight cancer and tumor formation. (17) If you want to eat bread, choose whole grain bread with this listed as the first ingredient on the package. Some bread, labeled as wheat bread, hearty grain, or 9 grains, may not be whole grain bread. (18) There are recipes on the Internet on how to make healthy bread.

Avoid products that have the following ingredients in them.

- **Artificial colors:** Many of these are linked to allergic reactions, organ damage, birth defects, fatigue, asthma, hyperactivity, skin rashes, headaches, and cancer. The most common ones used are Red 40, Yellow 5, and Yellow 6. All of these have known carcinogens in them. (19,20)

- **High fructose corn syrup:** This ingredient is in many processed food items. Statistics show that the average person consumes over 60 pounds of this a year. (21) This sweetener has been linked to weight gain, diabetes, cancer, high blood pressure, heart disease, an increase in cholesterol levels, leaky gut, and fatty liver, and liver stress. (22)

- **Monosodium glutamate (MSG):** MSG is an excitotoxin, which has been found to cause damage to nerve cells, destroy brain cells, and cause neurological disorders. MSG has also been found to increase a person's appetite, causing weight gain, and is often found in canned vegetables, processed meat, Chinese food, potato chips, and soup stock. People who are sensitive to MSG may have reactions to it. Some of the symptoms include headaches and heart palpitations. MSG has many other names, so when looking at labels, we need to be educated consumers. Some of these names are: hydrolyzed vegetable protein, calcium or sodium caseinate, hydrolyzed plant or animal protein, yeast extract, glutamate, textured protein, soy protein isolates, barley malt, glutamic acid, vegetable protein extract, natural flavor, and malt extract. (23,24)

- **Partially hydrogenated soybean oil:** Not only does this contain trans fat, but it also contains soy. Often the soy is a GMO product, adding another harmful component.

- **Soy products:** Most soy products are genetically modified. They contain anti-nutrients and toxins. These interfere with the absorption of vitamins and minerals. Soy products may also affect Alzheimer's. [20] One report shows that soy can elevate the blood level of estrogen up to 22,000 times the normal level. Soy contains phytoestrogens, which can mimic estrogen and wreak havoc on both women who have too little or too much estrogen production in their bodies. [25,26] Soy can also block stomach enzymes and zinc absorption. Many believe the only safe soy products are organic fermented soy products, which rids the soy of the anti-nutrients it contains. [27]

Food for thought:

1. Are you spending money on food that is not nourishing you or your family's bodies, and is this food contributing to health issues?

2. How can you change your shopping habits so that you buy nutritious food that you and your family will enjoy?

3. What food substitutions can you implement at this time to help your family improve their diets?

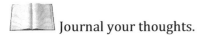 Journal your thoughts.

Day 5

JUICING AND SMOOTHIES

Nugget of the day: I realized that no one can discover everything God is doing under the sun. Not even the wisest people discover everything, no matter what they claim (Ecclesiastes 8:17).

Wouldn't it be nice to understand everything God has planned for our lives? What if every time we opened the Bible, we had a clear understanding as to what God had to say? Would we stay in the Word? Sometimes we have to sit back and marvel at the greatness of our God. He is capable of doing anything at any time. Our God is the only Being that could write a book which continues to baffle and challenge even the most knowledgeable scholars yet is simple enough for the ordinary person to read and find comfort in it. Who else could pen a verse that can address the needs of many people and also provide insight into many situations? The Bible is written with such supreme wisdom that it is the only book that is as alive and fulfilling today as it was when first penned because it never ages. Not only is the Bible still alive, but so is our God. He still performs miracles in our lives, and He continues to have an active role in the world. Rather than trying to figure God out, we need to appreciate His superiority and allow Him full access to our lives. Rather than question Him, we need to trust Him and let Him guide us. Any good soldier obeys his captain and knows the captain is privy to information that he cannot always share with those beneath him. We need to know that we are not privy to all the information that God possesses. As the captain, God knows that too much information could be detrimental or cause us to make irrational decisions.

My prayer is that you realize that God is in control, and He has far more knowledge than you can ever imagine. Take some time to appreciate just how great our God is and thank Him for being in control and leading you through life. Accept that God always has your best interest at heart. He will protect you and watch over you when you step out of the way and follow Him. Good soldiers place trust in their leader and allow the captain to give the orders. Imagine how much easier your life would be if you would surrender to our all-knowing and all-powerful God and let Him be in charge.

****

Do you ever take the time to marvel at how much thought and love God put into giving us food for life? God has given us a beautiful array of colors, shapes, and tastes to choose from when nourishing our bodies. Nutrients abound in these foods, and each one has a unique purpose. These fruits and vegetables not only serve to nourish us, but to maintain a healthy body and help heal our bodies from many sicknesses and diseases. There are so many varieties of fruits and vegetables to choose from that our pallets will never get bored. We have dulled our taste buds by giving them so many man-made foods that we have lost our taste for real food. Let's return to eating real, God-given foods, and our taste buds will rejoice once again.

There are so many fruits and vegetables that offer us so many nutrients, but we cannot eat them all in one day. By juicing or making smoothies, we can compact these fruits and vegetables to get more nutritional value out of our foods. Juicing involves extracting the juice from the pulp of the fruits and vegetables and removing much of the fiber. In smoothies, the fruits and vegetables are finely chopped and pureed so that it retains all of the fiber and juice in this thick drink.

Juicing and smoothies are similar in that they can combine a variety of vegetables and fruits in one drink so that we get many of the nutrients our bodies need daily. They also present unique advantages. Eating these vegetables and fruits instead of juicing or blending them can fill us up too quickly, limiting our nutritional intake during the day. For many people, juicing and smoothies are the only way to get the recommended daily intake of vegetables and fruits.

We should be careful not to allow too much of our diets to be taken up with too much meat or food that offers little or no nutritional value. The recommended daily serving of vegetables and fruits is 6-8 servings. Drinking juice or smoothies can help you reach this goal. Another advantage of blending our vegetables and fruits is that our bodies utilize the nutrients much better when the blending process breaks them down.

People who are actively receiving cancer treatment may find blending their produce a much easier way to get the nutrients they need to keep their bodies strong to enable them to fight cancer. Juicing and smoothies are especially helpful for those who have trouble swallowing.

Benefits of juicing or drinking smoothies include:
- **Providing the body with phytonutrients.** These are essential in helping fight cancer and boosting our immune system.
- **Making it easier for the body to digest vegetables and fruits.** We don't often chew the fruits and vegetables enough to break them down so that our bodies can utilize the nutrients. When they are in liquid form, it is easier for our bodies to digest.
- **Detoxifying the body**. When using the right combination of vegetables, juicing and smoothies are an efficient way to detoxify the liver and intestines.
- **Providing the body with a broader array of vegetables and fruits in our diet**. They allow us to ingest vegetables and fruits we usually would not eat due to taste or texture.
- **Hydrating the body**. Watery fruits and vegetables can hydrate our bodies.
- **Retaining the nutrients**. Cooking and baking vegetables and fruits often reduce the number of nutrients in the food. Using produce in the raw form preserves the nutrients.

Juicing and smoothies have specific advantages and disadvantages.

Advantages of juicing: Drinking twelve ounces of juice allows us to take in two to three pounds of vegetables and fruit. [1] It is best to juice mostly vegetables, with minimal fruit, since fruit is higher in sugars and calories.

Juicers extract the juice from the fiber. Nutrients are digested more quickly when the fiber is not present in a drink. By removing the pulp, a person can get more vegetables and fruits at one sitting. Juicing places less stress on the digestive system. We can extract seventy percent of the nutrients from the produce when juicing, and because there is no insoluble fiber, our bodies absorb one hundred percent of these nutrients. (2)Juicing is better if you are having intestinal problems or difficulty breaking down your food.

Disadvantages of juicing: When juicing, the fiber is eliminated, therefore allowing the juice to get into the bloodstream very quickly, which can cause a spike in blood sugar. Juicing cannot be used as a meal replacement because juice does not have protein. It is more expensive at first due to the cost of a good juicer, and it requires more fruits and vegetables to juice. Juicing takes more time and has more waste. It can be difficult and time-consuming to clean the machine.

Advantages of smoothies: They can be made using a blender. Smoothies retain the fiber, which aids the digestion system and improves elimination. Since there is fiber in the smoothie, it allows for the slower release of the nutrients and helps to remove the toxins in the digestive system. The slow release of nutrients helps us to feel fuller for an extended period and does not cause a spike in the blood sugar. Chia and flax seeds can be added to provide the body with healthy omega-3 nutrients and protein. Adding protein to a smoothie makes it a meal. Using a blender to make smoothies can be more cost-effective.

Disadvantages of smoothies: Some of the nutrients attach to the fiber and therefore, are eliminated rather than utilized, so it loses some of its nutritional value. It is harder on the intestines due to them having to digest and absorb the fiber. Some people do not like the consistency.

How to make juice/smoothies:

1. Blend the chia seeds and flax seeds first. The body digests flax seed and chia seeds more efficiently when they are ground. Grind them first because when they are put in with fruits and vegetables, they often don't get ground entirely.

2. Keep produce as cold as possible. Using cold produce to help prevent the blades of the blender from getting too hot because if the ingredients get overheated, it may decrease their nutritional value. Chop up the produce into small chunks and do not overload the blender since this makes the blades work harder, thereby increasing heat. Frozen fruits and vegetables work great, and they do not spoil.

3. Use organic vegetables and fruits when possible, especially for produce that is more prone to being contaminated by pesticides. If we are eating healthy, we want our bodies to consume the most nutritious foods possible.

4. Start slowly. Juice vegetables that are easier to digest and that you enjoy. As you get used to juicing, you can gradually add new vegetables.

5. Be cautious with the fruits and some vegetables. It is best to use mostly vegetables with only one serving of fruit so that there is not a lot of sugar released into the bloodstream. Also, be cautious with using excessive amounts of vegetables that have high sugar content.

6. Don't always use the same produce. By alternating the vegetables and fruits, we allow the body to get different vitamins and minerals it needs to maintain its health.

7. Use lemon or limes. These counterbalance the bitterness of some of the vegetables. They are also useful to help improve the alkalinity of the body.

8. Make only enough juice to use in one sitting. The nutritional value starts to decrease after fifteen minutes of air exposure, so it is best to drink immediately. (3) If you make excess, it will store for up to twenty-four hours in an airtight glass jar. If there is air in the jar, it will cause oxidation.

9. Drink a smoothie on an empty stomach. It is best to drink two hours after a meal or wait twenty minutes to eat a meal. Other food prevents the body from absorbing the nutrients quickly.

The best vegetables and fruits to use for juicing and smoothies are: aloe, apples, avocado, beets, berries, bok choy, broccoli, cabbage, carrots, celery, citrus fruits, cherries, cranberries, cucumber, dandelion greens, ginger, kale, mustard greens, papaya, parsley, pineapple, spinach, tomatoes, and wheatgrass.

THE DANGERS OF SUGAR

How can something that tastes so sweet be so wrong for us? Many people associate sugar with being a special treat and use it as a reward for doing something good. Sugar is often misused in our diets. As I have become more aware of the dangers of sugar, I am concerned about how we allow it to control our lives and destroy the people we love. I have been guilty of using sweets as a reward for my children and myself. I have allowed sugar to interfere with my health, leading to excessive weight. It took hard work and determination to get sugar out of my diet. Rather than see it as a treat, I now see it as a vice that can damage my body. Take a look around you and see how sugar has caused harm to your family and friends. How many of your loved ones have illnesses that are caused by or worsened by sugar?

How has sugar disrupted your family or friends' lives?

As I look at my surroundings, I struggle with how sugar disrupts the lives of those around me. I am frustrated as students who receive meals from school are fed chocolate muffins and chocolate milk for breakfast and are told this is a well-balanced diet. Later these same children eat entrees with little nutritional value, consume fruit cups with heavy syrup, and get juice laden with sugar for lunch. They are told this is a healthy diet, and it will give them energy. I also see parents send their beloved children to school with lunchboxes packed with chips and cookies because they are giving them a special treat, only to see these children struggle throughout the day. At first, these children cannot sit still and then later, as the sugar high wears off, they cannot stay awake. I see teachers continually reprimand students all day for being unable to sit still and having poor behavior, and then when they finally do sit quietly, give them candy as a reward. It is hard to watch as people who struggle to perform their daily activities due to obesity continue to consume large amounts of sugar. Then there are those who work out regularly in the gym so they can go home and eat some sweet treat as a reward and they cannot understand why they can't lose weight.

When I was at the cancer center, the clinic only offered sweet treats to patients and had large candy bowls filled with chocolate on the counters. I cringe when I hear doctors tell cancer patients sugar does not have a role in causing cancer, affecting its progression, or altering their prognosis.

Holidays are a time of overindulging in cookies and candies and people laugh about putting on weight during these seasons. For many, rather than find this appalling, they see it as a holiday tradition. Some people plan their vacations around dining out and visiting all their favorite eateries such as bakeries, ice cream shops, and candy stores. When people quit looking to food as the central part of the vacation, they will be in better health to be more active. They will have the energy to take hikes and see the available sights.

Sugar is highly esteemed in American society. The ironic thing is that when consumed, this reward only lasts for several seconds, maybe several minutes if a person takes time to savor the sweetness. Then it is gone, but the consequences of the few moments of heavenly bliss remain in our bodies for a more extended period. Please don't tune me out because I am talking about a subject that you find brings comfort in your life. For some people, there is nothing wrong with enjoying a sweet treat on a special occasion. Sugar becomes a problem in our lives when it controls us, causes us health problems, interferes with our lives, or is an obsession.

You need to carefully evaluate whether or not one piece of candy or a sweet treat will trigger you to overindulge in sugar. For some, abstaining from sugar is the right thing to do to ensure that it does not control you. Others can eat sugar sparingly.

Have you ever taken the time to contemplate what the sweet item you are about to put in your mouth is going to do to your body?

How can you use visualization as a tool to discourage you from eating sugar, knowing what it is going to do to your body?

"Keep watch and pray, so that you will not give in to temptation. For the spirit is willing, but the body is weak" (Matthew 26:41)!

Temptation: the desire to have or do something that you know you should avoid. Something that seduces or has the quality to seduce. (1)

Would you say sugar could be a temptation?

How does Jesus advise us to deal with temptations?

We all have vices. We frequently realize these vices are not suitable for our well-being. For some, these vices are food related, and sugar can be the biggest culprit. They cause us to gain weight, limit our activity, or have food-related health issues. No matter what the vice is, we need to deal with it for us to live fulfilling lives.

Have you ever taken the time to think that sugar, when it is an addiction, is something the devil can use to prevent you from fulfilling your calling and living a joyous life?____ If you do, how is he using it?

The serpent was the shrewdest of all the wild animals the Lord God had made. One day he asked the woman, "Did God really say you must not eat the fruit from any of the trees in the garden" (Genesis 3:1)? The devil knows each one of our weaknesses, and will use them against us and it is to his advantage to keep us sluggish, immobile, and unhealthy. When we are not feeling our best, we are unable to put our best effort into fulfilling our God-given calling. We need to realize that sugar may be the tool he uses against us.

Do you see sugar interfering with your calling?   If so, in what way?

Not all sugars are harmful for us. There are two different types of sugar. **Natural sugars**, which come from fruits and vegetables, are called fructose and glucose. Glucose is essential to our bodies as every cell depends on it for energy. (2) Our bodies can use glucose immediately as fuel. The remainder of the glucose is stored as glycogen in our liver and muscles for further use. The brain and nerve cells depend on glucose, as this is their only energy supply. The body stores excess glucose as fat.

Fructose is not as versatile. The body finds fructose harder to break down because the liver is the only place this process occurs. The benefit of getting fructose from fruits is that fruits also contain many other essential nutrients, vitamins, antioxidants, and fiber. An advantage of the fiber is that it allows the body to absorb the fructose slowly so that it can break down this sugar. This slow process will not overload our liver or cause the fructose to turn into fat unless we eat excessive amounts of fruit.

Refined sugars are processed sugars. Our bodies utilize these sugars differently. Refined sugar is digested quickly, causing blood sugar to spike. Because of this rapid spike, a person does not experience a full sensation and will continue to consume more food. (4,5,6)

We could consider refined sugar as the Satan of the food world. Sugar deceives our bodies into thinking they need the sugar rush, and then it wreaks havoc in our bodies, causing us to have to deal with its consequences, including sickness and pain that could be avoided just by abstaining from this terrible vice. We Americans are often fooled into thinking that sugar enhances our lives, rather than hindering them. All one has to do is watch television for half an hour and see the commercials which show us how sugar can transform our fatigue into energy. They try to convince us that sugar will make us happy when we have a bad day, or that it is a reward we deserve. Sugar-laden food promotions lie to us about their benefits and fail to warn us about the problems it can cause in our lives. Since we seldom see commercials promoting healthy foods, it is easy to be tricked into thinking we want and need refined sugar in our diet.

The average American consumes one hundred thirty pounds of sugar a year. (7) We are not always aware of how much sugar we are consuming because manufacturers have come up with new ways to disguise sugar in their products. We need to familiarize ourselves with these other names and check the labels for these forms of sugar. We are most familiar with high fructose corn syrup or corn syrup, but there are many others. Here is a list of some of the most common aliases for sugar: fructose (natural sugar from fruits), rice syrup, lactose (natural sugar from milk), sucrose (made from fructose and glucose), barley malt, maltose (sugar made from grain), glucose (simple sugar, product of photosynthesis), fruit juice, and dextrose (form of glucose). (8) These added sugars contain empty calories. Empty calories are mostly made of sugars and solid fats and offer little or no nutritional value to our diet. The body is unable to use up all these calories, and so it stores it as fat in the body. In 2010, the National Institute of Health reported that in children between the ages of two and eighteen, forty percent of the calories they consumed were considered empty calories. (9)

How does it make you feel to know that you are throwing away your hard-earned money to buy foods that have little nutritional value with high amounts of sugar, which can contribute to increased weight problems and other health issues?

There is research available saying both that sugar affects cancer cells and that it does not. So for a moment, let's play the devil's advocate and say that sugar does not affect the cells. Does this mean that we should go ahead and allow this in our diet and not be concerned with how much we consume? What is one of the high risks of cancer? Obesity. What is one of the leading culprits of obesity? Sugar. Sugar is responsible for making the brain think it is hungry. Therefore, people eat more food, and then sugar is stored as fat in the body, creating a vicious cycle. (10) Statistics show that the average American takes in twenty teaspoons of sugar each day. (11) The excess sugar we take in is turned into body fat, which, in turn, leads to many diseases such as heart disease and hypertension, type 2 diabetes, dementia, and cancer. (12) Some of the fat produced from excess sugar, not stored in our fat cells, is stored in the liver, which contributes to non-alcoholic fatty liver disease. The role of the liver is to remove the toxins in our bodies, process the food nutrients, and regulate body metabolism. (13) The liver is also responsible for regulating and getting rid of excess sex hormones. Excessive estrogen can be a contributing cause of cancer. (14) When the liver gets overloaded with toxins, it fails. Hmmm, it sounds like we want to keep our liver healthy to assist our body in preventing sickness or allowing our body to heal from any illness or disease. So we need to eliminate sugar.

Other research has shown that sugar is taken up by cancer cells at a rate of ten to twelve times more than healthy cells. (15) To detect sugar-hungry tumor cells, the PET (positive emission tomography) scanners use radioactive glucose. A PET scan is one of the most accurate tools for identifying cancer growth. (9)

As I mentioned previously in this book, sugar addictions can be hard to break because of the release of dopamine into the brain. Our bodies crave this "high" sensation and will continue to want to experience this feeling, thus craving more sugar. We need to find replacements, such as exercise, that can release the dopamine into our brains. To break our sugar addictions, we need to detoxify the body. We will be much more likely to break our sugar addiction if we quit cold turkey. Unfortunately, sometimes this comes with withdrawal symptoms. Not only do we have to deal with the physical withdrawal, but also the emotional withdrawal, which can be more significant. The physical withdrawal from sugar usually only lasts a few days. Some of the symptoms may be fatigue, anxiety, irritability, depression, poor sleep, heart palpitations, or rapid heartbeat. (16) These withdrawal symptoms are due to toxins leaving the body while breaking the addiction.

Remember, if we go back to eating sugar because we do not like going through the withdrawal, we will have to go through the whole process again the next time we try to quit eating sugar. Rather than focus on the symptoms, focus on how our bodies are ridding themselves of these nasty toxins. Visualize how our bodies are recovering. I find relief when I offer myself a reward for getting through a tough time. Make sure the reward is something that will enhance your healthy lifestyle such as a hike on a favorite trail, a fun activity, or a new book on healthy living. When you look at the positives as you make the changes, and see the good things that are happening in your life, it is much easier to be victorious.

Ways to beat your sugar addiction and eat healthier:

Pray for God to help you overcome your sugar addiction. Ask God for the strength to overcome this weakness. Post Bible verses on the refrigerator and pantry shelves so that you are reminded to seek God's assistance in moments of weakness.

Remove foods with refined sugars from your home. Remove all the foods that will tempt you to eat refined sugar. Clean out your pantry, refrigerator, and freezer.

Adopt new comfort foods. We all like to have a special treat now and then. Find something that tastes good and can give you some nutrition when you eat it. Finding a healthy food that you may not always be able to afford as a regular staple can be a good comfort food when you need a treat. Try new healthy recipes and keep the ones that give you comfort in an easy to find place so that you can make them when you need something special.

Find a group of friends to share food ideas. When you have a friend or group of friends with whom to share new recipes and try new things, your new lifestyle can be an exciting adventure.

Choose healthy sugars such as fruits. The fiber in the fruit helps to slow the release of glucose into the bloodstream and helps to decrease the appetite. Be careful drinking fruit juice because there is no fiber, so the sugar is released quickly into the bloodstream. Although fruit has many health benefits, eat it in moderation.

Use cacao nibs. Cacao nibs can add chocolate flavor when added to the fruit. You receive the benefits of chocolate without adding sugar to your diet.

Exercise. Exercise will help to lower the extra glucose in the blood and also helps to decrease the body's resistance to insulin. Physical activity will also cause the brain to release dopamine, serotonin, and endorphins, which help to improve your mood and well-being.

Eat proteins and vegetables. Eat adequate amounts of protein and increase your vegetable consumption. Most experts agree that a person should have .36 grams per pound of body weight. Sufficient amounts of protein help to slow the rate of carbohydrate absorption and stabilize the blood sugar. When people lack protein, their bodies can crave sugar and carbohydrates.

Eat smaller quantities of food more frequently. This helps to balance your insulin and control your appetite.

Lose weight or control your weight. Abdominal weight gain increases insulin resistance, and the higher intake of simple sugar adds more calories, which can cause additional weight gain. [17]

Add fermented foods to your meals. Fermented foods can help control the urge to eat sweets. Fermentation also provides bacteria that helps with digestion and detoxing the body so that fructose is not as taxing on the liver. There are several good choices for this, including organic yogurt, kimchi, natto, sauerkraut, fermented vegetables, and kefir produced from grass-fed milk. [18]

Use natural sugars. Natural sugars have some nutritional value. If you must use some form of sugar in food, use natural sugars. These natural sugars have antioxidants, which help fight cancer. Some of these products are honey, maple syrup, and molasses. However, these should still be used sparingly in your diet. [19]

Use supplements. Vitamins B, C, and zinc, as well as the trace mineral chromium and amino acid L- glutamine, help to reduce sugar cravings and symptoms of sugar withdrawal. [16] The mineral chromium helps insulin control blood glucose and helps with energy production. It also regulates blood sugar, so it does not have ups and downs. Use 200 mcg once a day, at the start of any meal, to prevent the sugar surges that often leave you reaching for more sugar later. [20]

Reward yourself. Sugar is often a reward for many reasons in a person's life, such as making it through a hard day, celebrating an achievement, or having a good workout. Instead of using sugar, find something else that is healthy to reward yourself. These rewards could include a nice walk, watching a movie, or having a healthy meal with a friend. Set up milestones you wish to achieve as you embark on this journey. As you begin to lose weight due to your healthy lifestyle, look forward to buying new clothes.

Do not substitute artificial sweeteners for sugar. Artificial sweeteners have been proven to increase weight gain, causing people to overeat and crave sweets more. They trick your body into thinking it is going to get a high-calorie intake, which in turn alters the hunger signal. Many of these sweeteners contain genetically modified ingredients (GMOs) from soy, corn, or sugar beets. [21]

Food for thought:

1. There are many recipes for healthy smoothies on the Internet, find several and try them and report to your group how you liked them.

2. Do you consume excessive amounts of sugar in your diet, and how does this affect your health?

3. What foods could you use as your comfort food when you want a sweet treat that would not have an adverse effect on your health?

4. If you have a sugar addiction, what steps can you take to break this addiction and are you willing to make the effort to remove sugar from your diet?

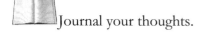Journal your thoughts.

Week 5

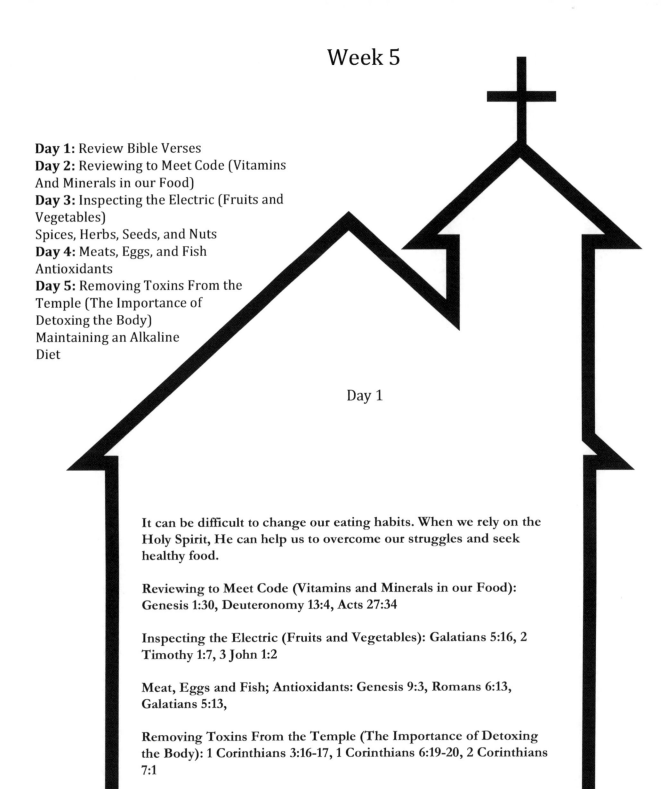

Day 1: Review Bible Verses
Day 2: Reviewing to Meet Code (Vitamins And Minerals in our Food)
Day 3: Inspecting the Electric (Fruits and Vegetables)
Spices, Herbs, Seeds, and Nuts
Day 4: Meats, Eggs, and Fish
Antioxidants
Day 5: Removing Toxins From the Temple (The Importance of Detoxing the Body)
Maintaining an Alkaline Diet

Day 1

It can be difficult to change our eating habits. When we rely on the Holy Spirit, He can help us to overcome our struggles and seek healthy food.

Reviewing to Meet Code (Vitamins and Minerals in our Food): Genesis 1:30, Deuteronomy 13:4, Acts 27:34

Inspecting the Electric (Fruits and Vegetables): Galatians 5:16, 2 Timothy 1:7, 3 John 1:2

Meat, Eggs and Fish; Antioxidants: Genesis 9:3, Romans 6:13, Galatians 5:13,

Removing Toxins From the Temple (The Importance of Detoxing the Body): 1 Corinthians 3:16-17, 1 Corinthians 6:19-20, 2 Corinthians 7:1

Weekly exercise: Try one new vegetable or fruit that is discussed this week.

REVIEWING TO MEET CODE
(VITAMINS AND MINERALS IN OUR FOOD)

The electrical code is a set of regulations established by the government. An electrician must adhere to this code when installing the wiring. An inspector will come to the temple and inspect it to make sure that the wiring meets the code.

Nugget of the day: Then God said, "Look! I have given you every seed-bearing plant throughout the earth and all the fruit trees for your food (Genesis 1:29).

God does not make mistakes. When He created us, He also made sure He provided all we needed to live on His earth. God gave us beautiful, nutritious food that would not only sustain us but also be pleasing to our palate. Why human beings thought they could improve on God's foods is something that baffles me. God added the perfect amount of nutrients to each variety of plants He created. He added no chemicals because He knew they would harm our bodies. As Christians, we are to adhere to God's teachings, and yet many of us miss the Bible verses relating to nourishing our bodies. God felt our physical well-being was essential and He included this frequently in the Bible.

My prayer is that you realize you must take care of your physical body if you are going to be able to fulfill your calling on this earth. God would not have given instructions on how to eat healthy if He did not see it as essential. If you struggle with eating right, ask God for guidance. Ask the Holy Spirit to give you the willpower needed to resist the temptation to eat foods that harm your body. Ask that He help break the addiction of food and help recondition your taste buds. Our loving Father knows best, but you cannot reap the benefits of living a good, quality life unless you listen to Him!

✳✳✳

When an electrician wires a temple, he has to follow specific guidelines for the temple goer's safety and protection. Following the code, helps ensure the electrician wires the temple correctly.

Our bodies need a combination of vitamins and minerals to be able to function efficiently. Poor nutrition leads to obesity, stress, fatigue, and illness. We cannot nourish our bodies adequately if we do not know what nutrients they need to maintain a healthy state. I have included a list of the nutrients found in the various foods that God has provided for us. Take some time to become familiar with these nutrients. These are God's code for good health.

Dear friend, I hope all is well with you and that you are as healthy in body as you are strong in spirit (3 John 1:2). We all know that good health is no accident. It takes hard work to keep our bodies in their optimal state and allow for healing when sickness is present. We cannot live life to the fullest if our bodies are depleted of energy or are sluggish due to receiving the wrong type of fuel. We are each responsible for educating ourselves and making sure that we are physically and spiritually fed on a daily basis, to live lives that are pleasing to our loving Father. *Pay careful attention to your own work, for then you will get the satisfaction of a job well done, and you won't need to compare yourself to anyone else. For we are each responsible for our own conduct (Galatians 6:4-5).*

How does it make you feel that God knowing that God went to all the trouble to create the vast array of natural foods available to us because He believes that nutrition is essential to us living healthy lives? Explain.

Are you making sure you are physically and spiritually fed a healthy diet daily?

What actions are you taking to ensure you are getting the right nutrition?

If God expects us to take pride in ourselves, shouldn't that include taking care of our bodies and minds so that we are as healthy as possible?

Are you taking pride in the body and life that God gave you?

Studies have shown people who eat diets rich in fruits and vegetables reap many benefits such as lower risks of cancer, heart problems, diabetes, and fewer illnesses overall. Each food has a specific combination of nutrients that make it unique, just as each one of us is a unique creation in Christ. Because each food has a unique makeup, our bodies do best when we add variety to our diet. By eating a variation of the foods that God has provided for us, we can improve our quality of life.

When preparing meals, there are some guidelines we should follow to ensure our bodies get the proper nutrition at each setting:

- Fifty percent of each meal should consist of vegetables and fruits, and the majority of this section needs to be vegetables. Try to provide a variety of vegetables with different colors and textures to get a variety of nutrients at each meal.
- Twenty-five percent of the meal should consist of whole and intact grains, quinoa, or brown rice.
- The last twenty-five percent should be a protein such as fish, organic chicken, beans, or nuts.
- Add herbs and spices to the meal to enhance the flavor as well as to add additional health benefits.
- Remember that when using oils for cooking the food, we need to make sure it is a healthy oil, such as coconut oil. Use olive oil to garnish vegetables that are not heated.
- The beverage of choice should be filtered water.

There are so many foods God has given us that I cannot list all of them. I have tried to include the most nutritious ones. If there are some new foods on this list you have never tried before, be adventurous. Remember to make healthy living a fun hobby; get excited about trying new foods and finding new recipes. Take time to study the vegetables and fruits before eating them and look at how beautifully God created them. Enjoy the smells and savor the taste, taking time to acknowledge how much love God has put into the food that He has prepared for us. The more we appreciate these foods, the more we will want to eat them.

Each vegetable and fruit comes with a unique composition of vitamins and minerals. When we become familiar with the nutrients our bodies need and the roles each one fulfills, we can become more aware of the foods we need to eat to ensure we are getting the proper nutrition.

Antioxidants: Antioxidants are chemicals produced by the body or obtained from fruits, vegetables, and grains. These chemicals neutralize free radicals, which are found in our bodies and can cause damage and promote sickness and disease. Free radicals are highly reactive chemicals formed when an atom or molecules either loses or gains an electron causing it to be unstable. Our bodies require some free radicals for healthy cellular function. However, when there is a high concentration of these free radicals, they damage our cells and cause many health problems. The antioxidants bind to the free radicals neutralizing them and preventing cell damage.

Vitamin A: This vitamin is key to maintaining eye and skin health, promoting proper bone growth, and supporting the immune system. It also helps promote cell growth, which helps develop and keeps the heart, lungs, and kidneys. Vitamin A presents with antioxidant properties, helping to fight inflammation in our bodies.[1]

Vitamin B: This is called B complex when it has all eight of the B vitamins contained in it. When individualized, each B vitamin has a specific role to maintain our health. [2]

B1 (Thiamine): This vitamin helps fight stress by protecting the immune system, helping break down simple carbohydrates, and helping the body make new cells.

B2 (Riboflavin): This vitamin helps produce red blood cells, works as an antioxidant, and may help prevent aging.

B3 (Niacin): This vitamin helps to increase our healthy cholesterol.

B5 (Pantothenic acid): Helps to manufacture red blood cells as well as the sex and stress hormones produced by the adrenal glands and maintain a healthy digestive tract.

B6 (Pyridoxine): Vitamin B6, in conjunction with other B vitamins, helps regulate the amino acid level in the body, metabolize our food, and stabilize our blood sugar. It also helps to make antibodies and improve our sleep and moods. B6 helps the body manufacture serotonin, melatonin, and norepinephrine.

B7 (Biotin): This vitamin helps strengthen our nails and promotes healthy hair and skin. It is essential during pregnancy to help support healthy development of the baby and possibly helps with depression and memory loss.

B9 (Folate or folic acid): Women who are pregnant need this vitamin to help prevent birth defects and assist with the healthy development of the fetus. It may also help with depression and memory loss.

B12 (Cobalamin): This vitamin, in conjunction with B5 and B9, helps produce red blood cells, which protects us from anemia. It also helps iron create hemoglobin. B12 is needed to help maintain a healthy heart, skin, nervous system, and digestive system.

Vitamin C (Ascorbic Acid): Vitamin C helps to make collagen, heal wounds, promote the growth and repair of tissues, maintain healthy bones and teeth, and absorb iron. [3]

Calcium: This mineral is essential for maintaining good bone, heart, muscle, and nerve health. For the body to absorb calcium, it needs vitamin D. [4]

Choline: This micronutrient helps to maintain proper liver, nerve and brain function, as well as energy levels and metabolism. It also helps with muscle movement. [5]

Copper: This trace element helps with the development and maintenance of our immune system. It works with iron to help form red blood cells and aids with iron metabolism. [6]

Vitamin D: This vitamin helps regulate calcium and phosphorus absorption, maintain healthy teeth and bones, and regulate insulin levels. It helps with cancer prevention and supports heart, lung, nervous, and immune system health. [7]

Vitamin E: This is a powerful antioxidant and may help protect our bodies from many health issues, including cancer, vision problems, and memory loss. [8]

Iron: This mineral is an essential component of hemoglobin. Hemoglobin transports oxygen from the lungs to the tissues of the body. [8]

Vitamin K: This vitamin is essential for bone formation and blood clotting, which helps prevent excessive bleeding. People who are using blood thinners need to avoid eating too many foods high in vitamin K [8]

Lycopene: This antioxidant helps prevent macular degeneration and cardiovascular disease, lowers bad cholesterol and blood pressure, helps prevent some cancers, and protects the immune system. [8, 9]

Magnesium: Magnesium is essential for bone and dental health, to regulate blood pressure, to convert food into energy, and to sustain our heart rhythm. It also supports healthy enzyme, gene, nerve, and muscle function. [10]

Manganese: This trace element helps with forming our bones and connective tissue, and it helps with carbohydrate metabolism. [8]

Omega-3 fatty acids: These are essential to maintaining our heart health. Omega -3s help sustain our heart rate, improve blood vessel function, lower blood pressure, and decrease inflammation. They may also help with controlling lupus, rheumatoid arthritis, and some cancers. [11]

Phosphorous: This mineral is vital for all cell functions. It is also needed to maintain our energy levels. Phosphorous helps promote healthy bones and maintain proper pH. [12]

Potassium: This mineral helps maintain a proper fluid balance in our bodies as well as regulate our blood pressure, muscle contractions, heartbeat, and insulin secretion. [8]

Selenium: This trace mineral helps with maintaining good cognitive function, controls inflammation, helps with fertility, and supports the immune system.

Zinc: This essential trace mineral helps with maintaining our skin, hair, immune system, and aids in protein metabolism. [8]

Food for thought:

1. When you look at how God has carefully designed a variety of foods to nourish your body correctly, does that change how you view the food that you serve yourself or family?

2. Are you serving the correct proportions of food at your meals?

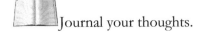Journal your thoughts.

INSPECTING THE ELECTRIC
(FRUITS, VEGETABLES, SPICES, HERBS, SEEDS, AND NUTS)

Once the electrician has completed his work, it must be inspected one final time. Everything must meet the legal safety standards (code) of the local government. Anything that does not pass the inspection must be repaired or replaced.

Nugget of the day: *You won't spend the rest of your lives chasing your own desires, but you will be anxious to do the will of God.* (1Peter 4:2)

It is so easy to get caught up in the ways of this world. It is easy to justify our behavior by the way others act. Watch television at night or follow celebrities, and our lives seem calm in comparison. We should not compare our lives to the world's standards. We need to look toward Heaven. We should ask ourselves, "are we doing what pleases God?" On that great day, when we meet Him face to face, God will not compare us to anyone else. God will not accept the answer that "everyone else did it, so it must be okay." God has given us His set of rules. He sent His Son to instruct us on how to live healthy, fulfilling Christian lives. We have no excuses. God gave us these commands, not to be in control of us, but to provide us with greater freedom. He knows when we live up to His standards our lives will become less worrisome and less complicated. Living lives of sin has us always looking over our shoulder, making it hard to trust others and causing undue stress in our lives. Eating healthy diets enable us to have more energy and do what God has called us to do.

My prayer is that you examine your life using our loving Father's standards and make a sincere effort to improve in areas you have failed in the past. You need to know our Father is a forgiving Dad. He will forgive you for the sins you have committed when you confess to Him and make a sincere effort to change your behavior. Seek God's wisdom and let Him guide you so that you make the correct decisions as to how to live a healthy lifestyle. Ask Him to help you to restore your temple. I pray that you experience the life our loving Father intended for you to live. After all, God does know best, trust Him!!!
****

Once the work is completed, it needs to be inspected to make sure the temple is safe before it can be given a permit to open it's doors to the congregation. If the work is done incorrectly, the faulty wiring could start a fire or shock someone when touching an outlet or switch. If mistakes are found, they need to be corrected before the temple can be operational. Our human temples also need to be inspected to make sure they receive the proper nutrition so that they do not short circuit or run out of energy. When we do not feed our bodies the proper diet, we waste money and cause them to not perform to the optimal potential.

For the rest of this week, we will explore the food that we eat and how they can maintain or improve our health. I have provided you with basic nutritional information of various foods so that you can nourish your body correctly. God has given us a nutritional code, which is perfectly balanced with all the nutrients we need for our bodies to perform at their optimal levels. Let's make sure our food source is up to code. I have given suggestions on how to prepare some of these foods so you can include them in your diet.

Cruciferous vegetables
These are classified as superfoods because they offer so much nutrition and loaded with vitamins A, C, K, and folic acid. They also provide the fiber needed in the diet. They are most beneficial when eaten raw but can be lightly steamed.

Arugula: This plant is an excellent source of fiber and is high in protein. It is also known for decreasing bad cholesterol and improving good cholesterol. Arugula contains vitamins A, C, and K as well as folate, calcium, iron, phosphorous, potassium, and manganese. It contains antioxidants, which help maintain the immune system, strengthen the bones and teeth, support brain health, and decrease the risk of breast, cervical, colon, and prostate cancers. Since it contains folate, it is excellent for prenatal care. [1] Arugula blends well with other greens to make a healthy salad.

Bok choy: This plant has many antioxidants, vitamins, and minerals essential for maintaining good bone and heart health and decreasing cancer risks. This plant may also help lower blood pressure, improve sleep, and reduce inflammation. Some of the vitamins and minerals in bok choy are potassium, vitamin A, calcium, selenium, folate, niacin, and choline. After chopping it up, let it sit for 5 minutes before cooking. [2] It tastes best when sautéed with fresh garlic and ginger. I often use bok choy in my green smoothies.

Broccoli: Broccoli is a cruciferous vegetable that contains cancer-fighting properties. It has sulforaphane, which may detoxify harmful substances in our bodies. The broccoli stalk also has lots of antioxidants, so it is important to include this in the diet. Broccoli may also help with decreasing allergy symptoms and is good for bone health. [3] Broccoli tastes good when steamed and sprinkled with lemon juice or eaten raw with hummus. Broccoli is also an excellent addition to smoothies or salads. The stalks can be used in soups or stews.

Brussels sprouts: These are an excellent source of vitamins B, C, K1, and the minerals manganese, potassium, and choline. They also have sulfur compounds in them, which help to detoxify the body. Brussels sprouts improve heart health and may help prevent some cancers. [4] They can be roasted and served with Parmesan cheese and a small pat of organic butter. They can also be steamed and drizzled with olive oil.

Cabbage: This plant is rich in vitamins K, B, C, and the mineral iodine. It also contains sinigrin, which helps prevent some cancers and has potent antioxidant and anti-inflammatory properties. Cabbage is good for maintaining the digestive tract, the heart, the skin, and the nervous and endocrine systems. Cabbage juice may help heal ulcers. [5] It is best eaten stir-fried or raw to retain its nutrients. I use cabbage in my smoothies or make a vinegar slaw.

Cauliflower: This is rich in vitamins and minerals and contains a sulfur compound, which is an excellent cancer-fighting agent. It also has anti-inflammatory properties. Cauliflower helps detoxify our bodies, protect them from ultraviolet radiation, maintain our electrolyte balance, maintain our neurological system, and strengthen our immune system. [6] Cauliflower is also good for heart health. It works as a substitute for pizza crusts and is delicious when steamed or eaten raw with hummus.

Collard greens: These greens provide us with vitamins A, C, and K as well as the minerals folate, manganese, magnesium, riboflavin and iron. Collard greens are rich in sulfur and have antioxidant and anti-inflammatory benefits for our bodies. Collard greens can lower our cholesterol, help improve bone strength, and protect our eyes. [7] The greens help to detoxify our bodies and may help prevent cancer. They are easy to prepare. Steam the greens for four to five minutes and then warm 1teaspoon coconut oil in a skillet. Add the greens and sauté and season with salt, pepper, and a pinch of cayenne pepper. When done, sprinkle with olive oil and red wine vinegar. Collard greens are also good when used in green smoothies.

Kale: This plant has phytochemicals to prevent tumor growth and helps block cancer-causing agents from affecting the cells. It is another good source to help detoxify the body and provide heart health. [8] Kale is high in fiber and low in calories. It is a good source of iron, vitamins A, C, K, and calcium. Not only is kale good for detoxifying our bodies, it also helps maintain our immune system, liver, eyes, and skin, and it prevents bone loss. [9] Different varieties of kale have different flavors. Kale is a key ingredient in many green smoothies and is good in salads. To make a kale salad, drizzle olive oil and lemon juice on the kale and let it sit in the refrigerator for one to two days. Before serving, add pumpkin seeds, sunflower seeds, and Parmesan cheese.

Radish: Radishes are potent detoxifiers. They have been associated with helping treat cancers due to their detoxifying abilities and the antioxidants they possess. Radishes may help to kill cancer cells by not allowing the cells to reproduce. [10] Use radishes in salads and smoothies or eat them raw.

Spinach: Spinach is rich in so many vitamins, minerals, and phytonutrients. It is an excellent source of iron as well as potassium, manganese, zinc, magnesium, iron, and calcium. It has carotenoids, which remove free radicals from our bodies before they can cause damage. Spinach also has folate and fiber to help decrease cancer risks. It helps improve eyesight, provides skin protection, maintains healthy blood pressure, and helps prevent arteriosclerosis and heart attacks. It also helps our neurological system and bone mineralization as well as promoting healthy fetal development. (11) It tastes better in the colder months when the frost makes the leaves crisper and sweeter. Spinach is best eaten raw, lightly cooked, or sautéed. Spinach is one of the best leafy plants to eat. It is an essential ingredient in green smoothies and salads.

Swiss chard: This plant has anti-inflammatory and antioxidant properties. It is rich in calcium and magnesium and supports our bone health. It mixes well with other greens to make a healthy salad.

Other vegetables:
Asparagus: Asparagus is packed with vitamins and minerals, including vitamins A, C, E, K, and B6. It also contains folate, iron, chromium, copper, calcium, protein, and fiber. Asparagus is both an anti-inflammatory and antioxidant. It also helps support the heart, improves brain function, is a natural diuretic, and regulates blood sugars. (12) It is best stored in the refrigerator with the ends wrapped in a damp towel. One way to prepare this is to steam it. Then add garlic and sprinkle with lemon juice and fresh Parmesan cheese. Another delicious option is to sprinkle with garlic, salt, and pepper, and then roast it in the oven at 425 degrees for about ten minutes.

Beets: Both the root and the greens provide the body with great nutrition. Beets do contain a high amount of sugar and carbohydrate content, so they need to be consumed in small quantities. Beets have been shown to lower blood pressure, increase stamina during exercise, fight inflammation, and help ward off cancer. Being rich in nutrients and fiber helps ward off osteoporosis and helps with detoxification. (13) Beets contain betalain, which helps to purify the blood and liver. The greens also provide the body with protein, fiber, phosphorous, zinc, magnesium, potassium, copper and manganese, vitamins A and C, calcium and iron. The green leaves of the beets are healthier than the beet itself. They are higher in iron than spinach. There are studies using beetroot extract to fight pancreatic, breast, and prostate cancer. (14) Beet greens are good in smoothies or sautéed with other greens. When using in smoothies, be careful to use small amounts at first to help develop a taste for them.

Carrots: Carrots contain beta-carotene that may protect cell membranes from toxic damage, slow tumor growth, help slow aging, and maintain heart, skin, tooth, and gum health. (15) Cooked carrots may have more nutrients and are best steamed or boiled whole to prevent the loss of nutrients. They are also very good eaten raw with hummus or put into salads or smoothies.

Celery: Celery is a low-calorie vegetable. Celery contains antioxidants, which strengthens the immune system. It also works as a diuretic and helps protect the digestive system. It tastes good eaten raw with hummus, tossed in a salad, or sautéed in a stir-fry. (16)

Chili peppers and jalapenos: These peppers contain capsaicin, which may neutralize cancer-causing substances, works as an anti-inflammatory, and promote healthy blood flow. They also help with weight loss. To decrease their heat, cook them or remove the seeds and white membrane. These peppers add flavor to salsas, tacos, and salads. (18)

Cucumbers: *"We remember the fish we used to eat for free in Egypt. And we had all the cucumbers, melons, leeks, onions, and garlic we wanted"* (Numbers 11:5). This vegetable contains vitamins B, C, and K and the minerals copper, potassium, and manganese. Cucumbers are beneficial to us because they help decrease our cancer risks and maintain a healthy digestive system and a healthy weight. They also act as an anti-inflammatory agent and provide the body with antioxidants. (19) Cucumbers enhance the flavor of salads and taste good in smoothies. To make a cucumber salad, add cilantro, olive oil, and lime juice to sliced cucumbers.

Eggplant: Eggplant provides the body with iron, calcium, vitamins B6, C, and K, niacin, folic acid, phosphorus, copper, potassium, manganese, and fiber. It helps improve circulation, prevents osteoporosis, increases cognitive function, decreases stress, helps prevent cancer, helps manage diabetes, lowers bad cholesterol, prevents blood clots, and promotes heart health. [20] Eggplant is delicious baked, sautéed and served with tomato and mozzarella, or sautéed in vegetable broth with bell peppers and other vegetables. After cooking, drizzle olive oil and lemon juice over it.

Garlic: The phytochemicals in garlic have been shown to halt the formation of nitrosamines. These are carcinogens formed in the stomach. Some studies show that people who have an increased intake of garlic have a lower risk of some cancers, including breast and prostate. [21] Garlic also speeds DNA repair, kills cancer cells, and helps to fight bacteria in our bodies. Crushing the garlic helps release beneficial enzymes. After crushing the garlic, let it sit fifteen to twenty minutes before cooking. Crushing garlic activates the enzymes and releases the sulfur-containing compound that is so beneficial.

Mushrooms: Mushrooms are not actual vegetables. They are fungus, but I have included them in the list because of their many benefits to our health. Mushrooms help strengthen the immune system. They contain lectins, which attack cancerous cells and keeps them from multiplying. Mushrooms have been shown to stop breast cancer tumor growth and inhibit breast cancer metastasis. [22] Research has shown mushrooms help the body to detoxify, slow tumor formation, halt cell mutation, and protect the DNA while leaving healthy cells intact. They also help lower bad cholesterol, increase energy, improve brain function, improve our immunity, provide our bodies with vitamin D, and decrease inflammation. [23] Mushrooms taste good in many vegetable dishes, sauces, and salads. Many people have a difficult time eating them due to the texture. Cutting them up into very small pieces may help with this issue.

Onions, leeks, scallions, and chives: Onions contain quercetin, which is an antioxidant flavonoid. They help lower cholesterol, thin the blood, fight infections, and help fight asthma as well as hay fever. Onions may also help lower cancer risks. Onions are rich in sulfur-containing compounds, which are essential for detoxing the body, especially helping rid the liver of toxins. Once onion is cut, it should be used because it does attract bacteria even if stored in the refrigerator.

Quinoa: Many people classify this food as a grain, but in actuality, it is the seed of a plant. [24] Quinoa is high in protein. It is considered a complete protein because it has all nine essential amino acids. This food also contains iron, B vitamins, vitamin E, calcium, phosphorus, manganese, copper, folate, and antioxidants. It has excellent anti-inflammatory properties. Quinoa is good for energy production, may help to control weight loss, control blood sugar, improve heart health, and support bone health. [25] The seeds should be stored in an airtight container and will last three to six months if kept in the refrigerator. Before cooking quinoa, it is best to gently rub them while rinsing the seeds in a fine-meshed strainer. Quinoa is easy to prepare by adding one cup of quinoa to two cups of water or vegetable broth and bringing it to a boil. It can be used as a substitute for rice in recipes, used for breakfast cereal, mixed with fruit, seasoned with herbs, or made into a salad. Quinoa also tastes good in stir-fry.

Seaweed and other sea vegetables: These vegetables contain beta-carotene, protein, and vitamin B12. Seaweed is a cheap and complete source of all known minerals and trace elements found in the ocean. Seaweed can play a major player in detoxifying destructive radioactivity in the body. It also contains high levels of iodine, which helps suppress tumor formation and growth. [26] You can grind up seaweed in the blender and pour into a saltshaker or mix it with sea salts. Seaweed can be added to smoothies and other dishes.
Use these with caution so that we do not overload our bodies with iodine.

Squash: There are a variety of squash plants. These plants have many antioxidants and anti-inflammatory properties. They contain a large number of vitamins and minerals, including vitamins A, C, E, B6, thiamin, folate, magnesium, potassium, copper, calcium, and iron. Squash helps to regulate blood sugars, boosts the immune system, improves lung, bone and eye health, and helps reduce ulcers. [27] The rind has nutrients as well. Squash is a good substitute for pasta and can be used as a replacement for spaghetti or other noodles in recipes. Purchase a spiralizer and use it to make the squash into thin strips resembling noodles.

Sweet Potatoes: These contain beta-carotene, which may protect DNA in the cell nucleus from cancer-causing chemicals outside the cell membrane. [28] The abundant amount of beta-carotene also helps protect the skin from sun damage and is good for eye health. Sweet potatoes contain twice as much fiber as any other potato. [29] These potatoes are good for the heart since they have large amounts of vitamin B6 to help keep the arteries flexible and blood flowing. Sweet potatoes are also high in potassium, which helps with lowering blood pressure and regulating the natural rhythm of the heart. They also help maintain our brain and central nervous system health. Sweet potatoes contain manganese, which helps maintain healthy blood sugar levels. Sweet potatoes are delicious when baked or mashed with cinnamon and organic butter added to them. They can also be cut into thin slices, brushed with coconut oil, and seasoned with herbs, salt, and pepper, and then baked in the oven.

Fruits

The Bible specifically lists six fruits: apples, dates, pomegranates, grapes, figs, and melons. **Remember that although fruit has many benefits, due to the amount of fructose, fruits need to be consumed in moderation to not cause a spike in our blood sugar.**

Apples: *Strengthen me with raisin cakes, refresh me with apples, for I am weak with love (Song of Solomon 2:5).* Apples are a good source of fiber, vitamin C, and phytochemicals, including quercetin, which helps maintain the nervous system while decreasing the risk of Alzheimer's. They contain pectin, which is a fiber that works as a prebiotic, so they are good for gut health. Other benefits of eating apples may be that they help with heart health, weight loss, and fighting cancer. [31] Apples make a great mid-day snack or taste good in salads.

Apricots: Apricots are rich in fiber, which helps relieve constipation. They contain many of the minerals necessary to maintain good bone health. Some of these minerals are calcium, phosphorus, manganese, iron, and copper. Iron helps prevent anemia, improves heart health, maintains proper fluid balance in our bodies, and helps with detoxification. Apricots have also been found to decrease the risk of cancer. [32] They are very flavorful and can be eaten raw or dried.

Avocados: This fruit has powerful antioxidants that attack free radicals and may help prevent cancer. Avocados are loaded with vitamins C, B5, E, healthy fats, folate, fiber, beta-carotene, and high levels of potassium. Avocados are higher in potassium than bananas. This fruit helps lower cholesterol, protects the eyes, may help relieve arthritis symptoms, and assists with weight loss. [33] Use avocados to make guacamole, eat with an egg for breakfast, or add to a smoothie or salad.

Bananas: This fruit has high amounts of potassium and pectin, as well as antioxidants. They also contain magnesium, and vitamins B6 and C. Bananas help with weight loss, protect against developing type 2 diabetes, improve the nervous system, and maintain bone and eye health. They also help with white blood cell production. [34] Bananas are an excellent addition to a smoothie, taste good in fruit salads, or can be eaten plain.

Berries: All berries have phytonutrients and rank higher than most fruits and vegetables in regards to their number of antioxidants. Berries are delicious when eaten plain or make a great addition to smoothies, fruit salads, or green salads.

Acai berries: This berry is considered a superfood. It is rich in healthy mono and polyunsaturated fats as well as fiber. Acai berries are powerful antioxidants. They may also aid in losing and maintaining weight, improve digestion, improve skin and cell health, and boost the immune system. These potent berries may also help slow aging, increase energy, and improve brain function. [35]

Blackberries: These berries are rich in antioxidants. They have been shown to help improve digestion, strengthen the immune system, aid in skin care, maintain bone health, and enhance memory and cognition, as well as helping with weight management. [36]

Strawberries: These berries are high in antioxidants and flavonoids, which suppress an enzyme that damages

DNA and helps inhibit tumor growth. They have quercetin in them, which helps with heart function and cancer prevention. Other benefits include helping to regulate blood sugar and possibly reducing constipation. [37]

Blueberries: These are high in anthocyanin, which reduces inflammation and are also a powerful antioxidant. Blueberries help to protect the brain from degeneration due to aging. These berries have also been shown to decrease cancer risks, including breast cancer. Other benefits include helping with weight loss, being good for the skin, improving vision, adding digestion, and promoting good heart health. [38]

Cranberries: They contain vitamin C and dietary fiber as well as being very high in antioxidants. These berries help prevent and fight urinary tract infections, help maintain heart, neurological, and immune system health, help prevent cancer, and work as an anti-inflammatory. [39]

Goji berries: These berries have high levels of antioxidants. They improve immune function, fight cancer, maintain skin, protect eye health, increase energy, detoxify the liver, and help maintain blood sugar levels. [40] I love to eat goji berries on my salads or put them in power bars.

Cantaloupe: This fruit is loaded with beta-carotene and fiber. The cantaloupe is also rich in vitamins A, C, B6, niacin, and minerals potassium, and folic acid. This melon helps boost our immune system, maintains healthy skin and eyes, helps with stress and anxiety, and helps with arthritis. [41] The seeds of the cantaloupe are also healthy for us to consume. The seeds provide a good amount of plant protein; they are high in fiber and contain vitamins A, C, and E as well as the minerals magnesium, phosphorous, and potassium. [42] The seeds can be added to a smoothie or roasted.

Cherries: Cherries have less sugar than most fruits, so they are an excellent snack to eat. One study has shown that due to the melatonin, drinking a glass of cherry juice thirty minutes after waking up and then another glass thirty minutes before dinner will help improve sleep. Cherries are also good for improving memory, decreasing osteoarthritis symptoms, helping with colon cancer, preventing stroke, and helping with skin care. [43] Cherries are a great antioxidant and anti-inflammatory with tart cherries being a better anti-inflammatory than sweet cherries.

Dates: *Then he gave to every Israelite man and woman in the crowd a loaf of bread, a cake of dates, and a cake of raisins. Then all the people returned to their homes (2 Samuel 6:19).* Dates contain fiber, potassium, copper, manganese, magnesium, and vitamin B6. Dates have been shown to help women have a healthy labor and delivery when eaten for four weeks before birth. They also work as an anti-inflammatory, decrease blood pressure, promote heart and digestive health, and relieve constipation. This fruit does have high sugar content, so it needs to be eaten in small quantities. Dates are a good substitute for sugar and can be used to make power balls with a variety of nuts and seeds to provide our bodies with energy. [44]

Powerball recipe

2 cups pitted dates, ½ cup almonds, 2 cups raw cashews, 1 cup dried figs, 1 tablespoon vanilla, ½ cup raw coconut, ½ cup cacao powder, ½ cup organic peanut butter, 2 teaspoons cinnamon, 1 cup oats, ¼ cup flaxseed, 3 tablespoons chia seeds, and ⅓ cup water. Walnuts, goji berries, and cacao nibs can also be added to give more flavor to these energy balls. Blend all ingredients in a blender. The mixture should be moist but not sticky. Roll into balls and store in a glass container in the refrigerator. Add extra water as needed so the mixture is not crumbly.

Figs: *They also gave him part of a fig cake and two clusters of raisins, for he hadn't had anything to eat or drink for three days and nights. Before long his strength returned (1 Samuel 30:12).*
Then Isaiah said, "Make an ointment from figs." So Hezekiah's servants spread the ointment over the boil, and Hezekiah recovered (2 Kings 20:7 NIV)! Figs are high in fiber, pectin, vitamins K, and B6. They also contain the minerals copper, potassium, magnesium, and manganese. They help prevent constipation, lower cholesterol, improve diabetes, decrease asthma and bronchitis symptoms, and assist in the prevention of some

cancers. [45] Figs, like dates, have high sugar content and need to be eaten in small amounts. Figs can be made into a paste and used as a sugar substitute.

Grapefruit: This fruit is rich in vitamin C, antioxidants, and lycopene. Grapefruit helps to decrease cholesterol, prevent kidney stones, protect against colon cancer, and may lower risks of some cancers. [46]

Grapes: *"When you enter your neighbor's vineyard, you may eat your fill of grapes, but you must not carry any away in a basket (Deuteronomy 23:24).* Grapes contain polyphenolic antioxidants including resveratrol, vitamins, and minerals. Resveratrol is a compound that has been found to decrease stroke risks and help protect against cancers of the colon and prostate, heart disease, degenerative nerve disease, Alzheimer's, and viral and fungal infections. Other benefits of grapes are that they help maintain blood sugar levels, help with the effects of aging, and may help to increase lifespans. Red and purple grapes are the most beneficial. The seeds of the grapes also contain antioxidants that help with protecting cell membrane lipids against oxidative damage and help protect our bodies against infection, heart disease, aging, and cancer. They also strengthen arteries and veins. [47] Grapes are delicious when eaten alone or added to fruit or green salads.

Kiwi: Kiwis are high in nutrients and low in calories. They are high in vitamins A, B6, C (five times more than an orange), and E, the minerals potassium and copper as well as fiber. They may have many health benefits, which include promoting a healthy heart, lowering blood pressure, and aiding in maintaining healthy skin. Kiwis may also improve sleep and help prevent constipation. [48]. This fruit also can help control blood sugar, help with asthma symptoms, and promote a healthy colon. Kiwis contain many nutrients in the peel as well, so it too can be used in smoothies or fruit salads.

Lemons: Lemons contain fiber and many vitamins, including vitamins C and B-complex, as well as the minerals calcium, magnesium, and potassium. They are one of the richest sources of vitamin C. Since lemon juice can be hard on tooth enamel, it is best to dilute the juice with lukewarm water. When drinking lemon water, keep the seeds out of the water since citrus seeds are not good for the body. Avoid adding sugar, honey, or other sweeteners as these may reduce the benefits. Drink warm lemon water fifteen to thirty minutes before breakfast for best results. Lemon water boosts the immune system, reduces inflammation by decreasing acidity in the body, and removes uric acid in joints. It also flushes out toxins, relieves tooth pain and respiratory issues, helps with throat infections, and acts as a blood purifier. Lemons help reduce digestive problems such as bloating and heartburn. Lemons can aid in weight loss and help reduce bad breath. [49] Oranges and lemons stimulate cancer-killing immune cells. [8] Lemons can be added to smoothies. The rind of organic lemons and oranges are packed with antioxidants and can be used in teas, smoothies, or grated in salads. Apply lemon juice to the skin to help reduce scars and dark spots.

Oranges: This fruit offers us fiber, vitamin C, thiamin, folate, and antioxidants. Oranges are good for our digestive system and may help prevent kidney stones and anemia, in addition to improving heart health. [50] They, like lemons, also have cancer-fighting properties.

Papayas: This fruit provides a rich source of vitamin C, flavonoids, B vitamins, folate, potassium, magnesium, copper, and fiber. Papayas help protect against heart disease and colon cancer, improve the immune system, promote digestive health, and are anti-inflammatories. [51] Papayas add flavor to fruit salads.

Pears: Pears are a good source of potassium, fiber, vitamin C, antioxidants, copper, and iron. They are beneficial to the diet because they help with wound repair, cancer prevention, circulation, and heart health. **[52]**

Pineapple: Pineapple is one of the highest sources of bromelain, which works as an anti-inflammatory, cancer fighter, and pain reliever. Pineapple is high in fiber and helps with constipation. It boosts the immune system, helps with circulation, and contains manganese, which helps with bone formation. Overdosing on pineapple may cause vomiting, nausea, and headaches. [53,54] Pineapple tastes good in salsa and mixed into fruit salads. The core of the pineapple has more nutrients than the fleshy part. It has the same great taste as the flesh but is a rougher texture. Use the core of the pineapple in smoothies.

Pomegranates: *When they came to the valley of Eshcol, they cut down a branch with a single cluster of grapes so large that it took two of them to carry it on a pole between them! They also brought back samples of the pomegranates and figs (Numbers 13:23).* Pomegranates are another superfood. Pomegranates contain many vitamins and minerals, especially vitamins A, C, E, potassium, and folic acid. These fruits have three times as many antioxidants as green tea. Pomegranates may help with fighting prostate and breast cancers. They have been shown to inhibit estrogen synthesis. Other benefits of this fruit include decreasing the risk of heart attack or stroke, decreasing dental plaque, helping with osteoarthritis, supplying iron to the blood to decrease anemia, and helping to keep the skin healthy. (55) Pomegranates are a great snack or taste good in salads.

Tomatoes: Tomatoes are most beneficial when cooked. Cooking tomatoes increases the amount of lycopene the body can absorb because it breaks down the plant's cell walls. Some lab tests have shown lycopene helps keep cancer cells from growing. Lycopene is a powerful antioxidant. Other foods containing lycopene are watermelon, pink grapefruit, and red bell peppers. Tomatoes are good for maintaining heart, skin, eye, and bone health. They act as an anti-inflammatory and may help reduce risks of some neurological diseases, including Alzheimer's. (30) Raw tomatoes are good in salads. When cooked, tomatoes are good in chili and squash pasta.

Watermelon: *"We remember the fish we used to eat for free in Egypt. And we had all the cucumbers, melons, leeks, onions, and garlic we wanted" (Numbers 11:5).* Watermelon has the highest concentration of lycopene in any vegetable or fruit. Lycopene helps fight heart disease and some cancers including ovarian cancer. Watermelon is rich in calcium to help with bone health and also helps with inflammation in the body. The other benefits of watermelon are that it may help with detoxifying the kidneys, preventing macular degeneration, and repairing damaged tissue. (56) The rind and seeds also provide nutrition for our bodies. The rind contains chlorophyll as well as the amino acid citrulline. This amino acid is important in maintaining the immune system as well as heart health. The black seeds contain iron, zinc, protein, and fiber. (57) Use the rind and seeds in smoothies. Cold watermelon is refreshing to eat on a hot summer day or when added to a fruit salad.

Legumes, beans, and whole grains

Beans: *"Now go and get some wheat, barley, beans, lentils, millet, and emmer wheat, and mix them together in a storage jar. Use them to make bread for yourself during the 390 days you will be lying on your side" (Ezekiel 4:9).* Beans are high in protein, fiber, folate, and lignans. Beans are especially beneficial for someone consuming a vegan or vegetarian diet because of the protein they contain. Beans help fight breast and prostate cancers. Other benefits may include their ability to help lower cholesterol, help with weight loss, and manage diabetes. Beans have been found to trigger migraines in some people. (58) There are a variety of types of beans with many uses, including salads, chili, soups, and sauces.

Oatmeal: Oatmeal provides high levels of fiber, magnesium, and protein. It contains lignans and antioxidants, which protect against heart disease and cancer. The unique fiber in oatmeal helps neutrophils travel to the site of an infection more quickly and allows the body to eliminate bacteria it finds there. (59) It is best to eat steel cut oats. Steel cut oats can be prepared ahead of time and stored in the refrigerator. They taste good when mixed with berries and seeds.

Brown rice: Brown rice is much healthier than white rice. White rice has been refined, and therefore, some of its nutritional value has been lost. Brown rice still contains its side hull and bran. Brown rice contains selenium, manganese, naturally occurring oils, antioxidants, and fiber. Because of these nutrients, brown rice helps to prevent colon cancer, stabilize our blood sugar levels, control cholesterol levels, and protect our reproductive and nervous systems. (60)

Lentils: *They brought sleeping mats, cooking pots, serving bowls, wheat and barley, flour and roasted grain, beans, lentils, honey, butter, sheep, goats, and cheese for David and those who were with him*

(2 Samuel 17:28-29). Lentils contain high concentrations of fiber and folate. They support good heart health, contain iron to increase energy levels, act as a powerful antioxidant, help alkalize the body, and help stabilize blood sugar. (61)

SPICES, HERBS, SEEDS, AND NUTS

So their father, Jacob, finally said to them, "If it can't be avoided, then at least do this. Pack your bags with the best products of this land. Take them down to the man as gifts—balm, honey, gum, aromatic resin, pistachio nuts, and almonds" (Genesis 43:11).

Then the Lord said to Moses, "Collect choice spices—12 ½ pounds of pure myrrh, 6 ¼ pounds of fragrant cinnamon, 6 ¼ pounds of fragrant calamus, and 12 ½ pounds of cassia—as measured by the weight of the sanctuary shekel. Also get one gallon of olive oil. Like a skilled incense maker, blend these ingredients to make a holy anointing oil *(Exodus 30:22-25 k).*

Then she gave the king a gift of 9,000 pounds of gold, great quantities of spices, and precious jewels. Never again were so many spices brought in as those the queen of Sheba gave to King Solomon (1 Kings 10:10).

What common thread do you see in each of these verses?

Each one of these verses shows how valued herbs, spices, and nuts were to the people in the Bible. There are many other records of people using these plants and seeds for their health and well-being. They were used to make sacred oils and as gifts to kings. They were used for medicine and to provide nutrition.

This is what the Lord says—your Redeemer, the Holy One of Israel: "I am the Lord your God, who teaches you what is good for you and leads you along the paths you should follow. Oh, that you had listened to my commands! Then you would have had peace flowing like a gentle river and righteousness rolling over you like waves in the sea (Isaiah 48:17-18).

The Bible tells us we will have peace when we heed God's commands. How does this relate to eating a diet that is pleasing to God?

We often say we trust God and want to do what He commands us to do, and yet, we make exceptions. One big exception is in our diet. Rather than making sure we have the proper nutrition to live a healthy lifestyle to have fulfilling lives, we justify eating unhealthy food.

Do you believe God has given us direction as to how to eat?

If you said yes, do you eat a diet that pleases God?

How can you improve in this area?

God does not make mistakes. He has provided us with such valuable plants that not only enhance the taste of our food but also provide us with an excellent source of nourishment and health benefits. These herbs and spices are unique and offer us different vitamins, minerals, and essential amino acids, which in turn provide us with energy and strength. These nutrients strengthen our bones, help prevent and heal some illnesses and diseases, boost our immune systems, and repair cell damage. We need to get back to the basics if we want to live our lives to the fullest. To use these gifts from God, we need to become more familiar with them and how each one can uniquely provide us with specific nutrients necessary in our diet.

Five of the most potent cancer-fighting spices are turmeric, curcumin, cayenne pepper, oregano, and garlic.

Turmeric: This spice is commonly used in Indian food. It is rich in fiber, B6, potassium, and vitamin C as well as manganese and iron. It is a natural, potent anti-inflammatory, antibiotic, and analgesic. Turmeric's active ingredient is curcumin, which has been shown in studies to slow the growth and spread of tumors. [1] It decreases the time it takes for wound healing, improves digestion, acts as a blood purifier, strengthens ligaments, and helps minimize coughs. It can help reduce arthritis symptoms. It may also lower cholesterol and prevent gas and bloating. It may improve skin conditions, assist with maintaining weight, and aid in fat metabolism as well as reducing the side effects of chemotherapy. [2] Turmeric should be a regular additive to our diets. It is recommended to use about 100 to 200 mg (roughly one to two teaspoons) daily. Research has shown that when turmeric is used for long periods, it lowers the rates of certain cancers. [3] For increased potency, use the capsule form. If a person is pregnant, on blood thinners, has diabetes, gallbladder problems, or stomach issues, they should consult their doctor before using turmeric.

Curcumin: This is the active ingredient extracted from turmeric and is very powerful in treating many diseases. Curcumin is not the same spice as turmeric. It is an extract of turmeric, but because turmeric only contains two to five percent of the curcumin, a person needs a significant amount of turmeric to get the benefits of the curcumin. [4] Therefore, it is best used in the extract form. Curcumin is an anti-inflammatory and antioxidant. Some research has shown that it can enhance the effectiveness of chemotherapy drugs [5] and radiation while it protects the healthy cells from their toxic effects. It is also helpful in dealing with cancer, Alzheimer's, osteoporosis, depression, heart disease, rheumatoid arthritis, diabetes, and irritable bowel syndrome. By adding fish oil, olive oil, coconut oil, or black pepper to curcumin, it helps the body use it more readily and increases the effect it has on cancer. [6]

Cayenne pepper: This spice contains capsaicin, which may help kill cancer cells. It also has excellent detoxification properties - the hotter the pepper, the better the results. Cayenne has vitamins A, E, B6, C, K, and fiber. It is a good source of vitamin A, partially due to having beta-carotene. Beta-carotene is not only an anti-inflammatory, but it is converted in the body to vitamin A, which is essential for healthy epithelial tissues. The epithelial tissue includes the mucous membranes that line the nasal passages, lungs, intestinal tract, and urinary tract. These tissues are the first line of defense of the body against pathogens. This spice may also help in reducing asthma and arthritis. Its antioxidant properties help with preventing free radical damage that can lead to atherosclerosis, colon cancer, heart disease, and nerve damage due to diabetic complications. The cardiovascular benefits may include the reduction of blood cholesterol and lower risk of both heart attacks and stroke. The heat of the pepper helps stimulate secretions to clear mucus. [7] Cayenne pepper enhances the flavor of many vegetable dishes, including potatoes and beans. It also tastes good on air-popped organic popcorn.

Garlic: This is an excellent source of selenium, which may help to protect the body from cancer. It does this by causing the cells to die before having a chance to spread. It has anti-inflammatory, anti-bacterial, and anti-viral properties. Garlic may also help with improving iron metabolism. It is best to buy garlic that is plump and has unbroken skin. Store it in a cool, dark place since it does not have to be refrigerated. When preparing garlic, it is best to chop or crush it to get maximum health benefits. You should wait ten minutes before adding it to any recipe. [8] It is best to add the garlic after the dish is cooked, but if you cannot tolerate raw garlic, add it at the end of the cooking time. Garlic is good to sauté with steamed spinach and lemon juice. Add garlic to vegetable smoothies.

Oregano: This herb has potent antioxidant and anti-bacterial properties. It is also a rich source of vitamin K. Oregano also helps with muscle pain, bloating, heart conditions, respiratory tract disorders, toothaches, and intestinal parasites. There is a study that shows oregano may slow or help prevent breast cancer. [9] Season potatoes, eggs, pizza, pasta, and meat with this spice. Oregano is also good on a variety of vegetables.

In addition to these five, the following spices, herbs, and nuts are also essential for our health.

Cinnamon: This is an excellent source of calcium and iron. Cinnamon has anti-clotting agents, which help to prevent clumping of platelets. It also helps stop the growth of bacteria and control blood sugar. The scent of cinnamon boosts brain function. Cinnamon is an excellent source of fiber and manganese. It has been found to help with colon health and protect against heart disease. Cinnamon is found to help fight the flu and colds. [10] Cinnamon is best stored in tightly sealed glass containers in a cool, dark place. Ground cinnamon stores for six months and cinnamon sticks last one year. Storing in the refrigerator can increase the shelf life for both. To see if it is fresh, smell it. It should have a sweet smell.

Ginger: Ginger is useful for many medicinal purposes. The most commonly used part of the plant is the root-like stem that grows underground. It is a very potent anti-inflammatory, clears congestion, helps a cough, and aids with indigestion. Ginger has also been found to help decrease toothache pain, swelling, upset stomach and nausea, and relief of cold and flu symptoms. It is very good for helping decrease pain, including pain from osteoarthritis. Ginger helps especially with decreasing knee pain. Ginger also reduces side effects associated with chemotherapy, including dizziness, nausea, vomiting, and cold sweats. [11] Ginger helps with the treatment of several cancers, including ovarian, colorectal, lung, and breast. [12] Ginger is very concentrated, so large amounts are not needed. Use 1 or 2 ½" slices in a cup of hot water to settle the stomach or mince up a small amount (one teaspoon full) and swallow it. Adding a slice of ginger in cooked foods may help arthritis. Fresh ginger is much better than powder. Make sure the root is firm and smooth and it can be stored in the refrigerator for up to three weeks. Storing it unpeeled in the freezer will help it last six months. It's great to use to make baked apples, add to pureed sweet potatoes with orange juice, use in salad dressing, put in rice dishes, or mix into a smoothie.

Peppermint: This herb has many means to improve our health. Its leaves and stems contain menthol, which is used medicinally, in food flavoring, and cosmetics. Studies have shown that peppermint helps to decrease headaches, works as a decongestant, soothes sore throats, and eases itching and skin irritations from plants. Peppermint has been found to relax the muscles of the stomach, which allows bile to flow more freely, helping with indigestion. Peppermint helps to relieve gas. Several studies have shown peppermint to be effective in treating irritable bowel syndrome. [13] Peppermint should not be given to infants or small children. Do not use it if you have gastroesophageal reflux.

Rosemary: This herb stimulates the immune system, increases circulation, and improves digestion. It also helps with increasing blood flow to the brain to improve concentration. Fresh rosemary herbs can be preserved and stored by trimming their stems, placing them in a glass of water, putting a paper towel or baggie over the glass, and placing it in the refrigerator.

Curry powder: This spice contains turmeric, fenugreek, coriander, cinnamon, and ginger. Because of these components, curry powder helps with detoxification and cholesterol management. It has anti-cancer benefits and aids in blood sugar control. [14]

Aloe vera: This plant has also been called the plant of immortality and the medicine plant. The Egyptians used this plant for treating burns, infections, and parasites. [15] This plant is composed of ninety-five percent water, but it is the other five percent that makes it such a potent healer. It has minerals, vitamins, enzymes, glycoproteins, amino acids, and essential oils that have healing properties. The plant can be used externally for burns or skin conditions by cutting off a piece of aloe, slicing it in half, and using the gel to soothe the burns. It can also be used to stop itching and take the sting out of bites or sunburn as well as to keep the skin elastic. Aloe can be made into a juice that helps with colitis, peptic ulcers, and digestive tract irritation. Aloe is now being studied for its potential in curing cancer. Research has shown that taking aloe vera with chemotherapy helps improve the quality of life and reduces side effects. [16] Aloe is good to add to smoothies. Some people have noticed diarrhea, stomach pain, sick feeling, or skin rash when ingesting an aloe vera supplement.

Cumin seeds: These are an excellent source of iron, which helps with energy and aids in digestion and immune function. These seeds are also a good source of manganese. They have anti-cancer properties because of their free radical scavenging abilities and ability to help detoxify the liver. You can use cumin seeds to make tea by boiling the seeds and then letting them steep eight to ten minutes. They can also be used to season legumes, brown rice, or mixed vegetables. [17]

Flaxseed: These seeds are a great source of omega-3s and antioxidants, as well as a good source of lignans and fiber. Studies show they may help with reducing the risk of breast, endometrial, and ovarian cancers. Flaxseeds have been shown to help with clearing the skin, enhancing our mood, protecting against radiation, decreasing inflammation, and improving joint health. Flaxseeds promote healthy blood pressure, boost the immune system, and aids with digestive and eye health. The seeds have more nutritional benefit than flaxseed oil. [18] When eaten whole, the body is unable to digest them. It is best to buy them whole and grind them yourself since the outer shell keeps the fatty acid inside protected. Grind the seeds daily to get the most nutritional value. If you buy them ground, keep them in the freezer to maintain the nutrition value. Whole flaxseed can be stored at room temperature in a dark place for up to one year.

Chia seeds: These seeds are a great source of omega-3 fatty acids. They are also high in antioxidants, help protect the body from free radicals, and contain the minerals calcium, phosphorus, magnesium, and manganese. They are also a good source of fiber, protein, and healthy fats. These seeds contain the phytochemicals quercetin, myricetin, and kaempferol. They have six times more calcium than milk. These seeds have a longer shelf life than most seeds. They can last for up to two years stored in your pantry. Chia seeds are best used after they are ground or soaked. You can use them to replace eggs in a recipe by mixing one tablespoon of seeds with three tablespoons of water and letting them sit for fifteen minutes. Chia seeds can be used as a topping by adding them to many dishes, including yogurt, cereal, smoothies, and salads. Chia seeds will become gelatinous when mixed with liquid, so if you prefer them dry, add to the dish right before serving. Chia seeds can also be used as a breading. Mix the seeds with finely ground nuts and spices. [19] A healthy breakfast could consist of a bowl of steel cut oatmeal, berries topped with ground chia seeds, flax seeds, pumpkin seeds, and sunflower seeds. Some people report feeling gassy after consuming these seeds. Most of these people find if they soak the seeds before using them, they will not experience gas. Soaking the chia seeds (also called sprouting) helps to increase the nutritional benefits you receive from these seeds and make them easier for the body to digest. Mix ⅓ cup chia seeds and two cups water in a jar and shake for two minutes. Then leave it in the refrigerator overnight. In the morning, add to a smoothie or other recipes.

Pumpkin seeds: They are high in magnesium, manganese, copper, zinc, and protein. Pumpkin seeds also have phytosterols and free radical scavenging properties. Pumpkin seeds are good for immune system support and have anti-diabetic effects by regulating insulin. These seeds are rich in phytoestrogens, which increase good cholesterol, decrease blood pressure, ease joint pain, and help relieve post-menopausal symptoms such as hot flashes. They have anti-inflammatory effects and may help to improve sleep. [20] They are the only seeds that are alkaline-forming. The best way to consume these seeds is raw. If you want to roast them, do it at no higher than 170 degrees for fifteen to twenty minutes. Sprinkle with Himalayan salt.

Hemp seeds: These contain all twenty amino acids, including the nine amino acids our bodies cannot produce. They are a great source of protein and a rich source of phytonutrients. They are also the richest source of essential polyunsaturated fatty acids. [21] Hemp seeds help to protect our bodies' immunity as well as the bloodstream, tissues, skin, and organs.

Sunflower seeds: These seeds are the highest natural source of vitamin E. One-quarter cup of these seeds will provide almost the entire daily recommendation for vitamin E. These seeds also provide protein and fiber, along with magnesium and B vitamins. Sunflower seeds help keep the skin hydrated, smooth and glowing since they contain healthy fat. These seeds also contain selenium, which is an antioxidant. Selenium has been shown to stop the growth of cancerous tumors by keeping the cancer cells from multiplying. Sunflower seeds also contain magnesium, which can help improve your mood and be useful when dealing with depression and anxiety. [22]

Almonds: These nuts contain a lot of fiber, protein, and healthy fats as well as manganese, magnesium, and vitamin E. Almonds help with good brain function, nourish the nervous system, help with controlling the blood sugar, and alkalize the body. Almonds can help reduce hunger. [23] Almonds provide us with an excellent source of antioxidants. They have phosphorous, which helps maintain healthy bones and teeth.

Brazil nuts: These nuts contain protein, which assists in the healing of wounds and cellular growth and repair. They also contain fiber, selenium, zinc, vitamin C, and omega- 3 fatty acids. They help with digestion, maintain a healthy heart, skin, thyroid, and immune system, help with hormone balance, and can help prevent constipation. These nuts are high in calories and should be eaten in small amounts. [24]

Cashews: Cashews provide the body with vitamins, minerals, and antioxidants, which are required for normal functioning. Cashews contain high levels of copper and proanthocyanidins. [25] Proanthocyanidins are a class of flavonols, which fight against tumor cells by stopping them from dividing further. Cashews may also help prevent colon cancer. Cashews are low in fat compared to other nuts and are cholesterol-free. The magnesium in them helps lower blood pressure as well as help with bone and nerve health. They help the body utilize iron properly and eliminate free radicals. " Two handfuls of cashews can be as effective as an antidepressant since the essential amino acid L-tryptophan is broken down into anxiety reducing, snooze inducing niacin. Cashews can filter ultraviolet rays thus help prevent macular degeneration. [26]

Hazelnuts: These nuts contain eight-six percent of the daily recommendation of vitamin E as well as magnesium and the B vitamins. These nuts can improve healthy aging, help improve brain function, work as a powerful antioxidant, and promote heart health. [27]

Macadamia nuts: These nuts contain vitamins A and B as well as iron, fiber, folate, good fats, and antioxidants. They help maintain our heart health, decrease our appetite, strengthen hair, nails, and skin, improve gut health, and support our bones and nervous system. [28]

Pecans: Pecans contain the minerals manganese, potassium, calcium, iron, magnesium, zinc, and selenium as well as vitamins B6, riboflavin, niacin, thiamin, and folate. These nuts are a good source of energy. They also help to decrease bad cholesterol and increase the good cholesterol. They help protect against cancer and protect our skin. [29]

Pine nuts: These nuts are the main ingredient used in pesto. They contain pinolenic acid, which is only found in these nuts. Pinolenic acid helps to make us feel fuller faster, helping with weight loss. They also contain the minerals and vitamins C, D, protein, magnesium, and iron, which help support our bones, boosts our immunity, helps maintain our circulatory and nervous systems, and give us a good source of energy. [30]

Pistachios: Many people consider these a nut, although technically they are a seed. Pistachios provide the body with protein, B6, and thiamin. Three ounces daily of these seeds also elevates levels of probiotics in the digestive tract.

Walnuts: These are potent antioxidants. Walnuts are high in manganese, copper, and biotin, as well as a good source of magnesium. One-quarter of a cup provides us with the daily requirement for omega-3 fats. Consuming these nuts gives us many health benefits. They help with weight loss, maintain bone health, decrease the risk of osteoporosis, and improve heart health. Research has shown that two handfuls of these nuts may assist with preventing prostate and breast cancer as well as decrease tumor growth. [31] The phytosterols have been shown to block the estrogen receptors in breast cancer cells. When eating walnuts, make sure to keep the white outer coating on since up to ninety percent of the antioxidants are found in the skin. [32]

There are many herbs, spices, nuts, and seeds that can benefit our health. I have tried to share some of the best ones so you can start including them in your diet. I encourage you to continue to explore this area more as you begin to add more foods to your diet and want to enhance flavor and broaden your options.

Don't be afraid to spice up your diet with these foods. Experiment with them, use new spices, nuts, seeds, and herbs in your favorite dishes.

Food for thought:

1. After reading this section, are there any new foods you want to try?

2. If possible, try at least one new suggestion on preparing these foods and share how you liked it with your group.

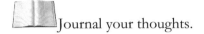Journal your thoughts.

Day 4

MEATS, EGGS, AND FISH

Nugget of the day: remember how the Lord your God led you through the wilderness for these forty years, humbling you and testing you to prove your character, and to find out whether or not you would obey his commands. Yes, he humbled you by letting you go hungry and then feeding you with manna, a food previously unknown to you and your ancestors. He did it to teach you that people do not live by bread alone; rather, we live by every word that comes from the mouth of the Lord (Deuteronomy 8:2-3)**.**

When we finally give God our lives, He continuously exposes areas that need improvement. We are like an onion, and God continues to peel back the layers. Sometimes God gently peels off a layer and lets us ease into the new change, and other times He quickly rips off the peel and leaves us burning. For many of us, this is frustrating because we feel as if we will never live up to God's expectations. But we need to look at it from God's perspective. God sees us as His children, children He loves very much. He knows we are capable of so much more. God knows our potential, and He does not want us to look back on our lives and say, "what if ...?" On that great day, when we meet our Dad face to face, He wants us to say, "I did my best. I gave you my all, and I became a better person because of following you."

My prayer is that when God exposes your weaknesses, rather than feeling as if you are failing, you see it as a challenge. Also, appreciate that our loving Father knows you are capable of so much more. He knows you are capable of doing good in this world and making a difference. Our loving Father knows you better than you know yourself. Take some time to thank our Dad for not giving up on you. Ask Him to give you the strength and knowledge to grow to your full potential.

****

Everything that lives and moves about will be food for you. Just as I gave you the green plants, I now give you everything (Genesis 9:3 NIV). There is much controversy over whether or not humans should consume meat. Meat provides the much-needed amino acids that our bodies need to make various proteins. Our bodies need protein for many of our bodily functions. If we are going to exclude meat from our diet, we must make sure that we include some other form of protein. Our bodies need approximately .4 grams per pound of body weight daily. Other types of protein include quinoa, beans, lentils, eggs, nuts, green peas, broccoli, and leafy greens such as spinach, oatmeal, chia seeds, sunflower seeds, and sesame seeds.

Proteins provide specific and vital roles in maintaining our health. Proteins are in every cell of the body and provide the structure and support for our cells allowing our bodies to move. They also function as antibodies to remove viruses and bacteria. There are messenger proteins, which are hormones that coordinate various biological processes in our systems. Proteins also work as enzymes to assist in the multitude of chemical reactions occurring in our bodies. [1] When we have a protein deficiency, our bodies begin to break down our muscles, and we experience decreased energy, have an increased risk of injuries when exercising, and increased risk of infection. Protein deficiency can stunt our growth and slow wound healing. Protein is essential for pregnant and lactating mothers. [2]

Not all people do well maintaining a vegetarian diet and eating only plant-based protein. Some people's bodies function better when they have some meat protein in their diet. However, consuming the right type of meat is critical to our health. If we are going to spend money on our food, we want to get the best quality. Meat is not supposed to be the main staple of our meal. It should be about twenty-five percent of our plate. The average serving should be four to six ounces. When eating meat in the proper proportion, higher quality meats will feed us for several meals. We should be buying our meat for quality, not quantity. The best quality of meat is one hundred percent grass-fed beef, venison, grass-fed lamb, wild game, or organic, pasture-raised poultry.

When you buy beef that is one hundred percent grass-fed, this means that the cattle are fed grass their entire lives. Make sure when purchasing meat, you read the label to make sure the cattle were not given a grain option or fed grain at the end of their lives. Grain-fed cattle often receive drugs to help prevent and heal diseases since they are more susceptible to illnesses. They are given hormones to help them mature more quickly so that they can be slaughtered sooner, reducing the cost and time to the farmer. Many of the grain-fed animals are fed corn and soy, which can be a GMO product. A recent U.S. Department of Agriculture (USDA) inspector's report showed that there were two hundred and eleven different drug residues contaminating beef sold in the US. It is estimated twenty percent of these drugs may still be in the meat we purchase. [3] Remember that if an animal eats something, you too will consume it when you eat the animal. You are what you eat; so only eat the best meat possible.

Benefits of grass-fed beef vs. grain-fed beef: [4, 5]

Grass-fed beef is leaner, so there is less fat in the meat you consume.

Grass-fed beef higher in Omega 3s. These fatty acids are critical to maintaining a healthy heart and nervous system, as well as assisting the body with handling stress.

Grass-fed beef provides us with CLA (conjugated linoleic acid). This is a fat that has been shown to reduce the risk of cancer, diabetes, and other immune disorders. It also assists with weight loss and improves brain function.

Grass-fed beef helps regulate the omega-6 to omega-3 ratio. The American diet often allows a person to consume too much of the omega-6s, causing an imbalance between the omega 6s and 3s. [6] Grass-fed beef has up to five times as many omega-3s, which helps to balance this ratio. [7]

Grass-fed beef provides us with more vitamins and trace minerals. Grass-fed meat contains more iron, potassium, calcium, and magnesium as well as vitamins A and E.

Organic chicken: Chickens are fed grain. When the chickens you buy are organic, it means that they are fed organic feed, which cannot be a GMO product. The farmers cannot give the chickens drugs, antibiotics, or hormones, and they must be able to go outside. (8) According to one study, these chickens offer us up to twenty-eight percent more omega-3 fatty acids in our diet. (9) When given the option of getting organic, pasture-raised, or free-range, choose pasture-raised. These chickens are allowed to forage on the food they prefer: grass, seeds, and worms rather than grain as their main staple. (9) It is essential to know your meat source. Some farmers know how to do the bare minimal to sell their chickens as free-range chickens.

Organic eggs: These eggs offer your body up to three times more omega-3 fatty acids, forty percent more vitamin A, and two times more vitamin E, according to studies. (10) These eggs have also been found to have higher levels of beta-carotene, less cholesterol, and less saturated fat. (11) Conventionally raised eggs have a higher risk of being contaminated with bacteria such as salmonella. (12)

Fish: Fish is an excellent source of lean protein, vitamins A and D, and omega-3 fatty acids. Unfortunately, our waters have become polluted with mercury, therefore contaminating our seafood. Because fish have higher levels of mercury, your fish intake should be limited to twice a week. Taking good probiotics and eating fermented foods can help reduce the effects of mercury on our bodies. (13) Smaller fish have fewer toxins. The best types of fish to include in our diet are wild-caught salmon (avoid farm-raised), tilapia, shrimp, scallops, sardines, and freshwater trout. Wild salmon is high in vitamin D, which may help block the development of blood vessels that feed tumors. They are also rich in omega-3s, which promote heart and eye health, decrease cancer risks, help maintain good brain function as you age, and reduce the risk of depression.

ANTIOXIDANTS

Antioxidants are essential to help maintain a healthy body. They help to combat free radicals that produce oxidation in our bodies. These free radicals are created in our bodies by natural cell functions such as respiration, inflammation, food metabolism, and as byproducts of cellular reactions. We need some free radicals as they play a role in many cellular processes. The liver produces free radicals to help with detoxification. The white blood cells use these free radicals to get rid of viruses, bacteria, and damaged cells. (1) Some of the external factors, which cause free radicals, are pollution, x-rays, strenuous exercise, pesticides, industrial solvents, and smoking.

When we have an excess of free radicals due to an antioxidant imbalance, they can damage our bodies, causing sickness and disease. Oxidation occurs when cells gain or lose an electron. (2) The body tries to stabilize these free radicals by stealing an electron from another molecule. That molecule, in turn, must take from another molecule. This chain reaction continues until an antioxidant attaches to the unstable molecule or the reaction decays. (3) This chain reaction is a natural occurrence in our bodies. When these free radicals are produced at high levels so that the body cannot regulate them, oxidative stress occurs. (4) The excess free radicals can cause bodily damage to the cell's DNA, cell membranes, and proteins. Some of the issues that may occur are an exacerbation of the aging process, production of mutant cells, and damaged tissues. Some of the diseases that can be related to these free radicals are cancer, arteriosclerosis, heart disease, stroke, diabetes, rheumatoid arthritis, cataracts, Crohn's disease, and ulcers. (5)

Our bodies produce some antioxidants, and others are from external sources such as fresh fruits, vegetables, and herbs. (6) Antioxidants can be found in foods which contain beta-carotene, other carotenoids, selenium, manganese, lycopene, and vitamins C and E. (9) Organic produce appears to have more antioxidants than conventionally grown produce. Fruits and vegetables that have darker colors are best since many of the antioxidants come from plant pigment. (7) It is important to eat fruits and vegetables of different colors since each color has various health benefits. Lycopene, which provides produce with its pink or red color, is found in tomatoes, watermelon, and pink grapefruit. Beta-carotene makes carrots orange, and anthocyanins make blueberries blue. We need to have at least three to four servings of these foods daily.

There are many health benefits to having a diet rich in antioxidants. These benefits include: slowing down of the aging process, healthier skin, boosting our immune system, reducing cancer risks, decreasing the risk of dementia, and improving eye and heart health. Some antioxidant-rich foods include artichokes, acai berries, beets, black beans, blackberries, blueberries, carrots, cherries, cilantro, cranberries, dandelion tea, dark chocolate, elderberries, Goji berries, green tea, kale, kidney beans, lentils, pecans, pomegranates, pumpkin seeds, strawberries, tomatoes, and fresh, wild-caught Alaskan salmon. (2,6) Herbs and spices include cinnamon, cloves, oregano, cumin, basil, ginger, and thyme. (2)

When using supplements, you should be careful because high doses of antioxidant supplements may cause health problems due to causing an imbalance between the free radicals and antioxidants or the antioxidants being different than those produced in the body. (8)

Food for thought:

1. What are the benefits of eating grass-fed meat or organic pasture-raised chicken?

2. Are you incorporating a variety of antioxidants in your diet on a regular basis?   If you are not, how could you improve this?

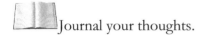Journal your thoughts.

Day 5

REMOVING TOXINS FROM THE TEMPLE
(THE IMPORTANCE OF DETOXING THE BODY)

The atmosphere of the temple is vital in making the congregants welcome. People will find a new temple to worship if they are uncomfortable at the one they attend.

Nugget of the day: Then Jesus explained: "My nourishment comes from doing the will of God, who sent me, and from finishing his work (John 4:34).

Some people have a refrigerator full of food and sit down to eat healthy meals every day, and yet they are starving. Food cannot only serve to feed our body, but it also is a mask to hide our real hunger. We all need God, and we need to know that we have a calling in this world. God is the only One who can nourish our spirits and fill us to help us find our real purpose in life. We deny ourselves wholesome food by not accepting that God is the driving force in our lives. To substitute, we have to feed this hunger with "junk food." Junk food can come in many forms: addictions, unhealthy habits, overindulgence, being a workaholic, and spending a lot of time in front of the television. These are only a few of the ways people compensate for their spirits starving and not having the means to fill them. They can become toxic to our bodies and souls. There is no denying there is only One true God. Idols of any sort cannot replace Him. Christians can claim to follow God and accept Jesus as their Savior and not invest the time in feeding their faith. Rather than looking to God, people look to those around them and never get to fulfill their purpose in life. When we do not feed our spirits with the right nutrients, we starve. Our outward appearance may look okay, but inside, our spirit is withering away. We can experience lethargy, pain, lack of energy, and depression when we deny our spirit food.

My prayer is that you realize just as your physical body needs to be nourished several times a day, so does your spirit. You cannot feed the spirit one time a week and expect to be able to stay connected to God and hear His call for your life. Spend some time asking for guidance in areas you are starving your spirit. Let God expose areas that are not getting the proper nourishment. If you have not accepted Jesus as your Savior, do so today. Ask Jesus to reveal Himself to you. Spend some time seeking Jesus and let Him feed you. It will be the best thing you can do to replenish the nutrients your spirit is craving.

****

The atmosphere of the temple is a determining factor as to whether or not visitors will return and want to become members. When a person walks in the doors, they can get a feeling as to whether or not they are welcome. A warm, genuine welcome makes the visitor want to enter. An intimate atmosphere makes people feel as if they fit in and not isolated from the members. No one wants to attend a place of worship where they feel unwelcome or unappreciated. The demeanor of the pastor, as well as the congregation, is evident as the visitor partakes in the service.

When we load our bodies with toxins, we can feel sluggish and uncomfortable. We have studied ways to make our bodies become more efficient, have more energy and be healthier. To best put into practice what we have learned, it is essential that we also detox the body periodically. A good detox will rid the bodies of toxins and allow us to use the nutrients we are fueling our bodies with more efficiently, thus reducing inflammation, increasing energy and mental alertness, and aiding in weight loss.

Toxins constantly bombard our bodies. Some of these toxins we can control and others we cannot avoid. One report shows that since the beginning of the industrial revolution, over eighty thousand toxic chemicals have been released into our environment. Many of these chemicals have not been tested to ensure our safety. [1] These toxins are in our air, water, food, clothing, cleaning supplies, and health and beauty products. Toxins can be a cause of many of our medical problems. Dr. Mark Hyman has listed some of the most common symptoms of having chronic toxicity. These symptoms include: fatigue, muscle aches, joint pain, sinus congestion, postnasal drip, constipation, bloating, gas, diarrhea, foul-smelling stool, heartburn, sleep problems, difficulty concentrating, food cravings, water retention, difficulty losing weight, rashes, skin problems, acne, puffy dark circles under the eyes, PMS, and bad breath. [1]

God designed our bodies to remove waste efficiently. Several systems can do this for us. These systems are the skin, gastrointestinal (liver, gallbladder, colon, and GI tract), lungs, lymphatic (immune system), and urinary (kidneys, bladder, and urethra). [2] Each one has a specific role in keeping our bodies clean, and when one of these becomes congested, it can wreak havoc on the other systems.

Our skin eliminates waste through sweat glands. The urinary tract works as a filter for our blood and removes the waste through urination. Our gastrointestinal tract converts the nutrients the body does not utilize into stool. The liver functions as a filter to break down and remove toxins from our blood and regulates our hormones. The respiratory system eliminates toxins every time we breathe by exhaling carbon dioxide. [3] The lymphatic system is part of the immune system and transports fluids out of the tissues and returns it to the blood. It also rids our bodies of waste, debris, dead blood cells, pathogens, toxins, and cancer cells. [4]

No matter how hard we try and avoid all the toxins, we will still be exposed to some of them. Our job is to maintain healthy lifestyles by eliminating as many toxins as we can by eating healthily and taking care of our bodies. Detoxing will help us to counterbalance the effects of the toxins we cannot control.

Even healthy eating does not always rid our bodies of toxins that cause us to become sluggish and not properly digest our foods. So what else can we do to rid our bodies of some of these toxins? We can do a detox regularly basis to allow our bodies to operate as optimally as possible. It is recommended we detox two times a year and detoxing can last between three days to several weeks. There are several levels of detox.

Some supplements can be used to assist in this process, and there are a variety of detox programs. Detox programs can be very specific or general, depending on which plan you chose. The primary goal of a detox program is to rid the gut of debris stored up in the body over time with as little stress as possible. During this time frame, fuel the body with nutritious foods that require little effort to break down. Then the toxins need to be flushed out with large amounts of water. To eliminate the stress on the digestive system, remove meats, dairy products, sugar, grains, processed food, and alcohol during the detox. [5]

One form of a detox is to do a juice fast and water diet, giving the digestive system a rest. Another simple detox is using the guidelines established in the Daniel Fast, which requires a person to eat only raw fruits, vegetables and vegetable juices while drinking plenty of water to flush out the system. [6] There are many detox recipes available on the Internet. During this time, it is also helpful to include a probiotic to help with the digestion while detoxing. Some foods that are an excellent source of probiotics are yogurt (with active or live cultures) kefir, sauerkraut, kimchi, kombucha, and pickles. Natto can also work as a probiotic for our diet. [7]

Helpful ideas to detox your body regularly:

- Drink eight to ten glasses of water a day. Using lemon, lime, or orange slices in the water is also beneficial. Water not only helps you to stay hydrated, but it also flushes out the toxins.
- Detox the liver by using beets, turmeric, grapefruit, milk thistle, dandelion root, burdock root, and green tea in your diet. [8,9] Asparagus helps detox the liver and urinary tract as well as helps with digestion. [10] Green tea also helps clean out the toxins.
- Get regular exercise. Exercise stimulates the cardiovascular system as well as the lymphatic system to help rid your body of toxins. Rebounding on a trampoline or jumping rope is an excellent way to help stimulate the lymphatic system.
- Another way to boost the lymphatic system is to take a hot shower for five minutes and then turn on cold water for thirty seconds and repeat three times.
- Allow the body to sweat several times a week. You can do this by working out, taking hot baths using Epsom salts, or using a sauna.
- Make sure to eliminate bodily waste by having a bowel movement one to two times a day. Regularity is essential to prevent buildup in the intestines.
- Take a good probiotic daily.
- Use homemade cleaning supplies instead of store-bought to eliminate chemicals in your home. Many of the substances can cause toxins to build up in your body.
- Take time to relax each day and calm your nervous system. Calm bodies help aid in digestion. Perform deep breathing to increase oxygenation of the body. Make sure to get adequate sleep each night so the body can rejuvenate.
- Get regular massages. Massages help remove toxins from your body. It is essential you drink lots of water after the massage to help flush out the mobilized toxins.
- Eat foods that are known to help detox the body. You should have eight to ten servings of fruits and vegetables a day, with the majority of these being from cruciferous vegetables. Garlic and onions are also effective to help detox the body. Use organic and pesticide-free fruits and vegetables whenever possible. Other foods to include are green tea, seeds, and nuts.
- Avoid eating processed foods, including flour and sugar.
- Use as little medication as possible.
- Watch the air you breathe. You cannot control all of this, but you can stay away from second-hand smoke and not visit areas that have highly polluted air and fumes. You should avoid using paraffin candles and chemicals in your home.

If you are under a doctor's care, make sure you talk to the doctor before doing a detox to make sure you do not have any restrictions.

MAINTAINING AN ALKALINE DIET

Our bodies have been designed to perform optimally when they are in an alkaline state. We can test the body's alkaline/acid state by checking the pH levels. A neutral pH is 7.0. Optimally the body's blood pH is in the 7.35 to 7.45 range, which maintains a slightly alkaline state. The pH of our bodies will vary depending on our diet and external factors. The organs of the body will also have different pH levels, depending on their function. For example, the stomach is highly acidic because it has to break down the food.

The foods we eat vary as to whether they are acidic or alkaline. Due to the changes in our diets from when we were hunters and gathers, to now being buyers of processed food, there has been a significant change in the overall balance of minerals which affects the body's pH. (1) A diet that consists of a higher ratio of alkaline foods and lower amounts of acid-forming foods will enhance our overall performance, giving us more energy and lower our risk of illness and disease.

There is research showing that an alkaline diet may improve our cardiovascular health, bone density, memory and cognition, and reduce the risk of strokes and hypertension. By maintaining a more alkaline state, it may help in reducing the morbidity and mortality from these diseases. (2) Dr. Axe reports that an alkaline diet helps to decrease the calcium accumulation in the urine, decreases muscle spasms and muscle wasting, prevents plaque buildup in the blood vessels, strengthens the immune system, prevents kidney stones, and strengthens the bones. It also helps improve the body's ability to absorb minerals and prevent magnesium deficiency. (3) Other research has shown that an alkaline diet can help decrease chronic pain, slow the aging process and help prevent some cancers. An alkaline diet can also assist in the effectiveness of some chemotherapies since some of these agents work best with a higher pH. (4) Produce that is organic and grown in mineral dense soil will have the greater alkaline properties.

The alkaline Diet consists of eighty percent of the food being alkaline and twenty percent acidic for all meals and snacks.

The following are some of the most common foods that are alkaline:

Beans: Lima and navy beans.

Fresh fruits: Apples, citrus fruits, figs, pumpkins, tomatoes, and watermelon.

Fresh vegetables: Asparagus, avocados, barley grass, broccoli, Brussel sprouts, cabbage, carrots, celery, cucumbers, green beans, kale, onions, red beets, spinach, and sweet potatoes. These foods are best eaten raw. However, they can be lightly steamed. Cooking vegetables can deplete the minerals, which help maintain an alkaline state.

Green drinks and smoothies: Green plants and grasses have chlorophyll. Chlorophyll helps to restore the blood to an alkaline state.

Herbs: Burdock root, cayenne pepper, dandelion root, garlic, ginger, mint, parsley, and turmeric.

Herbal teas: Alfalfa, burdock root, chamomile, elderberry, ginger, green, red clover teas.

Mushrooms: Button, portobello, reishi, shitake.

Nuts and seeds: Almonds, coconut, flax seeds, pumpkin seeds, sesame seeds, and sunflower seeds.

Oils: Avocado oil, coconut oil, flax oil, and olive oil

Sprouts: Sprouted seeds should be eaten within two to seven days of sprouting to get the maximum benefit. They contain enzymes which help the body break down and absorb the nutrition, rid the body of toxins, fight disease, help wound repair, and help with metabolic functions. Some of these sprouts are alfalfa, barley, bean, bittercress, buckwheat, and flax seed sprouts.

Acidic foods: alcohol, artificial sweeteners, caffeinated drinks, eggs, grains, lunch meats, milk, pasta, peanuts, processed cereal, processed foods (most contain high levels of sodium chloride), rice, walnuts, and wheat.

Food for thought:

1. After reading about diet and how important it is to your health, what changes do you want to implement immediately?

2. What areas do you think you need to research more thoroughly?

3. What are some of your short-term goals for improving your diet?

4. What are your long-term goals for improving your diet?

Journal your thoughts.

APPLE CIDER VINEGAR

Research continues to provide evidence that apple cider vinegar can offer many health benefits. Therefore, I have included it in this book. To get the health benefits, it must say apple cider vinegar (ACV) with the "mother" on the bottle.

The mother is the sediment on the bottom of the bottle. The mother is the essential part of the vinegar and is the raw enzymes and gut-friendly bacteria that promote healing. Clear vinegar is processed and does not have any of the benefits that raw ACV offers. When introducing ACV into your diet, start slowly, and gradually build up to one to two tablespoons daily added to eight ounces of water. Make sure to dilute apple cider vinegar because when taken plain it can be strong and hard on the esophagus and tooth enamel. It can also be added to tea and made into salad dressing. One of the most common brands on the market is Braggs Organic Apple Cider Vinegar with the Mother.

ACV has many health benefits:[1,2,3,4,5]

- Cider vinegar promotes alkalinity in the body. It is harder for cancer cells to grow in an alkaline body. The gut-friendly bacteria improves the digestive system by helping it to utilize the nutrients more efficiently.
- The pectin in the ACV can help treat diarrhea by forming bulk fibrous matter. It also creates a protective coating for the colon lining and reduces intestinal spasms.
- It prevents indigestion: Add one teaspoon of ACV and one teaspoon of honey to a glass of warm water and drink thirty minutes before eating.
- It acts as a detoxifying agent to the body by helping detox the liver and cleanse the lymph nodes.
- It helps clear sinus drainage.
- It helps stop hiccups.
- It can soothe a sore throat by mixing a quarter cup ACV and quarter cup warm water and then gargling every hour.
- It may decrease swelling by rubbing ACV onto the affected area.
- It may help relieve night leg cramps by taking ACV in water two times a day.
- It helps fight yeast infections. Soak in a bath with half cup ACV added to the water.
- It helps fight foot and skin fungus by soaking the infected area in ACV and water.
- It can increase the body's metabolism, thereby helping with weight loss.
- It may help control blood sugar levels.
- It helps to remove warts. Soak a cotton ball in vinegar and place on the wart with a bandage to keep it on all night. Repeat until the wart falls off. You must be careful as the vinegar can burn the surrounding skin.
- It soothes sunburned skin.

Before trying anything new, do your research. People taking medication should talk to their physician to make sure it does not interact with their meds. People taking diabetic medication need to speak with their doctors as it can decrease blood sugar levels. Large amounts of ACV for long periods could cause harmful effects on your health and can lower your potassium levels and bone density. ACV needs to be diluted in water or juice since it is highly acidic and undiluted ACV can damage tooth enamel, skin, and tissues of the mouth and throat. Each person responds differently to various foods and drinks, as with any new foods introduced to your diet, monitor how you react to the latest additions.

Week 6

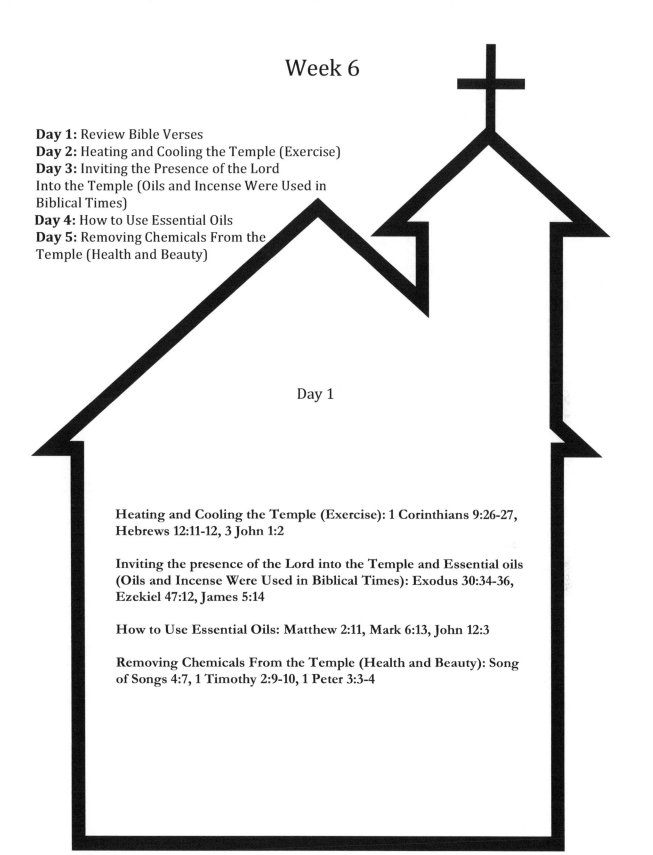

Day 1: Review Bible Verses
Day 2: Heating and Cooling the Temple (Exercise)
Day 3: Inviting the Presence of the Lord
Into the Temple (Oils and Incense Were Used in
Biblical Times)
Day 4: How to Use Essential Oils
Day 5: Removing Chemicals From the
Temple (Health and Beauty)

Day 1

Heating and Cooling the Temple (Exercise): 1 Corinthians 9:26-27, Hebrews 12:11-12, 3 John 1:2

Inviting the presence of the Lord into the Temple and Essential oils (Oils and Incense Were Used in Biblical Times): Exodus 30:34-36, Ezekiel 47:12, James 5:14

How to Use Essential Oils: Matthew 2:11, Mark 6:13, John 12:3

Removing Chemicals From the Temple (Health and Beauty): Song of Songs 4:7, 1 Timothy 2:9-10, 1 Peter 3:3-4

Weekly exercise: Try one new form of exercise this week and report to the group about your experience.
Bonus Weekly exercise: Research several essential oils and their benefits and share with your group. Try one of them in your home.

HEATING AND COOLING THE TEMPLE
(EXERCISE)

A temple needs a proper heating and cooling system so that the congregants are comfortable when worshipping the Lord.

Nugget of the day: Don't you realize that your body is the temple of the Holy Spirit, who lives in you and was given to you by God? You do not belong to yourself, for God bought you with a high price. So you must honor God with your body *(1 Corinthians 6:19-20).*

This is a verse that is easy to skip over and not take to heart. We should know that we have the Holy Spirit living in us when we accept Jesus, but do we really understand the significance of this? When we possess something beautiful and of value, we take care of it, put it on a shelf to display it properly, or carefully pack it away so that it does not get scratched or dented. However, in the Holy Spirit, we possess something very powerful and sacred. Too often we do not do enough to protect it or value it. We should to take care of our bodies because they house something much more valuable than any material thing we own. Our bodies are temples, and we should treat them as such. We should respect them and expect others to respect our bodies too. Let us live healthy lifestyles so that our bodies are kept in the best possible physical condition as well. When we eat healthy, we fuel our bodies. When we exercise we keep our bodies strong and increase our endurance.

My prayer is that we all take time to appreciate the gift our loving Father has given us: the gift of the Holy Spirit. We need to commit to protecting this gift by taking care of our bodies. Let us realize that proper diet and exercise are not an inconvenience, but a necessity to live quality lives, which allows us to do the Will of our Father to the best of our ability. I pray that we treat our bodies with respect because we are the precious children of God and we deserve what is good. ***For we are God's masterpiece. He has created us anew in Christ Jesus, so we can do the good things he planned for us long ago*** *(Ephesians 2:10).*

✦✦✦

The heating and cooling system in the temple needs to be properly maintained to ensure good indoor air quality and make the building comfortable for the people. The architect makes sure that the unit that is being installed is energy efficient and powerful enough to maintain a comfortable temperature throughout the building. After the unit is installed, it needs regular maintenance to keep it running and prolong its life.

Our bodies also need to be maintained. Exercise generates heat in our bodies. The body temperature can be raised as much as 3 degrees when we exercise. God has given us a cooling system so that our bodies do not overheat. Sweating allows the body to release some of the heat. To keep our bodies efficiently running while exercising, it is imperative that we hydrate it. Drinking water before, during, and after exercise is the best way to keep our heating and cooling system running properly.

Exercise is often that dreaded thing we must do in our day because people tell us it is good for us. When we do not see any reason for exercising, lack motivation, or have a poor self-image, it makes it hard for us to remain dedicated to exercising on a regular basis. For some of us, our bodies have been a sore subject most of our lives. Our bodies have embarrassed us because people have told us we are too heavy or not beautiful. People often like to point out others' imperfections so they feel better about themselves. At times, when a person has a poor self-image, they may be afraid to exercise in a place where other people can see them.

What are some of the reasons that you use to keep from exercising?

How have others discouraged you from exercising?

Let's shed the image that the world projects on us and accept God's truths. Let's try to see ourselves as God sees us. When we do, we will be able to live our lives more fully. We are not on this earth to please people. We are here to please God. When we struggle with self-image or the inability to break the chains that others have bound us with, we could ask ourselves the following question: *Obviously, I'm not trying to win the approval of people, but of God. If pleasing people were my goal, I would not be Christ's servant (Galatians 1:10).*

We should not have to be embarrassed to put on a pair of shorts or sweats when working out. We do not need to feel as if our workout is inadequate. If we allow other's approval or acceptance of us to interfere with our changing our lifestyles, we could limit our ability to grow and become the person God has intended for us to become. *Fearing people is a dangerous trap, but trusting the Lord means safety (Proverbs 29:25).* God will always approve of us trying to better ourselves and making our temples more efficient to serve Him.

How does it make you feel to know that God is the One you need to please and you should quit trying to win the approval of other people?

Isn't it often easier to please God than other people?

How can changing your view of exercise make you more willing to do it regularly?

If you see exercise as a means to improve stamina so that you can serve God more efficiently, will this help motivate you?

When we exercise, try to look at it as a way to get fit, not just as something we are doing to improve our physical appearance. The Bible recognizes that physical strength is a much-needed component of being able to accomplish the plans that God has for us. Without strength and endurance, we will become fatigued and unable to complete our work on this earth. We do not have to spend hours in the gym or perform grueling exercises to be able to do God's work. When we put it into perspective as to why we are exercising, we will be much more inclined to work out on a regular basis. Paul referred to physical training several times in his books. Physical training allows us to do God's work. *"Physical training is good, but training for godliness is much better, promising benefits in this life and in the life to come"* (1 Timothy 4:8).

Have you ever thought that maybe the reason you are not fulfilling your calling, or in some cases not hearing from God, is because you do not have the energy or strength?

If this may be the case for you, what do you plan to do to about this?

The hardest part of exercising is the preparation. We often drag ourselves to the gym or slowly walk to the trail, grumbling the whole way as if what we are about to do is painful. We see it as a "have to do" rather than a want to do. After we begin the activity, we realize it is not so bad and wonder why we were complaining about it. Most likely we will start this whole routine over the next day. Exercise should not be that dreaded thing that takes up valuable moments of our time; instead, it should be the activity we look forward to because it enhances our day. Exercise makes the rest of our day productive. It gives us energy, it can change our attitudes, it improves our sleep at night, and it is beneficial to our overall health.

Exercise is not only essential to keep us energized, but also to decrease our risk of diseases, including cancer. Research has shown that regular exercise will cut down the risk of developing cancer as well as preventing its return. [1] Another study showed that the mortality rate of patients diagnosed with cancer was sixty-seven percent lower when they exercised two and half hours per week as compared to the patients who did not exercise. [2]

Overweight women produce and store more estrogen than women who have a good body mass index. This increase of estrogen increases the risk of breast cancer. For this reason alone, it is essential to exercise and get into shape. [3] Exercise also helps with improving moods, raises self-esteem, and decreases heart disease and diabetes risks.

The American Heart Association recommends one hundred fifty minutes a week of moderate exercise to improve cardiovascular health. To lower blood pressure and decrease the risk of heart attack or stroke, they recommend forty minutes of aerobic exercise three to four times a week. [4] The American Diabetes Association recommends thirty minutes a day, five days a week to improve the body's ability to utilize insulin. [5]

Exercise can also help us recover more quickly when we do face an illness. I can personally attest to the benefits of exercise while recovering from an illness. While receiving chemotherapy, my energy level increased while going through treatment and I lost sixty pounds. I credit this weight loss to both eating a clean diet and working out daily.

If you have not exercised in a while or are battling an illness, this may seem like too much effort. Start slow. Set goals for yourself and work up to the recommended times. Some exercise is better than no exercise. Build in activity throughout the day. Do chores around your house such as gardening and lawn cutting. Park your car farther away in the parking lot, so you have to walk further to the store. Take the stairs rather than the elevator. Get up from your desk every hour and walk around the office. Take a few minutes to do some arm and leg exercises. When watching television, perform an exercise during commercial breaks. Whatever you do, make sure you find time in your day to stay active. Dr. Mercola states that there is substantial evidence that supports sitting for long periods of time increase the risk of disease and mortality even when maintaining a healthy lifestyle. [6]

Exercise is classified as aerobic and anaerobic. Both aerobic and anaerobic exercises are important to do on a regular basis to maintain or improve your health.

Aerobic activities (also called cardio exercise) focuses on improving cardiovascular and respiratory endurance, burns fat, and helps to improve your mood. Performing aerobic exercises on a regular basis has also been shown to reduce or prevent some illnesses such as cancer, diabetes, cardiovascular disease, osteoporosis, and depression. Exercise is classified as moderate or vigorous. Moderate exercise consists of walking, yoga, and doing activities such as mowing the lawn or gardening. Vigorous workouts include jogging, swimming, and bicycling. It is recommended we perform aerobic exercises at least five times a week for at least thirty minutes per session.

Anaerobic activities improve muscle strength. Your body can burn calories more efficiently when it has a greater muscle mass. These exercises are done at a high intensity level in short bursts. Anaerobic exercises help to improve bone strength, protect the joints, boost energy, boost metabolism, and improve athletic speed, strength and power. Examples of this type of exercise include weight lifting, jumping, and sprinting. Anaerobic exercises should be done at least two times a week.

There are many exercise programs available, and each promoter will tell you why theirs is the best. Many will try to convince you that only their program can offer you all the activity needed to keep the body healthy. I believe, as with diet, each one of us has unique needs, and no cookie-cutter exercise program works for everyone. People benefit from a variety of programs depending on their season of life. I change my routine up quite regularly. I get bored quickly, and when I am doing the same thing each day, I burn out and quit exercising altogether. I also need to change my exercise routine depending on how my body is responding and how I am feeling during a particular period.

In the spring and summer months, I enjoy the outdoors and would much rather take a hike on a trail, so I spend much of my summer hiking. Hiking not only gives me the benefits of the exercise, but I also get the benefits of the sunshine. While walking, I put on my praise music and can spend some uninterrupted prayer time with God. It is often during this time that God clears my head and helps me find answers and gives me solutions to problems I am facing. I have found that no matter where I am exercising, in my home, at the gym or on a trail, when I spend time in prayer and praise the time passes quickly. I have also spent time walking the trails with a friend. Not only do I reap the benefits of the exercise, but we also enjoy good conversation and we can share my faith. Doing some form of exercise with our friends is an excellent way to "kill two birds with one stone." People choose to visit by eating at a restaurant or sitting around snacking, and this can lead to weight problems. Exercise is a healthy alternative.

If exercise is something you find hard to do or get motivated to begin, enlist the help of a friend. It is easier to do something when you are accountable to another person. For me, even on the days I do not want to walk, it is nice to have a friend reminding me of the importance of keeping active.

You can do exercise in your home or community center, or you can pay for a gym membership. Many gyms are inexpensive, are open twenty-four/seven, and offer a variety of classes at no additional charge. Some exercise routines can be done at home utilizing a variety of television programs and websites where you can find workout routines. You can also utilize surrounding parks and neighborhood trails or just walk around your neighborhood.

**If you are being treated for a medical condition, consult with your doctor first.

Because there are many types of exercises a person can do, take some time to explore what works best for you and which offers you the most benefit. Mix and match workouts to stimulate different muscle groups and to improve metabolism. When we do one type of activity, the body becomes accustomed to the routine, and we do not benefit as much from the exercise. The body becomes efficient at performing the routine and burns fewer calories. Changing up the routine also helps to keep our brains sharp.

Here is a listing of some of the exercises you can explore.

Strength training: Strength training is an integral part of your exercise routine. You should do this at least 2 times a week. It will help you lose unwanted body fat and prevent age-related muscle loss. Strength training also improves the cardiovascular system and stresses our bones, which helps to prevent osteoporosis by increasing bone density. The increase in muscle mass will help enhance the body's metabolism.

There are several ways to do this type of training. You can use body weight (such as pushups, squats, wall pushes), resistive tubing or band exercises, free weights, or machines. Before beginning to exercise, warm up with stretching and ten minutes of aerobics. Make sure to do the exercises correctly to prevent injury. Lifting excessive weights can cause you to lose control and stress the joints or injure the muscles.

There are different weight training programs you can do depending on the results you want to obtain. If a person wants to increase muscle mass and strength, then they should do no more than eight to ten repetitions per set using a weight that will fatigue the muscle. When using weight training to tone and condition the muscles, you should do ten to twelve reps per set. When you can do more reps with one weight, then increase the amount of weight next time. Weight training should be done two to three days a week and cardio training the other days. To train effectively, there needs to be a recovery period to allow the muscles to heal between sessions. Therefore, weight training should be done every other day or work different muscles groups on opposite days.[7,8]

Yoga: This program helps people focus on their breathing technique as well as improving strength and flexibility. Deep breathing is an essential component of good health. It can enhance a person's posture and improve lymphatic flow. Another benefit of yoga is that it can be relaxing and help focus the mind. It can be performed at different levels so that people with low energy or weak muscles can do a modified version until they build up their strength.

HITT (high-intensity interval training): This type of training requires a person to perform bouts of high-intensity exercise followed by recovery periods of low-intensity exercise. This program focuses on getting the heart rate up and burning fat in less time. After a person completes the routine, their metabolism can improve for up to forty-eight hours. Most of the HITT routines are done using only a person's body weight and can be performed anywhere and take less than thirty minutes to complete. [9]

Zumba, barre, and other classes: Many gyms and community centers offer a variety of classes. Check the site directory to see what the center provides. For some people, working out with a group can be highly motivating. Zumba is a dance fitness program that has choreographed moves done to music. It is a full-body workout and helps burn calories. Barre classes help improve posture, balance, and strength combining techniques from ballet, yoga, and Pilates. It uses a barre as a prop to maintain balance while doing the exercises.

Swimming: Swimming works all the muscle groups and is an excellent aerobic activity. The benefits of swimming are increased endurance, improved muscle strength, and cardiovascular fitness. The buoyancy of the water alleviates some of the strain on the joints, so it is good for people who have painful joints.

Walking: This is an excellent activity especially for someone just starting to exercise. Try and keep a brisk pace for a good cardiovascular workout. Brisk walking helps maintain a healthy bodyweight, strengthens the bones and muscles, is a good cardiovascular exercise, and improves balance, coordination, and a person's mood. Be careful when using a treadmill. Treadmills can alter gait patterns, so if you can walk on a trail or path, you will have a more natural gait. Another advantage to walking on trails or in neighborhoods is that the terrain varies from flat to hilly and can challenge the cardiovascular system. The HITT program can be done in combination with your walking program.

Bicycling and jogging: These programs offer the same benefits as walking. They can be a more intense exercise for the cardiovascular system. Therefore, they are excellent aerobic activities. Some people find these activities refreshing, and they look forward to doing them.

Stretching: This is important to do with all the exercise programs especially as our bodies age and become less flexible. Stretching before and after exercise helps reduce injuries.

Balance training: It is always good to incorporate some balance exercises. These exercises can help strengthen the lower extremities as well as improve our agility. As we get older, balance can become more of an issue. Performing activities to maintain our balance can be helpful to decrease the chance of falling as we age.

Video game programs: For people who enjoy video games, there are now many active game systems which can challenge you physically. The Wii® and Kinect® systems offer many options.

Ways to develop an exercise program that works for you:

Pick an activity that interests you. You will be more motivated to exercise when you enjoy what you are doing.

Find the time of day that works best for you. I like to work out first thing in the morning. Before going to work, I can spend time doing my exercises. I feel it helps me to be more alert at my job. You will have to determine what time of day works best for you. Some people like to exercise in the evening because they find it helps them unwind after a busy day.

Stick with it. Your body needs time to adapt to exercise. At first, it is hard to get into the routine, but as your body gets used to training, it begins to crave it. Establishing this routine may take several weeks before you want to exercise and it is no longer a chore.

Work out with an exercise buddy. Encouragement helps to keep us going. When you have a partner, it is not as easy to miss a training session. They help to hold you accountable for exercising regularly.

Use the time for prayer and or worship. You get the benefits of both exercise and God. I know that I can focus more clearly on God when I am active. Some of my best writing comes to me when I am working out.

Hire a trainer. Trainers can give you motivation and guidelines, especially when you are just starting out. They will teach you the proper way to do the exercises and vary your program so you work all the muscle groups. Using a trainer is another way to be accountable for following through with an exercise program.

Set small, achievable goals. It is much easier to be motivated to exercise when you see results. If the goals are long term and you don't see change, it will be hard to stay motivated.

Don't compare yourself to others. Everyone has to start at the beginning. People that can perform the routines and make it look easy most likely started where you did, at the beginning. When you expect to complete the exercise routine like someone else, you can get discouraged.

Keep an exercise log. Record your progress. When you do not feel productive or hit a peak, it is nice to be able to go back and see that you have made progress from where you started. It is easy to forget what your baseline was if you do not record it.

Journaling is so important as you strive to make changes. Take note as to how your quality of life improves. Sleep, energy, and productivity can all be enhanced with exercise. When you see the benefits in your life, you will be much more prone to continue your routine.

Food for thought:

1. What types of exercise are you interested in doing?

2. What time of day would work best for your schedule?

3. Do you have a friend who would be interested in exercising with you?

4. What are your goals for exercising?

Journal your thoughts.

Day 3

INVITING THE PRESENCE OF THE LORD INTO THE TEMPLE
(OILS AND INCENSE WERE USED IN BIBLICAL TIMES)

Oils and incense were used in Biblical times for performing religious rituals, anointing the sick, and helping to heal the sick.

Nugget of the day: All Scripture is inspired by God and is useful to teach us what is true and to make us realize what is wrong in our lives. It corrects us when we are wrong and teaches us to do what is right *(2 Timothy 3:16).*

Isn't it amazing? God gave us all the instructions on how to live the most productive lives possible. It is all here in the Bible. Too often, we think we can do so much better than God. He gives us foods that fuel the body, herbs, spices, and oils that help with healing, and commandments that keep chaos out of our world. These are guidelines for healthy living and building strong interpersonal relationships that, when followed, make for good, clean, stress-free life. And yet people continue to think we know more than God. We believe we can make foods from chemicals that will fuel the body more efficiently, alter the plants He gave us so we can make them bigger, treat every symptom with manmade drugs, make our own rules, and allow everyone to do their own thing. We think we can live in a me-centered world and do what makes us happy. Many people think they can live sedentary lives with no adverse effects. Look where all of our "improvements" have gotten us. More people are overweight and struggle with health issues. Don't you wonder what God must be thinking about all this? He knows if we would just listen to Him our lives and our world would be so much better.

My prayer is that you realize God did not give you the Bible to dictate your life. In actuality, it allows you to live a full, healthy, God-centered life that would give you less stress and more pleasure in this world. I pray you ask God for guidance on how to de-stress your life so you can live the way He intended for you to live and realize your body is a temple for God.

****

Incense and oils were first used by the Israelites in the tabernacle of Moses and has been use ever since for worship. God gave specific orders to the Israelites as to how to prepare them. They were instructed to never use this formula for personal use. *Then the Lord said to Moses, "Gather fragrant spices—resin droplets, mollusk shell, and galbanum—and mix these fragrant spices with pure frankincense, weighed out in equal amounts. Using the usual techniques of the incense maker, blend the spices together and sprinkle them with salt to produce a pure and holy incense. Grind some of the mixture into a very fine powder and put it in front of the Ark of the Covenant, where I will meet with you in the Tabernacle. You must treat this incense as most holy. Never use this formula to make this incense for yourselves. It is reserved for the Lord, and you must treat it as holy. Anyone who makes incense like this for personal use will be cut off from the community"(Exodus 30:34-38).* God knew the value of these oils and each one is significant.

Frankincense is an essential oil still used today for its healing properties. It has anti-inflammatory, local anesthetic, and anti-fungal properties. Research has also shown it may help with fighting cancer. (1) Besides its health benefits, frankincense is used during worship or a person's quiet time to draw closer to God. The book of Revelation also mentions the use of incense during prayer. *Then another angel with a gold incense burner came and stood at the altar. And a great amount of incense was given to him to mix with the prayers of God's people as an offering on the gold altar before the throne. The smoke of the incense, mixed with the prayers of God's holy people, ascended up to God from the altar where the angel had poured them out* (Revelation 8:3-4).

The oils used today are not the same as those in Biblical times. They did not have the same technology to extract the oils that we do now. They used oils that they could extract from the plant, but they also used other parts of the plants for healing and everyday uses. For example, frankincense in its resin form was used for perfume and incense as well as healing; cedar wood was also made into perfumes. [2] People used aloe plants for skin conditions and constipation. The entire anise plant (seeds, leaves, and stems) was used for getting rid of fevers.

Have you ever taken the time to contemplate that God created this world with such precision and purpose, not leaving out any detail? He gave us all the essential things we need to help us live healthy lives: spiritually, physically, emotionally, and mentally. God has also provided us with a means to heal our bodies when we encounter illness or disease. Take some time to appreciate the love that God invested in us when He created this world.

Many of us read the Bible and take bits and pieces of it and apply them to our lives, but seldom do we heed all of God's advice. I don't know about you, but the more I study healthy living, the more I realize just how great our God is and how much information He packed into the Bible. He included all aspects of healthy living in the Bible, it is our responsibility to mine God's Word and utilize the information so that we can live our lives to their full potential. God intended for oils to be used, and He gave us this insight in both the Old and New Testaments. *"Fruit trees of all kinds will grow along both sides of the river. The leaves of these trees will never turn brown and fall, and there will always be fruit on their branches. There will be a new crop every month, for they are watered by the river flowing from the Temple. The fruit will be for food and the leaves for healing"* (Ezekiel 47:12). The last chapter of the last book of the Bible refers to these oils. *It flowed down the center of the main street. On each side of the river grew a tree of life, bearing twelve crops of fruit, with a fresh crop each month. The leaves were used for medicine to heal the nations.* (Revelation 22:2)

Have you taken the time to really think about how important God's creation of trees and plants is to our survival?

God began the first chapter of the first book (Genesis 1:29) with this information, and He ended the last chapter of the last book with this information (Revelation 22:2).

How do these verses impact you?

God wanted to remind us just how imperative it is that we eat well and that we can use oils for healing while living on this earth. He also shows us that He would provide us with similar types of food and oils in Heaven.

Take a look at how essential oils were used in the Bible to get a clearer understanding as to just how potent these oils can be. Oils and fragrant incenses are mentioned in over two hundred verses. The Levite priests were in charge of diagnosing and healing disease through prayer and anointing with oils. [3] There are over six hundred references in the Bible to essential oils and the aromatic plants from which they are extracted. [4] At least 33 different essential oils or aromatic oil-producing plants are mentioned in the Bible. [4] There seventy-six verses about anointing with oil. [5] There are fourteen principle oils listed that were used by people in the Bible. The oils listed are myrrh, frankincense, calamus, cedarwood, cinnamon, cassia, galbanum, onycha, spikenard, hyssop, sandalwood, myrtle, cypress, and rose of sharon. [4]

The first time many of us were introduced to essential oils in our lives was when we heard the Christmas story for the first time. Frankincense and myrrh became part of our vocabulary before we ever knew what they were. *They entered the house and saw the child with his mother, Mary, and they bowed down and worshiped him. Then they opened their treasure chests and gave him gifts of gold, frankincense, and myrrh* (Matthew 2:11). The magi could have brought Jesus any gift they chose. And yet they decided on these because they knew how valuable these oils were and that these oils were significant enough to give to the King. When Jesus was older and His time on this earth was drawing to a close, Mary anointed Jesus with expensive oil. *Then Mary took a twelve-ounce jar of expensive perfume made from essence of nard, and she anointed Jesus' feet with it, wiping his feet with her hair. The house was filled with the fragrance* (John 12:3). Jesus understood the significance of this oil and appreciated the gift. *Jesus replied, "Leave her alone. She did this in preparation for my burial. You will always have the poor among you, but you will not always have me"* (John 12:7-8).

The people who lived in the Biblical times valued oils. They understood that oils had many useful purposes and used them for spiritual cleansing and purification from sin: *And Moses said to Aaron, "Quick, take an incense burner and place burning coals on it from the altar. Lay incense on it, and carry it out among the people to purify them and make them right with the Lord. The Lord's anger is blazing against them—the plague has already begun." Aaron did as Moses told him and ran out among the people. The plague had already begun to strike down the people, but Aaron burned the incense and purified the people* (Numbers 16:46-47). They also used these oils as perfume and to improve their moods: *The heartfelt counsel of a friend is as sweet as perfume and incense* (Proverbs 27:9).

The Bible associates healing of the sick with the anointing of the oils. *They drove out many demons and anointed many sick people with oil and healed them* (Mark 6:13 NIV). *Are any of you sick? You should call for the elders of the church to come and pray over you, anointing you with oil in the name of the Lord* (James 5:14) God does not waste space in His Word. He only includes what we need to know while on this earth. We should take time to understand that essential oils have a place in all of our lives.

Food for thought:

1. Do you have a new appreciation for the essential oils and all they can do?

2. What stands out to you in regards to essential oils and what they can do for us?

3. What smells do you find to be effective in calming you, increasing your energy level or bringing a smile to your face?

Journal your thoughts.

HOW TO USE ESSENTIAL OILS

Essential oils have many uses in our lives today. They can be used to improve focus, assist in healing, and for cleaning.

Nugget of the day: My child, pay attention to what I say. Listen carefully to my words. Don't lose sight of them. Let them penetrate deep into your heart, for they bring life to those who find them, and healing to their whole body (Proverbs 4:20-22).

To whom do you listen? Do you listen to the people around you or do you listen to our loving Father? At times, it seems so much easier to talk to other people and get their advice. But have you noticed that you can talk to 5 different people and get 5 different answers? Although people who love us want to help us, their solutions are often based on their life experiences and what benefits them. When we face struggles, we should go straight to the source and talk to our Dad. He will never steer us wrong because He truly knows what we need. He knows what our future holds, and He knows how our actions will affect those around us. Before you speak to others when they seek your guidance, consult with your Dad. Don't talk freely on your own accord, as it may not be God's will.

My prayer is that you seek our loving Father when faced with struggles. I pray you are patient and wait for a response before you act. There may be a reason God is slow to answer. You need to trust Him and know He will never guide you wrong when you truly listen to Him. When you do speak with others, pray first with them so that God's will prevails. After all, Father knows best!!!

****

The altar of incense in the Holy place of the tabernacle was a symbol of prayer from God's people. This altar was symbolic of Jesus, the intercessor. Incense is also a symbol of prayers from the faithful rising to Heaven. Revelation also addresses the importance of incense and prayer. *The smoke of the incense, mixed with the prayers of God's holy people, ascended up to God from the altar where the angel had poured them out (Revelation 8:4).*

How often do you smell a particular smell and it takes you back to another time? Maybe it reminds you of a childhood memory and brings back the good old days. Aromas are important for more reasons than just memories. Aromas can improve a mood, enhance sleep, increase focus, and assist in healing. Essential oils are highly concentrated plant components that have been used for thousands of years. These oils serve so many functions and can provide so many benefits to enhance healthy living. Some of these benefits include: using them for relaxation, improving our health, invigorate, making health and beauty products, improving our skin conditions, and cleaning our homes. They serve many purposes including medicinal, personal care, aromatherapy, stress relief, and cleaning. Using essential oils in your home to replace scented candles is an excellent way to not only keep your home smelling good but also keep the toxins out. Most candles are made of paraffin wax, which creates highly toxic benzene and toluene when burned (both are known carcinogens). The toxins released from paraffin candles are the same as those found in diesel fuel fumes. [1] If you want to use candles, use beeswax candles, which are natural air cleaners and produce negative ions.

Essential oils are not actually oils. They do not contain the fatty acids that make up oil. These oils are made from extracting different parts of the herbs and plants. It takes enormous amounts of a plant to make the oil. For example, it takes two hundred fifty pounds of lavender plants to make sixteen ounces of this oil. [2] This chapter is written to help you become familiar with a few of the many benefits these oils can provide in your life. I encourage you to do more research into the many different types of oils and all the benefits they can provide.

Essential oils can be diffused several ways.

Diffusers: There are different types of store bought diffusers. Some are ultrasonic and use water, and others us a fan with oil placed on a filter. I keep a diffuser in each room and use a variety of oils in them.

Cotton balls: Place several drops of oil on cotton balls and put them in your car vents. This is extremely helpful when driving long distances because the oil can help energize you. Eucalyptus in your car can help clear your congestion.

Plugins: These can be purchased online and will diffuse the oils in your home or car.

Furnace filter: Place several drops on your furnace filter to help give the whole house a clean smell.

Bathwater: When taking a bath, place several drops of oil in the tub.

Aromatherapy necklaces, bracelets, or pendants: They can be worn when going out to get the benefit of essential oil. Some parents find that when their children use essential oil while at school, it calms them or helps to improve their focus.

Reed diffusers: These use a glass vase. Place carrier oil in the vase and add several drops of an essential oil. Place reed diffuser sticks in the vase. If you use a vase with a narrow opening, the aroma will last longer.

Mists and sprays: Place eighteen to twenty drops of an essential oil in a spray bottle of water and shake well. Then spray in the air.

Tips for using oils:

1. Use high-quality therapeutic grade oil: pure, medicinal and steam distilled.

2. Most oils need to be applied to the skin using a medium such as a carrier oil or water. A few examples of a carrier oils that can be used are coconut oil, olive oil or avocado oil. You can dilute the essential oil by using 1-2 drops of an essential oil with 1teaspoon of the carrier oil. Many of the oils are highly concentrated and need to be diluted so as not to cause skin irritation or reactions. Lavender, German chamomile, tea tree, sandalwood, and rose geranium do not need to be diluted.

3. Talk to your doctor if you have any health concerns or issues using the oils. Before using an essential oil, research the benefits as well as any contraindications. There are some circumstances when a person should not use particular oils. If you are allergic to the plant the oil is extracted from, you will be allergic to the oil.

4. There is a difference between fragrance oils and essential oils. If it says fragrance or perfume, it is not a natural essential oil. Fragrance oils are artificially created and have chemicals in them.

5. Be cautious when using oils around infants or children and check all the precautions. Do not use undiluted essential oils on a baby or child because their skin is delicate and much more sensitive to the oils.

6. Avoid certain oils while pregnant or nursing. Some of these include jasmine, lemongrass, nutmeg, cinnamon, anise (aniseed), chamomile, sage, and cedar wood.[2] Before using oils during pregnancy, do your research to make sure they are safe for you to use.

Benefits of some commonly used oils

Before using these oils, you should consult an essential oil specialist to learn all the contraindications and proper ways to use these oils. I have included a small list of oils for you to become familiar with and to show you how valuable these oils can be in your life.

Cinnamon: Cinnamon oil helps to stimulate brain function, improve circulation, relieve depression, control blood sugar and sugar cravings, boost the immune system, and fight viruses. (3)

Cloves: This oil is an antiseptic and can help improve oral infections and canker sores. It is also beneficial for boosting your immune system, improving respiratory problems, and easing bug bites, earaches, and skin problems. Cloves can be used in your home to get rid of fleas or mosquitoes. (4)

Eucalyptus: This oil is known for its decongestive abilities. It is very useful for clearing up congestion and helping you breathe at night when you have a cold.

Frankincense: There is a reason the wise men brought this oil to the Baby Jesus. Not only does it help a person meditate and improve their spiritual connection, but it also has potent medicinal properties. The University of Leicester researchers in the U.K. have brought to our attention that the wise men brought medicine to the Baby Jesus when they presented Him with frankincense. Along with many of its healing properties, it shows promise in treating ovarian cancer. (5) Frankincense can help in healing many illnesses because of its anti-inflammatory properties. It is associated with boosting immunity, fighting infections, arthritis, colds and respiratory problems, helping digestive disorders, healing skin cuts and scarring, and improving oral and uterine health. (5, 6) Frankincense is not recommended for pregnant women or nursing mothers. It can be used in diffusers, on the skin, or by placing two to three drops under the tongue.

Grapefruit: This oil helps with migraines, improves the lymphatic system, helps treat acne, boosts the immune system, helps stimulate the brain, decreases cramps, eases stress and depression, helps remove toxins in the body, and can be used as a deodorant. (7)

Lavender: This oil is excellent for relaxing and helping fall asleep at night. If you do not have a diffuser, you can put several drops in bath water or on your pillow to get a good night's sleep. It is also a good oil to put in your bath to relax after a stressful day.

Lemon: Lemon oil helps reduce stress, boosts the immune system, helps with asthma, aids in weight loss, and helps with stomach problems. (8) It is also known for its ability to stimulate lymph drainage and as a bug repellant.(9) If used on the skin, it is best to stay out of the sun for twelve to twenty-four hours after use due to skin becoming photosensitive.

Oregano: Oregano oil helps clear up respiratory problems, is a potent antioxidant, helps rid the body of infections, improves skin conditions, and decreases arthritis pain and flu symptoms. (10)

Peppermint: This oil relieves nausea, can be an analgesic for muscle aches and pains, and can help with migraines. It is also useful for helping increase focus, boost energy, and decrease stress. Some teachers use this oil to help students do better on their tests. Do not use on children under thirty months. (11)

Roman chamomile: This oil helps to relieve anxiety, insomnia, and stress. It also is an anti-inflammatory, aids in digestion, may promote heart health, and eases arthritis pain. (12)

Rosemary: This oil has been shown to normalize low blood pressure. (13) It also helps fight cancer, decreases inflammation, improves mental clarity, and overcomes fatigue. It may also help with hair regrowth. This oil can increase blood pressure, so it should not be used if you have high blood pressure. (14)

Sandalwood: Sandalwood works as an antiseptic and anti-inflammatory, improves memory, helps with skin care, boosts the immune system, and helps decrease spasms. (15)

Tea tree: This oil is known for its ability to heal wounds, fight acne, get rid of nail fungus, and act as antiseptic for minor cuts and as a natural deodorant. (16)

Remember many oils need to be diluted before using. You must read the labels and see how the manufacturer recommends you use the oil. Some oils cannot be ingested. Not all oils are of the same therapeutic grade and can cause problems for the user. Research any oil you want to use to see what precautions or contraindications accompany the use of these oils. If you are receiving medical attention, make sure your doctor is aware of the oils you are using.

Besides using essential oils for health reasons, there are many other ways to use these oils to eliminate chemicals that are dangerous to your health.

Cleaning: Lemon and tea tree oil are great natural disinfectants.

Mosquito repellant: Lemongrass, citronella, and eucalyptus oils mixed with 1 teaspoon of coconut oil can be used on the skin to ward off mosquitos.

Eliminate odors: Use essential oils in the laundry, in vacuum cleaners, in trashcans, and in diffusers around the house.

Natural perfume: Apply several drops of your favorite oil on the wrists.

Eliminate mold: Tea tree oil is good for eliminating mold.

Ward off mice and ants: Place cotton balls with peppermint oil near areas where you have a problem with mice or ants.

Food for thought:

1. Were you surprised to learn that essential oils are well documented in the Bible?

2. What essential oils do you want to use in your home?

3. Do you see the value of using these essential oils?

4. What aromas are soothing and comforting to you?

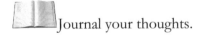Journal your thoughts.

REMOVING CHEMICALS FROM THE TEMPLE
(HEALTH AND BEAUTY)

We have worked very hard at rebuilding our temples. We should make sure that we are also eliminating the chemicals that can be toxic and harmful to our newly designed temples.

Nugget of the day: This is what the Lord says—your Redeemer, the Holy One of Israel: "I am the Lord your God, who teaches you what is good for you and leads you along the paths you should follow. Oh, that you had listened to my commands! Then you would have had peace flowing like a gentle river and righteousness rolling over you like waves in the sea (Isaiah 48:17-18).

As a parent, there are times that I am frustrated while watching my grown children doing something that will cause them added stress to their lives even though there is a more straightforward solution. Rather than listen to me, they want to prove they are independent and don't need my advice. It is hard for a parent to stand back and watch when we know how to help our children. God must be frustrated a lot. He has many children in this world trying to prove they can make it on their own and don't need Him to guide them. God does not want us to live in a state of unrest. He wants us to have peace and joy in our lives. The problem is that we are often too hardheaded to heed His advice and follow His direction. God even made it simple for us. He gave us the Bible, an entire book on how to find joy, how to get along with people, how to stay out of trouble, and how to keep our bodies and minds healthy. Yet we continually try to prove we can live our lives differently. The results are frustration, unhappiness, unhealthy bodies, and unnecessary struggles. Can't you just imagine God sitting on His throne shaking His head and asking the same question we earthly parents ask: When will they learn to listen to me?

My prayer is that you realize our loving Father does know best. He knows just what we need and when we need it. I pray that you adhere as closely as possible to the teachings of the Bible. Understand that God did not give you rules just to exert His authority, but to allow you to live a joyful and peace-filled life. So take some time to pray for guidance and the ability to submit to our Heavenly Father. You will find that when you trust God, your life will become less complicated.

****

There are many toxins that can be present in a temple. Many times, the administration is unaware of these culprits. For example, the construction materials such as paint and adhesives can emit volatile organic compounds (VOC's) into the air. These are gases emitted into the air from products or processes thus polluting the air and can cause a variety of illnesses. Another form of VOC's is cleaning supplies. The temple needs to be clean. However, great consideration needs to be taken when deciding what types of products should be used to ensure the safety of the members. Using commercial cleaning supplies can also have an adverse affect on the congregants who have chemical sensitivity.

When trying to keep contaminants out of our bodies, we must take into consideration that the skin absorbs many toxins as the skin is the largest organ of the body and is very porous. The pores allow our bodies to remove the toxins and prevent waste buildup. When chemicals clog the pores they no longer are able to do their job. The sebaceous glands in our skin produce oil that have bacteria to ward off disease. Chemicals applied to the skin can diminish this oil by blocking the duct and inhibiting our natural defense against some diseases.

If you want to rid your body of toxins, you need to not only consider what you put in your body but also what you put on your body. One study showed that women who use beauty products could expose themselves to 515 chemicals. When we consider a woman who uses deodorant, shampoo, conditioner, and makeup daily, uses a lot of products. Each product contains a large amount of chemicals, so the numbers add up quickly. Some of the chemicals can disrupt your hormone balance. It is important to read labels and become educated as to which ingredients you should avoid when selecting body care products. Many of the products have dyes in them, use synthetic fragrances and preservatives, and are made from petroleum derivatives. If the name of the ingredient is too hard to pronounce or the label reminds you of chemistry class, try a different product. There are so many ingredients you should try and avoid. Do your research about the products you use and be an educated consumer. Some of the ingredients to try and avoid in your beauty products are olefin sulfonate, mineral oil, synthetic fragrances, cocoamidopropyl betaine, triclosan, sodium lauroyl sarcosinate, potassium cocoyl glutamate, sulfates, parabens, and phenoxyethanol. (1) I have listed some recipes to help you begin your journey of healthy living. The Internet offers many ideas and recipes for clean living.

Hair and skin conditioner: Massage coconut oil into your hair before going to bed. Coconut oil also works like a gel on hair to spike it or give it some body. Coconut oil is also an excellent skin conditioner, makeup remover, and wound healer. It also helps to eases razor burns.

Homemade Shampoo: Put 1 tablespoon baking soda and 1 cup of water into a bottle and shake before using. Do not use every day because it can cause dryness to the scalp.

Another shampoo: ½ cup water, ½ cup Castile liquid soap, and 1 teaspoon vegetable oil or glycerine. If you want a scent, add a few drops of essential oil. Mix well and put in a bottle. Do not use vegetable oil if your hair is oily.

Hair conditioner: 1 Tablespoon apple cider vinegar and 1 cup hot water.

There are many other recipes for natural shampoo and conditioners on the Internet.

Detox bath: Fill a tub with water and use 2 cups Epsom salt, 2 cups sea salt, and ½ cup baking soda. Add several drops of lavender or frankincense essential oil. Soak in the tub for 20 minutes to help remove toxins from the body. The essential oils help to decrease stress.

Homemade deodorant recipe: Combine ¼ cup baking soda, ¼ cup arrowroot powder. Then add 8 tablespoons of coconut oil and mix so that it looks like the consistency of the deodorant you buy. If it is too moist add more cornstarch. This mixture can be put in old deodorant dispensers or stored in another container. If you have sensitivity to this deodorant before applying you can spritz your under arm with cider vinegar and water.

Homemade toothpaste: Mix equal parts of Arm and Hammer baking soda and coconut oil with several drops of peppermint extract.

Teeth whitener: Turn a piece of banana peel inside out and rub it on the area you want to treat. As you knead, the nutrients will be absorbed into the teeth. Then brush your teeth.

Treatment for acne, pimples, and brown spots: Take a piece of banana peel, turn it inside out, and rub it on the affected area until the peel becomes brown (a few minutes). As the skin dries, it will absorb the nutrients from the skin. Do not wash the skin for 30 minutes. Let the nutrients soak into the skin.

Brown spot remover or highlight your hair: Lemon juice can be used on the skin to remove sunspots or highlight your hair.

Sunburn balm: Use apple cider vinegar and apply with a washcloth or add 1 cup to your bath water.

Lip gloss: Use coconut oil.

Coconut oil moisturizer: Place 2 cups coconut oil in a mixer and whip it. Add several drops of essential oil. Then place in a jar and use as a lotion.

Avocado honey face mask: Use 1 fully ripened avocado (with skin and seed removed) and 1 tablespoon honey. Mash the avocado and add honey until well mixed. Apply to the skin and let stay for 10-15 minutes. Rinse your face with lukewarm water and pat dry. This mask is perfect for dry skin.

Body scrub: Mix 1 tablespoon chia seeds, ¼ cup coconut oil, and 1 teaspoon lemon juice together and store in a container. To apply, dampen your face or body and apply in a circular motion. Let sit for 2 minutes and then remove with a wet towel.

Poison ivy and bug bite salve: Make a paste out of baking soda and apple cider vinegar. Apply to the affected area. It will dry up the poison ivy and stop the itch.

Food for thought:

1. What are some changes you can make right now to eliminate using unnecessary chemicals on your body?

Journal your thoughts.

Week 7

Day 1: Review Bible Verses
Day 2: Cleaning the Temple (Cleaning and Decluttering the Home)
Day 3: Final-Walk Through (Reviewing Your Goals)
Day 4: Taking Possession of the Temple (You Now Have the Basics to Live a Healthy Lifestyle)
Day 5: Consecrating the Temple (Dedicating Your Hard Work to God)
Conclusion

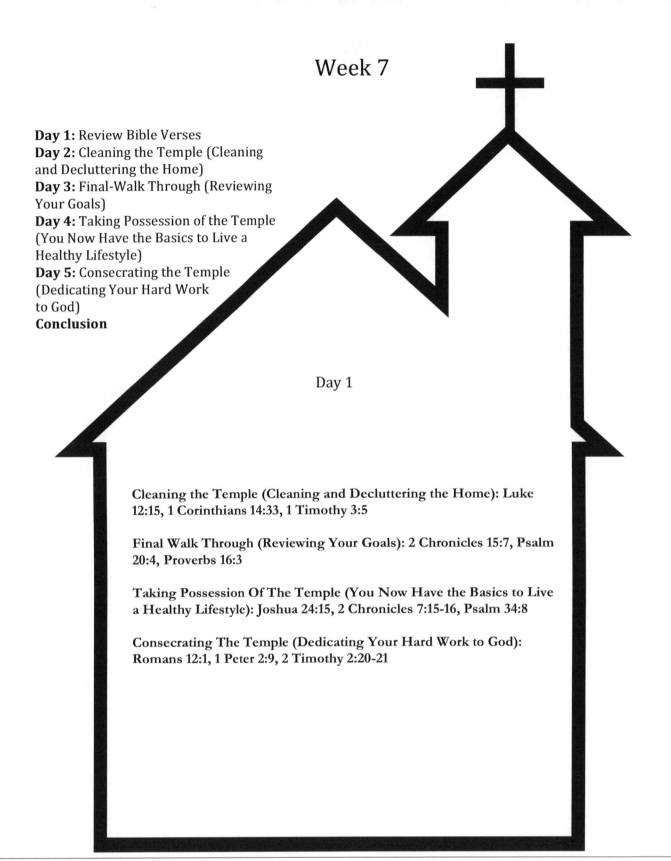

Day 1

Cleaning the Temple (Cleaning and Decluttering the Home): Luke 12:15, 1 Corinthians 14:33, 1 Timothy 3:5

Final Walk Through (Reviewing Your Goals): 2 Chronicles 15:7, Psalm 20:4, Proverbs 16:3

Taking Possession Of The Temple (You Now Have the Basics to Live a Healthy Lifestyle): Joshua 24:15, 2 Chronicles 7:15-16, Psalm 34:8

Consecrating The Temple (Dedicating Your Hard Work to God): Romans 12:1, 1 Peter 2:9, 2 Timothy 2:20-21

Weekly exercise: Try one homemade cleaning supply, and report to your class what the effects were in your home

CLEANING THE TEMPLE
(CLEANING AND DECLUTTERING THE HOME)

Construction is a messy job. It is best to clean up as you go along so that the mess does not become overwhelming and hinder your or the other workers' ability to complete the project.

Nugget of the day: You say, 'I am rich. I have everything I want. I don't need a thing!' And you don't realize that you are wretched and miserable and poor and blind and naked. So I advise you to buy gold from me—gold that has been purified by fire. Then you will be rich. Also buy white garments from me so you will not be shamed by your nakedness, and ointment for your eyes so you will be able to see *(Revelation 3:17-18).*

This world loves to give us a false sense of security. The world tells us we are nobodies if we don't drive a nice car, live in a big house, or have designer clothes. There is nothing wrong with having nice things as long as we understand these things do not define us. What truly matters is our faith and how we live our lives. What if people could see straight into one another's souls? What would others see in your soul? Is your soul nicely clad, pure in thoughts, and clean in actions or is your soul tattered with impure thoughts and dark with sin? God sees our soul. He does not even look at our outer appearance. On that great day, when we meet Him face to face, we will stand before Him baring our souls.

My prayer is that we all prioritize our lives. We remove things that bog us down and obstruct us from living healthy lives. I pray you realize that God loves you regardless of your material wealth. Ask God to help you remove obstacles that obstruct your relationship with Him. Decluttering our lives of material things is freeing and allows us to focus on what is important. Vow to stay committed to our loving Father.

****

We all know what clutter can do in a temple. The buildup of clutter and debris can happen quickly and without much warning. While we are remodeling our temples, we need to make sure to keep this mess under control so that we can continue to build. If the distractions become too much, it can overwhelm us. Taking the time to clean periodically relieves stress.

For if a man cannot manage his own household, how can he take care of God's church (1 Timothy 3:5)? We often do not take the time to understand how our homes can affect our moods, the stress level in our homes, our ability to focus on our projects. When we are at peace, the immune system has a greater ability to fight and heal us. Taking care of our homes requires us to establish our priorities. These priorities require us to make decisions as to whether our house is going to be calm and peaceful or chaotic. No one intentionally decides that his or her house is going to be chaotic. We all want to have a home that is inviting and can allow us to relax after a hectic day. We need to make conscious decisions as to how our homes look. The décor, the knick-knacks that we set around our homes, and the clutter can affect how we feel. We have to ask ourselves who are we trying to impress with the way our home looks? This may seem like a trivial question, but whom are you trying to impress? People believe the look of their home determines their self-worth and how others see them. Instead of going for comfort, people design their homes to look as if they are something out of a magazine. Rather than being able to relax, they are worried about the formal appearance of their home. Then there is the other extreme, where people believe the more they have, the better off they appear. *Then he said, "Beware! Guard against every kind of greed. Life is not measured by how much you own* (Luke 12:15).

People tend to collect "stuff." At first, a collection or hobby can be fun, but some times it takes over our homes and lives. What once was fun and relaxing now becomes a chore to manage. Clutter can cause us to become distracted and take away from the things that should be a priority in our lives: things such as spending time in God's presence and restoring our bodies. We should evaluate our colors and patterns in our homes. Sometimes the colors we choose to paint our rooms can be fun and exciting initially, but eventually, they prove to be too stimulating for us to relax fully. If we truly want to allow ourselves, family members, and guests find our homes warm and inviting, then we should take an honest look at how our homes are set up. Our homes can be an unsuspecting cause of chaos in our lives, putting our brains and family on overload. Research has shown there is a link between depression, stress, anxiety, and clutter. When a family is used to clutter, they may not recognize the correlation because the clutter has been part of their home life for a while.

Take some time to walk through your house, as a visitor might, and try and see the home with a fresh set of eyes.

When you enter your home, does it look warm and inviting so that you want to relax, or do you feel as if you are in a display home and everything needs to be kept in perfect order? Rather than relaxing, do you feel as if you need to be formal and/or straighten anything that is out of order?

Look around. Does the clutter or amount of knick-knacks that are displayed easily distract you? Are your eyes constantly moving around the room so that you are unable to focus on another person or the task at hand?

Do you feel as if you have to spend time rearranging to make room for more stuff?

How are your color choices and patterns affecting you? Sometimes bright colors are fun and exciting, but when the newness wears off, they can be over-stimulating. Take a look around and see how the colors affect your mood.

I can personally attest to how a house can affect life. I was a collector. I loved to collect many different things and display them in every room. I became a slave to my home. Rather than enjoy it, I felt as if I constantly had to dust and clean it. I always had to make room for new pieces I brought into my home. I was in a constant battle to keep up with everything I owned. I got to a point where I no longer enjoyed the things. Instead, I felt obligated to keep building the collections and finding new places to display them. I always felt as if I was in constant motion in my house. Between raising three boys and having to keep up with a chaotic home, it was hard to relax. Nine years ago all this changed. I made the changes gradually. At first, it was hard to declutter and let go of my possessions, but as time went on, it became easier and more freeing. I was finally able to clean my house in a few hours instead of it taking days.

I now look forward to coming home and enjoy being there. I know I will be able to relax. I still have knick-knacks that mean something to me, but they are neatly displayed. I have repainted my rooms so that the colors are bold and warm. I use Himalayan salt lamps, which are not only beneficial for my health but also give a warm glow to the room. I have oil diffusers in each room so that I enjoy the smell. My home is no longer a place of chaos, but a haven that I look forward to at the end of the day and miss when I am gone.

Not only do colors and décor affect our well-being, but smells also play a role in this. What odors or smells would a visitor notice?

Can you think of ways materialism has controlled your home life and/or you personally?
If the answer is yes, what can you do about it?

Remember, change does not occur overnight. Do not attempt to make drastic changes quickly, or you may revert to your old habits. The sooner you release yourself from the bonds of materialism, the sooner you will be able to direct your attention to the things that matter.

Not only does our décor and clutter affect our healthy lifestyles, but also what we use to clean our homes can have a significant impact on our health. We need to be careful as to how we clean our houses so that we are not polluting them with toxins. The media tells us that everything should be convenient. The store shelves are stocked with many cleaning supplies that we are told will make our lives much easier, but they are toxic. Many chemicals in our kitchens and bathrooms have been shown to cause health problems. They should be eliminated if possible.

Create in me a clean heart, O God. Renew a loyal spirit within me *(Psalm 51:10)*. As we recite this verse, let's not only pray for a clean heart but a clean home; a home that renews our energy and gives us peace. To live in a relaxing home, we need it to be clean. This requires us to use some cleaning supplies. Store bought cleaning supplies can be expensive, and they contain many toxic chemicals. Many of the chemicals are known or are suspected carcinogens. If we are eating healthy and keeping chemicals out of our diet, we should also keep them out of our homes.

There are four ways the chemicals we come in contact with can enter our bodies.

- We can inhale them.
- We can ingest them when we do not clean the chemicals off the surfaces we prepare food, or when we have the chemical residue on our hands.
- Contact with the chemicals. When we scrub with a rag or sponge, the substances may touch our skin. The skin is the largest organ of the body, and it is very porous. Anything that enters the pores can get into the bloodstream and wreak havoc on our organs.
- The chemicals can enter through a wound.

We must be cautious of products that claim to be "green," "biodegradable," or "natural." There are few regulations, and so these labels can be used loosely. Manufacturers are not obligated by U.S. law to list all ingredients in consumer products. Therefore, many substances can be used that cause people to present with symptoms such as headaches, lung irritations, cough, watery eyes, and sneezing. [1,2] One study revealed that using cleaning sprays has the same effect on a person's health as smoking a pack of cigarettes every day. [3] The women in the study had a decreased lung capacity and increased rate of asthma. Another study showed that nurses who cleaned surfaces with disinfectants regularly had a significant increase in lung disease. [4] Many of the cleaning supplies have antibacterial properties. The purpose of these chemicals is to kill the bacteria in which it comes in contact. The problem is that these chemicals may also alter the probiotic organisms in our body and disrupt microbial balance.

Health problems that have been linked to chemical exposure are as follows:
- Carcinogens: Chemicals that can cause cancer.
- Neurotoxins: Chemicals affect the brain and nervous system
- Endocrine disruptors: Some chemicals cause hormone imbalance, infertility, congenital disabilities, and early puberty.
- Respiratory problems: Chemicals that can cause breathing, asthma and lung problems

Many commercial product containers have WARNING or DANGER written on the label. All one has to do is read the container to see the range of adverse effects these chemicals can have on your body. These side effects can vary from acute symptoms such as respiratory problems or skin and eye irritations to chronic problems with the lungs, hormone disruption, heart problems, and even cancer. Bathroom cleaning products, for example, can cause light-headedness, dizziness, and breathing difficulty. Some companies make natural cleaning products, but you need to do your homework before using them to make sure the products are safe.

Although these chemicals may be convenient and advertise that they require less work to clean your home, you are compromising your health. Which is more important: using a little elbow grease and keeping your body free from toxic chemicals or saving a few minutes and exposing yourself to health hazards? If you choose health over convenience, homemade products will help you accomplish this. I have found that homemade products do just as good, if not a better job, without the harmful chemicals. They do not take any more time to get the same results.

It is not difficult to make your cleaning supplies. Many of them can be made in a short period of time. I bought spray bottles with different color lids to hold my cleaners. I then labeled them with the name and ingredients. I have included my labels for your use.

Shopping List for making cleaning supplies:
- Spray bottles
- Funnel
- Rubbing alcohol
- Dawn dish soap
- Cornstarch
- Olive oil
- Lemon juice
- White vinegar
- Baking soda
- Ivory soap
- Borax
- Washing soda
- Hydrogen peroxide
- Cream of tartar
- A couple of drops of essential oils can be added to the cleaners to give your home a pleasant smell.

All-purpose cleaner:
2 tsp. baking soda
4 Tbsp. Dawn
1-½ cups of water
Spray the mixture onto the surface and wipe clean.

Cabinet and wood floor cleaner:
½ cup white vinegar
1 cup of water
1-teaspoon olive oil
Several drops lemon essential oil
Spray the mixture onto the surface and wipe clean.

Car window de-icer:
⅔ cup of vinegar
⅓ cup of water
Spray on car windows and melt away the ice.

Carpet cleaner:
Pour a small amount of white vinegar onto the carpet to cover the stain. Sprinkle baking soda over the stain. Let this bubble up and absorb the stain. Rub away the stain with a damp white cloth.

Clothes whitener:
Add ½ cup lemon juice to the rinse cycle.

Drain opener:
Pour ½ cup vinegar and ½ box baking soda down the drain
Put the plug in the drain and hold in place until it stops fizzing. Wait 30 minutes and then pour boiling water down the drain, and the sink should drain. If it does not work the first time, repeat this process.

Dusting spray:
2 tsp. olive oil
1 tsp. lemon juice

¼ cup of white vinegar
1 cup of warm water
Pour all into a bottle and shake well.

Glass cleaner:
¼ cup rubbing alcohol
1 Tbsp. cornstarch
2 cups of warm water
Pour all into a bottle and shake well.

Granite counter cleaner:
3 drops Dawn dish soap
¼ cup rubbing alcohol
1 cup of water
20 drops essential oil (optional to give a pleasant smell)
Mix ingredients and spread on counters.
After cleaning, buff the countertop with a dry rag.

Grout cleaner:
½ cup baking soda
⅓ cup lemon juice
7 cups of water
Put in a spray bottle. Spray your grout and let sit several minutes. Then scrub with a toothbrush.

Laundry detergent:
1 bar Ivory soap
1 cup of washing soda
⅓ cup Borax
Heat 4 cups of water in a pan just before it boils. When done, shave the Ivory soap into the water and stir until dissolved. Fill a 5-gallon bucket with 3 gallons of hot water and mix in the Ivory soap mixture and stir. Then add 1-cup washing soda and ⅓ cup borax and stir. Let it sit overnight and then pour into cleaned out detergent bottles.

Lime buildup remover:
Cut a lemon and rub it on the faucet. Let it sit overnight and then wipe with a damp cloth.

Pot and pan cleaner:
Baking soda works well to clean most pots and pans. Mix baking soda with water to make a paste and then let it sit for several minutes before scrubbing the pot or pan. If this does not work, place 1-cup vinegar and some water into the pan and bring it to a boil. Then remove the pan and add 3 tablespoons of baking soda. After it is done fizzing, drain the excess liquid and scrub with the remaining paste.

Soap nuts: These nuts are berries, found in the Himalayans, and they contain soap in them. Soap nuts are gentle on the skin, so they are a good alternative for people with sensitive skin. I use them for my laundry and get good results. Soap nuts are an inexpensive alternative to buying laundry detergent. Five nuts are placed in a muslin bag and can be reused for four to five loads. The soap nuts can be ordered on the Internet.

Stove cleaner:
1 Tbsp. salt
1 Tbsp. baking soda
1 Tbsp. water
Mix to form a paste. Use a cloth dipped in the paste to clean the stove.

Tub and shower cleaner and soap scum remover:
1 part vinegar
1 part Dawn dish soap
Heat the vinegar and stir the ingredients together. Spray on the tub or shower and let sit for several minutes. Rinse. For heavy soap scum, allow the mixture to sit on the area for a longer time.

Weed killer:
1-gallon vinegar
2 cups Epsom salt
¼ cup Dawn dish soap
Mix and spray.

Cleaning tips
Dirt and rust stain remover:
Lemon juice mixed with salt will help remove these stains.

Garbage disposal cleaner: Use cut lemons to rid the disposal of any odors.

Cream of tartar (a natural bleach) Use a few tablespoons of cream of tartar with hot water or hydrogen peroxide to clean any rusty drains, stains in sinks, or in aluminum pans that are discolored.

Porcelain sink, tub, and commode: Rub the porcelain surfaces with cream of tartar to get rid of the stains.

Fabric stain: Mix a few teaspoons of cream of tartar with some glycerin and then spray on the stain.

Dishwasher: Use vinegar in the rinse dispenser to get rid of streaks and spots.

Walls: Mix 1-cup vinegar to a gallon of water and then clean with a rag.

Hydrogen Peroxide: This works as a disinfectant and as a bleach substitute. It can be used on cutting boards, to clean refrigerators, bathrooms, and on grout. To use on grout, scrub with a toothbrush along the lines.

Clean silver: Boil water in a large pot, getting the water as hot as possible. Remove it from the heat and place tin foil in the bottom of the pot. Next put the silver in the pot and then pour baking soda over it. It will fizz, and the tarnish will be removed. It works well, getting into all the crevices. Then wash the silver with soapy water to remove the film. This technique requires no elbow grease.

Whenever trying a new cleaning supply, it is best to try on an inconspicuous area first to make sure it will not leave a spot or harm the fabric. Make sure to read all the cleaning instructions in the owner's manuals or consult with the manufacturer of the product you are cleaning if you are unsure of the precautions of using certain ingredients.

Food for thought:

1. Do you see the value of eliminating cleaning products that can be hazardous from your household?

2. What are you going to do to do to decrease the number of chemicals in your home?

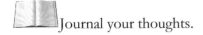Journal your thoughts.

FINAL WALKTHROUGH
(REVIEWING YOUR GOALS)

Before the owner accepts the completed job, there is a final walkthrough. Each part of the temple must be inspected to check for any problems. If there are problems, the builder addresses them before giving the temple the seal of completion.

Nugget of the day: And so, dear brothers and sisters, I plead with you to give your bodies to God because of all he has done for you. Let them be a living and holy sacrifice—the kind he will find acceptable. This is truly the way to worship him (Romans 12:1).

What holds you back from completely surrendering your life to God? The devil loves to mess with our heads. He loves for us to feel inadequate as if we have made so many mistakes or have so many flaws that God would not want us to witness for Him. And yet it is the struggles and errors that have given us all a testimony. We all sin, and we all have battles to fight in our lives. When we emerge victorious from these conflicts, we can testify how great our God is. God knows we are not perfect. He knows each one of us will make mistakes in our lives -and God still chooses to love each one of us. God does not give up on us. He keeps giving us signs that He is with us and He loves us. Until we breathe our last breath, God will be at our side, pushing us to grow as Christians and be the best we can be. He continues to expose areas in our lives that need improving upon so that we mature and draw closer to God. If you have not accepted Jesus as your Savior, He will lead you to the cross. If God does not give up on us, then we surely should not give up on ourselves.

My prayer is that you accept the fact that God loves you, not for what you do, but for who you are: His beloved child. Completely surrender your life to our Lord. Ask Him for forgiveness for mistakes you have made and then leave those mistakes at the cross. Quit carrying them with you and letting them take away the joy your Father wants you to experience in this life. Be willing to share your testimony with whoever will listen. Each one of us has a unique story, a story that God has given us. Be proud of who you are and bask in the love that your loving Father showers on you each day.

****

The final walkthrough is an exciting time. Often, this is the first time the new owners see the completed project. The debris has been removed and everything is in order. The owners finally get to see if their vision matches the finished product. If there are areas that were neglected or not done to specifications, this is the time to address them.

Let's take a walk through our temple that we have worked so hard on constructing. Let us take time to appreciate all the hard work we have done these past weeks. We should also reevaluate any areas that need further work. Don't be discouraged; no building is ever really complete. The remodeling of your temple was a huge undertaking. You had to address many issues and make changes that are hard to make. This temple is a work in progress.

The same is true in our lives. We will always have areas on which we can improve. It seems that when we get through one significant change, we find another area that needs work. Embrace these challenges. It is God's way of helping us draw nearer to Him. If we get too comfortable in life and do not have to rely on God for our strength, our relationships with Him often falter. When there are no challenges in life, it is easy to think we can handle life on our own.

You should embrace the new challenges because God knows you have more potential and are capable of fulfilling your calling. He wants to push you to be the best you can be. God loves to see you grow and become a stronger Christian. He also knows each one of us individually and understands how hard some of these changes are for us to make. God appreciates the effort we exert to build our temples more pleasing to Him. God knows how hard we must strive to live godly lives as opposed to living ungodly lives that many people in this world embrace and glorify. Keep up the good fight.

Take some time to review the work you did to remodel the inside of your temple. Spend some time revisiting the goals you developed when drawing up the blueprints. Inspect each area that was built and appreciate the accomplishments. Big or small, celebrate these achievements. If there are areas that still need some work, be honest with yourself about the work that you need to do. By addressing the issues that need improvements, you can have a plan in place to keep moving forward. When goals are written down, there is a better chance you will achieve them. If you are doing this study in a small group, take this week to celebrate together. Congratulate each other on a job well done.

Interior of the Temple: Lives are complicated. When the inside of the temple is not in order, there is chaos in your life. Forgiveness, repentance, strongholds, and unrest can wreak havoc. Many things can cause you to be unhappy or hinder your growth. Take time to appreciate how much you have improved in this study and address any issues that need work.

Interior walls: You need boundaries in your life so that you can accomplish your goals.
Goals accomplished:

Work that needs to be done:

Floor: When you hold onto negative strongholds, you can lose focus of your calling. You need to believe God's truths and not the enemy's lies.
Goals accomplished:

Work that needs to be done:

Ceiling: A positive attitude can make all the difference as to how you live your life. When we trust God we will find we can get through the tough times with less stress and draw closer to God.
Goals accomplished:

Work that needs to be done:

Sanctuary: Stress wreaks havoc on our lives. It causes our physical bodies pain, and it can cause us mental anguish. By restoring peace, it will decrease the stress in your life.
Goals accomplished:

Work that needs to be done:

Chapel And Vestibule: You can make changes in your life, but if you do not find contentment or have time to rest and rejuvenate, you can still struggle.
Goals accomplished:

Work that needs to be done:

Power Source: You need the power to make your home warm and comfortable. When you eat healthily, your temple is more energy efficient.
Goals accomplished:

Work that needs to be done:

Heating And Cooling: Exercise is essential to keeping your body in good shape. It is also crucial in helping to fight and prevent a variety of illnesses.
Goal accomplished:

Work that needs to be done:

Removal Of Chemicals And Toxins From The Temple: There are many things in your environment that you are unable to control so control what you can. When you eliminate toxins in your home and beauty and healthcare products, your body will be healthier.
Goals accomplished:

Work that needs to be done:

Remember to celebrate the victories. Do not give up on making changes in your life. When you trust God, He will continue to give you the strength to make changes and help you to continue to grow in faith and improve your lifestyle. *And I am certain that God, who began the good work within you, will continue his work until it is finally finished on the day when Christ Jesus returns (Philippians 1:6).*

Food for thought:

1. What improvements have you made in your lifestyle are you the proudest of?

2. How has your lifestyle changed since you have implanted new, healthy habits?

3. In what areas that you identified as needing improvement in can you begin to initiate change?

Journal your thoughts.

TAKING POSSESSION OF THE TEMPLE
(YOU NOW HAVE THE BASICS TO LIVE A HEALTHY LIFESTYLE)

Once the work is complete, the builder gives the keys to the new owner. This is a special day when the owner finally takes possession of the building.

Nugget of the day: The Lord had said to Abram, "Leave your native country, your relatives, and your father's family, and go to the land that I will show you. I will make you into a great nation. I will bless you and make you famous, and you will be a blessing to others (Genesis 12:1-2).

It is so easy to have the misconception that when we follow God and His calling, life will be easy. Often the opposite is true. When we listen to Him, we have to step out of our comfort zone and do something with which we are not familiar, requiring us to lean on God for strength. Following our calling can become an emotional roller coaster. One moment we are confident we can accomplish the task with God's guidance. The next moment we doubt whether or not we have the ability and question if God is going to help us. It can be frustrating as we muddle through blindly, taking the next step of faith hoping we are moving in the right direction. As we go along, there are periods of silence when God does not speak. Instead, He allows us to learn to trust Him and to have to struggle with finding the right way. If following our calling were easy, we would assume it was we who had accomplished the work. We would never get to see how active God is in our lives, and we would never learn how to trust God to guide us through this world. We would not stay in communication with Him and learn to speak to Him or include Him in our lives. There are many blessings when we dedicate our lives to Him. When we see how God can use us with all our imperfections and weaknesses to do the impossible, we have to stand in awe of how much interest He takes in each one of us. We get to hear Him speak to us and guide us. It is in these times we see God's role as a loving Father.

My prayer is that you realize God has a calling for your life. This calling may not be easy, and it may force you to take a leap of faith into areas you have never been. I pray you embrace the challenge and take the time along the way to appreciate all God is doing in your life. Use this time to draw closer to our Dad. God's calling will give you more rewards and joy than you can ever experience when you try and go at life alone without Him to guide you. God will show you His glory when you accept His calling.

****

Receiving the keys to the temple and taking ownership is exhilarating and scary at the same time. The owners have a responsibility to lead the congregants according to God's Word. The building is only a structure. It is the leadership, congregants, and the worship that makes it God's house.

Congratulations, you are holding the keys to a magnificent and wonderfully designed temple. The Architect designed this temple to be an original. Your temple was intended to house the Holy Spirit. If you are reading this chapter, you have worked hard on rebuilding and remodeling your temple to make it pleasing to God. It is time to celebrate your accomplishments and enjoy the temple you have built. All the hard work is worth it when you finally get to move into your new temple. You get to stand and marvel at all that has been done and appreciate the time and effort it took to build such a beautiful temple. But don't forget that receiving the keys also gives you responsibility. Anyone can call themselves a Christian. However, if you use this title, you need to act accordingly and heed the truths of the Bible.

By now, I hope that you are in awe of how great and knowledgeable our loving Father truly is. I hope that you, like me, are realizing that God has given us the keys to living successful and productive lives. It is up to us as to whether or not we accept these keys and heed God's advice so we can live the lives He has intended for us. The more I study the Bible, the more I realize that God has provided for all of His children from the beginning of time. He has given us a book of life's instructions to show us how to live fulfilling lives and to make the most out of our time here on this earth. God taught us the importance of having and maintaining a relationship with Him. He has also spoken about the importance of having and restoring relationships with one another. God has taught us how to have peace and joy in our lives, maintain the health of our bodies through nutrition and oils, and also exercise to keep our bodies fit. If we genuinely believe that God has a plan for our lives, then we also have to believe He has given us the means with which to fulfill this plan. However, just like anything we do, to be successful, we must do our part. Sitting back and waiting for God to work is not the answer. God has also given us free will. It is up to us to answer the calling and make an effort to be successful. He never promised us that it would be easy to fulfill our callings, but He has promised us blessings when we stay committed to fulfilling them.

I too, have grown in my faith and have learned to trust God. I first worked on changing my lifestyle and now have embarked on a new career. I am doing my best to heed His call. I have found that one of the hardest things in life to do is to surrender to God and be faithful in believing His promises. At times, I struggled with surrendering to His Will, and my writing was delayed because of this. He and I had many battles, and I let my mind fill with self-doubt. God was patient with me. He listened to my fears. In the end, God showed me that He was and is in charge. He was on this journey with me, and He will remain faithful even when I falter. This book was as much for me as it is for other readers. God has used this book to draw me closer to Him, strengthen my relationship, and teach me that I must look straight up instead of straight ahead when I need help.

I hope you have learned to look up for your strength. I also hope that you are learning to trust God with your calling, even when you do not see the immediate fruits of your labor. When God calls, He delivers on His promises, and He will not disappoint us. We miss out on seeing His glory because we quit before we complete the task He has put before us.

As you have worked through this Bible study, have you seen God more active in your life?   In what ways?

In what ways has God spoken to you through this study and throughout your journey?

In what ways has God challenged you to trust Him more thoroughly and turn over your struggles to Him?

Have there been times during this study that you felt as if things were overwhelming, and you could not make changes?   In what areas did you think you could not overcome the challenge?

How has God shown you that with His help you could not only overcome these challenges but that you can also address new challenges?

We cannot be successful in life if our bodies are not in the best shape possible. Whatever stage of life we are in, we must maintain our bodies, so we have the energy and stamina to get through our days.

Throughout this journey, we have talked about our bodies being God's temple. Do you take this to heart and try and live your life accordingly?

In what areas do you think you still need to improve to give God the honor and glory He truly deserves? (Remember, we are all human, and we will never be perfect. There will always be areas of our lives on which we can improve. When we are aware of these areas, we can focus on them and ask the Holy Spirit to help us improve.)

Take a moment to pray and ask God for His wisdom to help you become more aware of these areas and to guide you to make changes.

We have a responsibility as Christians to stay true to our faith and lead lives that bring others closer to our loving Father. *But those who trust in the Lord will find new strength. They will soar high on wings like eagles. They will run and not grow weary. They will walk and not faint (Isaiah 40:31).*

How have you found renewed strength in the Lord as you have worked on improving your lifestyle?

Have seen God's hand in restoring your temple not only physically but also spiritually and emotionally?

There is so much to see and do in this world. So many adventures await you. It would be a shame to miss out because you do not have the energy and stamina to participate in everything God has planned for you. *We do not want you to become lazy, but to imitate those who through faith and patience inherit what has been promised (Hebrews 6:12 NIV).* I often witness people sitting on the sidelines watching as others enjoy all life has to offer. They miss out because they have difficulty moving, find it hard to breath when they exert energy or do not have the endurance to walk very far. I see the hurt in their eyes, the embarrassment on their faces and the sadness in their demeanors because they are missing out. I know people who have dreams and callings and yet do not have the energy to fulfill them. Life is too short to miss out on all the opportunities God has provided for us in this world. *And so, dear brothers and sisters, I plead with you to give your bodies to God because of all he has done for you. Let them be a living and holy sacrifice—the kind he will find acceptable. This is truly the way to worship him (Romans 12:1)*.

As you have worked through this study, has your calling become more apparent, and if so, how?

Are you now ready and able to fulfill your calling, or are there physical, emotional, or mental barriers that need to be broken down first?

If you are still waiting for God to give you a new calling, do not be discouraged. Maybe your calling right now is to continue to work on the areas you are still struggling with, so you are prepared when He calls you. As you embark on this new stage of life, focus on God and let Him give you strength. Maybe you had tried to exercise before but were unable to stick with it, or life overwhelmed you. Take some time to pray to God and keep your eyes focused on Him as He guides you on this new journey.

I wish you the very best as you continue on your journey in life. If you have not already given your life to God, I pray that you do. I have seen what God is capable of doing when we trust Him and allow Him to take control. Life becomes an adventure, and God can amaze us with all He is capable of doing. If this study has drawn you closer to our loving Father, and you are learning to trust Him more with your life, then God has used this book for His glory. There is no sweeter joy than to be in love with our God and have a relationship with Him. *But you belong to God, my dear children. You have already won a victory over those people, because the Spirit who lives in you is greater than the spirit who lives in the world (1 John 4:4).*

Food for thought:

1. Do you see how God is working in your life to help you fulfill your calling?   Explain.

2. How have prayer and seeking God's guidance helped you to grow in faith and change your lifestyle?

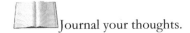Journal your thoughts.

CONSECRATING THE TEMPLE
(DEDICATING YOUR HARD WORK TO GOD)

Once the debt is paid off, and the owners own the temple free and clear. Therefore, the temple can be consecrated. Until the mortgage is paid off, the building may only be blessed, but not consecrated.

Nugget of the day: I heard a loud shout from the throne, saying, "Look, God's home is now among his people! He will live with them, and they will be his people. God himself will be with them (Revelation 21:3).

Research has shown that we need exercise to maintain our physical health. The same is true for our spiritual health. We must spend time in our spiritual gym. We need to flex our muscles of faith if we want them to grow stronger. When we spend time performing endurance training as we go through the trials of this life, we will be able to run the good race. We want to finish with arms raised in victory as we cross the finish line, look directly into the eyes of God, and hear those glorious words, "Well done, good and faithful servant." On that great day, we will not regret one moment of our spiritual training. All the trials we faced will have been worth the pain and suffering when we realize it prepared us to enjoy eternity in paradise. Every moment spent flexing our spiritual muscles and strengthening our faith will be worth the sacrifice of earthly pleasures to see God's glory first hand.

My prayer is that you realize if you want to enjoy all the promises God has given you, you need to live a Christian life. You need to stay in the Word and need to live by the rules God has given you. Work on your resistance training to stand against immoral values of this world, strengthen your faith, and run the good race. To train, you must have a daily faith routine. This routine will allow you to grow in your relationship with our loving Father. On that great day, when you meet our Dad face to face, all this training will have been worth it.

****

For I have chosen this Temple and set it apart to be holy—a place where my name will be honored forever. I will always watch over it, for it is dear to my heart (2 Chronicles 7:16). Solomon was able to build a temple for God, but only God can consecrate it and bestow His presence in it. The same was true for the Israelites. God gave the Israelites specific instructions as to how to build the temple in the wilderness. Everything had to be built exactly as God commanded. The Holy of Holies was where God resided in the temple. The Holy of Holies was separated from the rest of the temple by a curtain. Only the high priest could enter into the Holy of Holies, on the Day of Atonement. Jesus changed everything when He died on the cross, and the temple curtain tore, giving us direct access to God at all times.

Don't you realize that all of you together are the temple of God and that the Spirit of God lives in you? God will destroy anyone who destroys this temple. For God's temple is holy, and you are that temple (1 Corinthians 3:16-17). You were created to be a temple to honor God and house the Holy Spirit. You were given a valuable gift when you accepted Jesus as your Lord and Savior. I pray that as you complete this study, you see how important it is to maintain your beautiful temple.

And what union can there be between God's temple and idols? For we are the temple of the living God. As God said: "I will live in them and walk among them. I will be their God, and they will be my people (2 Corinthians 6:16). How does your temple resemble the temple that Solomon and the Israelites built?

Consecrate means to declare something sacred and to set it apart to serve God. People, places, or things can be consecrated. Many religious denominations will not consecrate the church until it is debt-free. You cannot consecrate your temple unless it is debt-free. The Good News is that you are debt-free! The blood of Christ has paid your debt. *With his own blood—not the blood of goats and calves—he entered the Most Holy Place once for all time and secured our redemption forever (Hebrews 9:12).* You have been given a gift you should cherish forever. The gift of salvation is something that will never grow old or become outdated. It is the only thing you will take with you when you leave your present body and join your Heavenly Father. When you accepted Christ, you consecrated your life to Him.

By consecrating your temple, you turn your life over to God. Your body is no longer your own. *Don't you realize that your body is the temple of the Holy Spirit, who lives in you and was given to you by God? You do not belong to yourself, for God bought you with a high price. So you must honor God with your body (1 Corinthians 6:19-20).* Spend some time reflecting on the meaning of this Bible verse. How are you going to allow it to be a guide as to how you live your life?

It is time to celebrate your accomplishments and enjoy the temple you have built. All the hard work is worth it when you finally get to move into your new temple. You get to stand and marvel at all that has been done and appreciate the time and effort it took to build such a beautiful temple. You can now consecrate the temple that you have worked so hard to rebuild.

Making changes in our lives is not always easy. We have been conditioned into believing we should be independent and live our lives the way we want to live. This is the human way of thinking. This independence has often gotten us into trouble and caused us heartache and many complications. It is when we surrender our lives, seek God's guidance, and live according to the Bible's commands that we see all that God is capable of doing in our lives. Many of us miss seeing God's blessings because we are too hardheaded to surrender and allow Him direct access to our hearts. *Then Joshua told the people, "Purify yourselves, for tomorrow the Lord will do great wonders among you" (Joshua 3:5).* When we let other people or worldly things influence our lives, we miss out on our real purpose. We also need to be on guard to not allow Satan to steal our joy. Satan wants us to miss out on seeing God's glory and reaping the benefits of following Jesus. *The thief's purpose is to steal and kill and destroy. My purpose is to give them a rich and satisfying life (John 10:10).*

God's ways are so much better than our ways. We are foolish not to let Him be in charge. By consecrating our temples, we are telling God we want Him to be in control. My prayer for you is that if you have trouble surrendering your life to God, you take the time to spend in His presence and ask Him to help you overcome your fears. Ask God to give you the courage to live the life only He can provide you. As you conclude this study, commit to staying connected to God. Include Him in every battle, decision, and celebration. Let Him be the first One you speak to in the morning and the last One you wish good night. Making a conscious effort to keep God ever-present in your life will keep you on the right path. When you stumble, your prayer life will get you back on track.

And so, dear brothers and sisters, I plead with you to give your bodies to God because of all he has done for you. Let them be a living and holy sacrifice—the kind he will find acceptable. This is truly the way to worship him. Don't copy the behavior and customs of this world, but let God transform you into a new person by changing the way you think. Then you will learn to know God's will for you, which is good and pleasing and perfect (Romans 12:1-2). As this study comes to a close, take this time to do just as Paul has asked. Consecrate your body to Christ. Know that you are now living for Him. In doing so, you will promise to try and keep your body, mind, and soul in the best shape so that you can fulfill your calling and enjoy the life God has prepared for you. Spend some time alone with God thanking Him for helping you achieve all you have these past 13 weeks. Enjoy this time with Him. If you are doing this study in a small group, have a ceremony to consecrate your newly renovated temple and then spend some time celebrating your accomplishments as a group.

Dear Heavenly Father,
Let this temple, which You have helped me rebuild, be a holy place. My temple is debt-free thanks to the blood of Christ. I am now able to consecrate this temple. Help me to live the life You chose for me many years before I was even born. Give me the strength and stamina to fight the good fight and run the race that you have set

before me. On this day, I consecrate this temple in your name. I pray that I may be a person that helps to draw others close to you. Let me be a light that shines in this dark world and let others know that I am a Christian by my actions. I vow to try and keep this temple to the best of my abilities: physically, mentally, and emotionally sound. My life is a gift from You, the Creator of the universe, and I want to honor you in all I do. I dedicate my service to You, almighty God, through Jesus Christ, our Lord. Amen

Food for thought:

1. How are you going to move forward and keep working on maintaining your temple?

2. Have you taken the time to ask God to continue to help you make changes and to thank Him for the help He has already provided you?

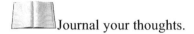Journal your thoughts.

CONCLUSION

In conclusion, I want to thank you for your dedication. This was an intense study, and it required you to explore many areas of your life and to address issues that were not always comfortable to address. There were changes that you made that took a lot of work and at times were very trying. There may have also been some changes that have already been reversed. Know there will be setbacks, but with God's help, you will get back on track. I want to encourage you to continue the fight to live a life that is pleasing to God. Continue to restore your temple. Until that great day, when you meet our loving Father face to face, He will continue to push you to your limits. When you clear one hurdle, God will make you aware of another obstacle that is interfering with your relationship with Him and keeping you from fulfilling your calling. *And I am certain that God, who began the good work within you, will continue his work until it is finally finished on the day when Christ Jesus returns (Philippians 1:6).* He loves us too much not to keep working with us and helping us to grow closer to Him.

For some readers, you have seen immense changes in your lifestyle and are seeing the rewards of the time and effort you have invested. I pray that you continue to live the lifestyle you have adopted and continue to see improvement. For others, this may have been your first attempt at changing your lifestyle. This information can be overwhelming, and it may take you some time to process all that you have studied. This book may have been a seed planted to give you the desire to make the changes necessary to live a healthy life. Take some time to go through the chapters again and work through them at a slower pace. Be patient with yourself and enjoy the journey of growing and improving your life. You may not have completed all you set out to do, but if you stay the course, change will come.

I pray that this book has given you the information you need to continue to work on your temple. There is no better way to thank our loving Father for all He is doing and will do in your life than to make your temple pleasing to Him. Healthy living, when adopted as a lifestyle, should not be a chore or something to dread. Instead, it should give you energy and excite you so that you want to continue along this path. There is so much to do in this world. So many places to go and people to meet, that you need to be in optimal health so that you can enjoy all the opportunities God is providing for you.

The purpose of this study is to serve as a guide and ignite a fire in you so that you want to delve deeper into many of the subjects presented. This book is just the first leg of your journey. There is so much more to learn and so many new things to try. I hope that you have accepted this new way of life as a rewarding hobby. A hobby you can enjoy and share with others. I hope that you now have a hunger to learn more. Review your journaling and research the areas you highlighted along the way so that you can continue to grow.

You should now feel empowered to take responsibility for your health. We all have choices and decisions to make that will affect our well-being. No one knows you better than you know yourself. No one doctor or other health professional has all the answers. You need to be an advocate for yourself. Some of the things that work for one person may not work for another. God created us as unique individuals. Because we are unique, we all have different needs and different opinions. Rather than just listening to another person, do your research, pray about your options, and then make an informed decision as to how you are going to improve or maintain your health.

I want to reiterate that the information I have shared in this book is something I found that worked for me and helped with improving my lifestyle. I hope I have shed some light on options that are available to you for enhancing your lifestyle. It is now your responsibility to determine what is best for you.

More than anything else, I pray each of you has come to know our loving Father in a more personal way. I hope that you have renewed your faith in God. I want you to feel His presence and know just how much He loves you. For those of you who already have a good relationship with God, I pray it has grown stronger and reached a new level of intimacy. There is nothing better in this world than to know the love of our Father. I cannot stress the importance enough that you develop a deeper trust in God so that you can hear His voice and follow His calling for you amidst all the chaos of this world. Though it is not always easy to follow God, the rewards outweigh the struggles. We have become so accustomed to doing things on our own and being independent that it takes energy and blind faith to give God our lives and let Him guide us. On those days when doubt and fear fill your mind, and you cannot find rest, I pray that you feel God's strong arms holding and comforting you. This world is a hard place to maneuver through without leaning on God and allowing Him to guide you. The more you trust Him, and lean into Him for support, the more you can accomplish. Our Father does know best. From the beginning, God has provided for you to meet all your needs and allow you to complete your calling successfully. God touched on every aspect of living a healthy life when He gave the earthly authors the words to pen in the Bible.

I thank you, the reader, for choosing this Bible study and allowing me to share my remarkable journey with you. Although it is not one I would have chosen for myself, I now know that God had a plan and He has always been in control. God has chosen a path for you as well. It may not be what you had planned, but trusting Him will surpass your highest expectations. Some are fortunate enough to understand God's plan in their life while on this earth, but for others, it will not be evident until we meet our loving Father face to face. It will be at that moment you will realize your earthly battles were well worth the fight. We will finally understand God's plan for our lives with the ultimate goal being to join Him in eternity. Until that day when we meet our loving Father, stand in awe of all His glory, and realize just how well-orchestrated our lives were, I urge you to continue *to fight the good fight, run the race, keep the faith and fix your eyes on the prize*. It will all be worth it when we hear those glorious words, *"well done my good and faithful servant"* (Matthew 25:23)!!!

In conclusion, I pray that God continues to guide you on your journey. Let Him give you the strength to withstand the temptations of this world and live the life He has designed specifically for you. I pray you can accept His love and walk through life knowing you are God's special child. He has called you by name, and He will never leave you.

Journal your thoughts.

Eating Habits Questionnaire

If you are going to change your eating habits to improve your diet, you need to become aware of your eating patterns and food consumption. Take time to evaluate what and when you are eating. If possible, keep a log of your food intake for the week and then review what you are eating.

1. How many times during the week do you eat meals at home?

2. How many times a week do you eat fast food?

3. How many times a week do you go to a sit-down restaurant?

   3b. How many times do you order healthy choices?

4. How many meals do you eat a day?

5. What does your breakfast primarily consist of?

6. What does your lunch consist of?

7. What does your dinner consist of?

8. How often do you snack throughout the day?

9. What do your snacks consist of?

10. What emotions cause you to eat more frequently and/or choose unhealthy foods?

11. What emotions cause you to eat less?

12. How often do you drink soda? Diet soda? Water? Sports drinks? Juice? Tea? Coffee?

   12b. Do you add anything to your drinks (sugar, creamer, etc.)?

13. What time do you stop eating at night?

14. Do you eat when you are not hungry?

15. What are your go-to foods for comfort?

16. What are your eating habits at parties?

17. When do you grocery shop?

   17b. Do you use a list or buy spontaneously?

If possible, make copies of this and record your daily food consumption for 1 week

Day:	What did you eat and drink?
Breakfast	
Snack	
Lunch	
Snack	
Dinner	
Snack	
Other	

This questionnaire is designed to help you think about how you can effectively exercise on a regular basis. If you lead a sedentary lifestyle, you may find it helpful to come up with a plan to start exercising. Remember, you do not have to do it all at once. Take the time to ease into the program. It is much better to start slow so that you progress, rather than jump in and not be able to keep up the pace and quit. By devising a plan and having it in writing, you may be more apt to stay with your program. You do not have to do the same exercises daily. It is best to mix and match because you will use different muscle groups and not get bored as easily. If you are currently under a doctor's care or have medical issues, talk to your doctor before starting an exercise program.

1. Currently, how often do you exercise each week? (Not at all, less than 1 hour a week, 1-5 hours a week, over 5 hours a week)

2. If you answered less than 1 hour a week, what limits you from doing a regular exercise program?

3. If you answered not at all, do you have any health limits to take into account before starting a new program?

4. What time of day do you prefer to exercise?

5. What type of aerobic exercises do you enjoy doing? (Examples of this are running, swimming, brisk walking, stair climbing, hiking, rowing, cycling, aerobic class and Zumba.)

6. Do you do best with a trainer who can push you or do you motivate yourself?

7. Do you like to exercise in a class, with a partner, or alone?

8. If you prefer to exercise with a partner, who can be your accountability partner to exercise with you and push you when you do not want to exercise?

9. Do you like to go to a gym, spend time outdoors, or exercise in your own home?

10. Do you like to do any sporting activities or play on a team?

11. Do you like to listen to music or watch television when exercising?

12. What types of activities do the local gyms or community center offer you?

13. How can you incorporate exercise in your daily routine? (Stair climbing, physical work, yard work, cleaning house, during childcare)

14. What are your goals for exercising? (Lose weight, get into shape, improve health.)

15. Write out your goals. Make them realistic so they are attainable. You can always go back and edit them as you reach each milestone.

16. What days work best for you to build weight-training exercise into your schedule? (It is recommended that these exercise be done at least 2 days a week.) Weight training can be done with weights, resistive tubing or body weight.

17. What days can you do 30 minutes of aerobic exercise? (It is best to do 5 days of aerobic exercise.)

18. Make an exercise log so you can record how long you are currently able to exercise and record your success as you improve your endurance.

Toxins and Chemicals Questionnaire

We are often unaware of how many toxins we are exposed to on a regular basis. Many of us feel as if we have created a safe environment in our homes and in our lives. Until we take the time to survey our lives, we do not realize how many chemicals we are exposed to every day. Find the time to look at your life and see what potential toxins and chemicals you come in contact with every day.

Not all of the products we use are toxic. By looking at the labels and sometimes do additional research you will become more aware of which products are safe to use in your home and which ones should be eliminated. We are all exposed to some toxins and chemicals in our everyday lives. Not all can be avoided. If we want to maintain our health, we should change the things we can change. Some of these things will be addressed in this study. In other areas, you may want to do some research to try and determine what changes you can make to improve your living conditions.

Rate how often you are exposed to these toxins. Use the following rating scale.
0= never
1= seldom
2=weekly
3=daily

Home: do you use ...
Air fresheners or plug-ins? ____
Candles? ____
Dryer sheets? ____
Conventional cleaning supplies? ____
Shower spray every time you shower? ____
Ammonia or bleach to clean? ____

Do you park your car in a garage attached to the house? ____
Do you have mold or untreated water damage in your house? ____
Has your home been flooded? ____
Do you smoke or are you exposed to second hand smoke? ____
Do you use pesticides, herbicides or other chemicals on your plants and in your home? ____
Do you use paint, wood stains or preservatives on a regular basis? ____
Are you exposed to chemicals when working on a hobby? ____
Are exposed to new carpet or furniture? ____

Health and beauty: How often do you use...
Cosmetics? ____
Cologne or perfume? ____
Deodorant? ____
Antibacterial soap? ____
Scented soaps, detergents or potpourri? ____
Products to dye or perm your hair? ____
Acrylic nail polish? ____
Prescription drugs? ____

Do you have mercury fillings in your mouth? ____

Diet: How often do you…
Eat fast food? ____
Eat non-organic fruits and vegetables? ____

Eat frozen meals? ____
Eat conventional meats and dairy products? ____
Cook with vegetable or canola oil? ____
Use artificial sweeteners? ____
Eat foods with food coloring or dyes? ____
Eat microwave popcorn? ____
Eat canned foods? ____
Store or heat up food in plastic containers or wrap? ____
Drink tap water? ____

Workplace:
Do you work in a place that has a damp or mildew smell? ____
Are you exposed to chemicals and/or dyes? ____

References

Trusting the Architect
(1) U.S. Department of Health and Human Services, National Institutes of Health, National Center for Advancing translational Science, Genetic and Rare Diseases Information Center. (2016). *Hematidrosis*. Retrieved Oct. 27, 2018, from https://rarediseases.info.nih.gov/diseases/13131/hematohidrosis.

The Sanctuary
(1) Salleh, M. R. (2008). Life event, stress, and illness. *The Malaysian Journal of Medical Sciences*, *15*(4), 9-18. Retrieved Oct. 27, 2018, from www.ncbi.nlm.nih.gov/pmc/articles/PMC3341916/.
(2) Mayo Clinic. (2018). *Exercise and stress: Get moving to manage stress*. Retrieved Oct. 27, 2018, from www.mayoclinic.org/healthy-lifestyle/stress-management/in-depth/exercise-and-stress/art-20044469.
(3) Australian Psychological Society. (2015). *Understanding and managing stress* [Fact sheet]. Retrieved Oct. 27, 2018, from www.guidelight.com.au/the-guidelight-psychology-blog/understanding-and-managing-stress.

Laying the Floor
(1) Holisticonline.com. (n.d.). *Therapeutic benefits of laughter*. Retrieved Feb. 17, 2017, from www.holistic-online.com/Humor_Therapy/humor_therapy_benefits.htm.
(2) Schoenfeld, T. J., Rada, P. R., Pieruzzini, P., Hsueh, B., & Gould, E. (2013). Physical exercise prevents stress-induced activation of granule neurons and enhances local inhibitory mechanisms in the dentate gyrus." *Journal of Neuroscience*, *33*(18), 7770-777. doi: 10.1523/JNEUROSCI.5352-12.2013.
(3) Mercola.com. (2015, April 27). *10 Superfoods for stress relief*. Retrieved Feb. 10, 2017, from https://articles.mercola.com/sites/articles/archive/2015/04/27/10-stress-relieving-superfoods.aspx.
(4) Mayo Clinic. (2016). *Stress relief from laughter? It's no joke*. Retrieved Oct. 27, 2018, from www.mayoclinic.org/healthy-lifestyle/stress-management/in-depth/stress-relief/art-20044456.

The Vestibule
(1) Answers.com. (n.d.). *How many verses are there in the Bible about money*. Retrieved Oct. 27, 2018, from www.answers.com/Q/How_many_verses_are_there_in_the_Bible_about_money.

The Chapel
(1) U.S. Department of Health and Human Services, National Institute of Neurological Disorders and Stroke. (2017). *Brain basics: Understanding sleep*. Retrieved Oct. 27, 2018, from www.ninds.nih.gov/Disorders/Patient-Caregiver-Education/Understanding-Sleep.
(2) Jockers, J. (2011). *Healthy sleep cycles balance hormones and burn fat*. Retrieved July 4, 2017, from www.naturalnews.com/031101_sleep_hormones.html.
(3) Swalin, R. (n.d.). *11 signs you're sleep deprived*. Retrieved July 4, 2017 from www.health.com/health/gallery/0,,20906153,00.html#you-think-you-ve-fallen-asleep-at-the-wheel-0.
(4) American Psychological Association. (n.d.). *Why sleep is important*. Retrieved July 4, 2017, from www.apa.org/topics/sleep/why.aspx.
(5) Harvard Medical School. (2018). *Blue light has a dark side*. Retrieved July 4, 2017, from www.health.harvard.edu/staying-healthy/blue-light-has-a-dark-side.
(6) Axe, J. (2017). *Do you sleep on an 'organic' mattress?* Retrieved July 4, 2017, from https://draxe.com/organic-mattresses-and-how-to-pick-the-healthiest-bed/.
(7) Ebrahim, I. O., Shapiro, C. M., Williams, A. J., & Fenwick, P. B. (2013). Alcohol and sleep I: Effects on normal sleep. *Alcoholism, Clinical and Experimental Research*, *37*(4), 539-549. doi: 10.1111/acer.12006.
(8) Mercola.com. (2013, May 2). *What are the five worst foods for sleep?* Retrieved July 4, 2017, from http://articles.mercola.com/sites/articles/archive/2013/05/02/worst-sleep-foods.aspx.
(9) McLaughlin, A. (2015). *Foods that increase serotonin and induce sleep*. Retrieved July 4, 2017, from www.livestrong.com/article/294169-foods-that-increase-serotonin-and-induce-sleep/.
(10) National Sleep Foundation. (n.d.). *Study: Physical activity impacts overall quality of sleep*. Retrieved July 5, 2017, from https://sleepfoundation.org/sleep-news/study-physical-activity-impacts-overall-quality-sleep.
(11) Ansel, K. (2011). 9 foods to help you sleep. *EatingWell*. Retrieved from www.eatingwell.com.
(12) Kirkpatrick, K. (2016). *5 foods that help you sleep*. Retrieved July 4, 2017, from https://health.clevelandclinic.org/2014/06/5-foods-that-help-you-sleep/.

Testing the Circuits for Overload
(1) Pratt, S., & Matthews, K. (2005). *Superfoods Rx: Fourteen foods that will change your life*. New York: Harper.
(2) Warren, M., Beck, S., & Rayburn, J. (2018). *The state of obesity*. Retrieved Oct. 27, 2018, from https://stateofobesity.org/.
(3) Smith, M., & Robinson, L. (2018). *Cancer prevention diet: How to lower your risk with cancer-fighting foods*. Retrieved July 5, 2017, from www.helpguide.org/articles/diet-weight-loss/anti-cancer-diet.htm.
(4) National Cancer Institute. (2017). *Antioxidants and cancer prevention*. Retrieved March 15, 2017, from www.cancer.gov/about-cancer/causes-prevention/risk/diet/antioxidants-fact-sheet.
(5) Schaeffer, J. (2008). Color me healthy—Eating for a rainbow of benefits. *Today's Dietitian*, *10*(11), 34. Retrieved Oct. 27, 2017, from www.todaysdietitian.com/newarchives/110308p34.shtml.
(6) Phillips, L. (n.d.). *Water—The most vital nutrient*. Retrieved Oct. 27, 2018, from www.meandmybody.com/browse_topic.php?topicId=22&all=1.
(7) Healthline. (n.d.). *Does exercise help you lose weight? The surprising truth*. Retrieved Oct. 27, 2018, from www.healthline.com/nutrition/does-exercise-cause-weight-loss.

Rewiring the Temple
(1) Klein, S. (2010, March 30). Fatty foods may cause cocaine-like addiction. *CNN*. Retrieved from www.cnn.com.
(2) Mercola.com. (2011, Feb. 25). *How to stop food cravings and prevent addictions*. Retrieved March 15, 2017, from http://articles.mercola.com/sites/articles/archive/2011/02/25/cant-beat-food-cravings-four-steps-to-help-you-kick-your-addictions.aspx.
(3) Body Ecology. (n.d.). *The top 3 most addicting foods, why they're destroying your health, and how to get your kids off them* [Blog post]. Retrieved Nov. 8, 2018, from http://bodyecology.com/articles/the-top-3-most-addicting-foods-why-they%E2%80%99re-destroying-your-health-and-how-to-get-your-kids-off-them.

Conserving Your Energy Supply
(1) Whole 9. (2012, Jan. 7). *Seasonal produce guide* [Blog post]. Retrieved Nov. 8, 2018, from http://whole9life.com/2012/01/seasonal/.
(2) The George Mateljan Foundation. (n.d.). *Eating in season: Your need-to-know basics* [Blog post]. Retrieved March 15, 2017, from http://whfoods.org/genpage.php?tname=george&dbid=461.
(3) Lee, R. (2016, Jan. 27). Consumer Reports: 'Natural' food labels misleading consumers. *CBS News*. Retrieved from www.cbsnews.com.
(4) George V. (2014, Feb. 16). *It says organic? Does that mean it's non GMO?* [Blog post]. Retrieved March 15, 2017, from http://wondergressive.com/organic-not-non-gmo/.
(5) Weil, A. (2013, March 5). *Are frozen vegetables healthy?* [Blog post]. Retrieved March 15, 2017, from www.drweil.com/diet-nutrition/nutrition/are-frozen-vegetables-healthy/.
(6) Johnson, J. (n.d.). *The health benefits of grass farming*. Retrieved March 15, 2017, from www.americangrassfedbeef.com/grass-fed-natural-beef.asp.
(7) Robinson, J. (n.d.). *Grass-fed basics*. Retrieved March 15, 2017, from www.eatwild.com/basics.html.
(8) Mercola.com. (2015, June 1). *The best fish for your health and the earth*. Retrieved March 15, 2017, from http://articles.mercola.com/sites/articles/archive/2015/06/01/best-seafood.aspx.

Cleaning, Story, and Preparing Food
(1) Mercola.com. (2011, Nov. 16). *How to store food without using toxic plastics*. Retrieved March 16, 2017, from http://articles.mercola.com/sites/articles/archive/2011/11/16/practical-options-to-store-your-food-without-contaminating-them-with-plastics.aspx.
(2) Duvauchelle, J. (2017, June 13). *What are the dangers of plastic food storage containers?* Retrieved Nov. 8, 2018, from www.livestrong.com/article/173172-what-are-the-dangers-of-plastic-food-storage-containers/.
(3) Toole, M. (2014, July 8). *Killer cookware: The dangers of Teflon*. Retrieved March 16, 2017, from www.healthy-holistic-living.com/dangers-of-teflon.html.
(4) Mercola.com. (n.d.). *Are you exposing your family to toxic fumes from non-stick cookware?* Retrieved March 16, 2017, from www.mercola.com/Downloads/bonus/dangers-of-nonstick-cookware/report.htm.

Using the Right Gauge Wire
(1) The Detox Project. (n.d.). *What's the connection between glyphosate and genetically modified crops?* Retrieved Nov. 8, 2018, from https://detoxproject.org/glyphosate/whats-the-connection-between-glyphosate-and-genetically-modified-crops/.
(2) American Academy of Environmental Medicine. (n.d.). *Genetically modified foods*. Retrieved March 16, 2017, from www.aaemonline.org/gmo.php.
(3) Smith, J. (2011, Aug. 25). *10 reasons to avoid GMOs* [Blog post]. Retrieved March 16, 2017, from https://responsibletechnology.org/10-reasons-to-avoid-gmos/.
(4) DeMarco, J. (2017, Jan. 6). *More good news for organic!* [Blog post]. Retrieved March 16, 2017, from www.cornucopia.org/2017/01/good-news-organic/.
(5) Barański, M., Średnicka-Tober, D., Volakakis, N., Seal, C., Sanderson, R., ... & Leifert, C. (2014, July 15). Higher antioxidant and lower cadmium concentrations and lower incidence of pesticide residues in organically grown crops: A systematic literature review and meta-analyses. *British Journal of Nutrition, 112*(5), 794-811. doi: 10.1017/S0007114514001366.
(6) Weil, A. (n.d.). *Foods you should always buy organic: The dirty dozen plus*. Retrieved Dec. 1, 2018, from www.drweil.com/diet-nutrition/anti-inflammatory-diet-pyramid/foods-you-should-always-buy-organic/.
(7) Mercola.com. (2010, Nov. 10). *10 organic foods that are worth the money*. Retrieved March 16, 2017, from http://articles.mercola.com/sites/articles/archive/2010/11/20/10-organic-foods-that-are-worth-the-money.aspx.

Cooking With Oil
(1) Gunnars, K. (2013, May 11). *Healthy cooking oils—The ultimate guide*. Retrieved March 14, 2017, from https://authoritynutrition.com/healthy-cooking-oils/.
(2) Dannie, M. (n.d.). *Is coconut oil good for frying on high temperature cooking?* Retrieved Oct. 3, 2017, from www.livestrong.com/article/446041-is-coconut-oil-good-for-frying-on-high-temperature-cooking/.
(3) Mercola.com. (2013, Nov. 18). *Countless uses for coconut oil—The simple, the strange, and the downright odd*. Retrieved March 14, 2017, from http://articles.mercola.com/sites/articles/archive/2013/11/18/coconut-oil-uses.aspx.
(4) Axe, J. (2018, May 21). *20 coconut oil benefits for your brain, heart, joints, + more!* [Blog post]. Retrieved Jan. 20, 2019, from https://draxe.com/coconut-oil-benefits/.
(5) Emily C. (2009, July 10). *Coconut oil* [Blog post]. Retrieved March 14, 2017, from www.nutrition.org/asn-blog/2009/07/coconut-oil/.
(6) Gunnars, K. (2018, Jan. 11). *Top 10 evidence-based benefits of coconut oil*. Retrieved Jan. 20, 2019, from https://authoritynutrition.com/top-10-evidence-based-health-benefits-of-coconut-oil/.
(7) Hyman, M. (2016, April 6). *Is coconut oil bad for your cholesterol?* Retrieved June 26, 2017, from drhyman.com/blog/2016/04/06/is-coconut-oil-bad-for-your-cholesterol/.
(8) Sinatra, S. (n.d.). *Heart health benefits of coconut oil*. Retrieved March 14, 2017, from www.drsinatra.com/coconut-health-benefits-for-heart-health.
(9) Axe, J. (2018, June 2). *Coconut oil pulling benefits and how-to guide* [Blog post]. Retrieved Jan. 20, 2019, from https://draxe.com/oil-pulling-coconut-oil/.
(10) Mercola.com. (2016, Dec. 17). *Is your olive oil fake?* Retrieved Jan. 20, 2019, from articles.mercola.com/sites/articles/archive/2016/12/17/fake-olive-oil.aspx.
(11) Levy, J. (2018, May 21). *Olive oil benefits for your heart & brain*. Retrieved Jan. 20, 2019, from https://draxe.com/olive-oil-benefits/.
(12) Patil, K. (2018, Oct. 29). *11 surprising benefits of olive oil* [Blog post]. Retrieved Jan. 20, 2019, from www.organicfacts.net/health-benefits/oils/health-benefits-of-olive-oil.html.
(13) Cicerale, S., Conlan, X. A., Sinclair, A. J., & Keast, R. S. (2009). Chemistry and health of olive oil phenolics. *Critical Reviews in Food Science and Nutrition, 49*(3), 218-236. doi: 10.1080/10408390701856223.
(14) Gunnars, K. (2018, April 13). *Are vegetable and seed oils bad for your health?* Retrieved Jan. 20, 2019, from www.healthline.com/nutrition/are-vegetable-and-seed-oils-bad/.
(15) Hyman, M. (2016, Feb. 2). *Dr. Mark Hyman: Why vegetable oils should not be part of your diet*. Retrieved March 14, 2017, from www.ecowatch.com/dr-mark-hyman-why-vegetable-oils-should-not-be-part-of-your-diet-1882164589.html.
(16) Axe, J. (2016, Dec. 20). *Stop using canola oil immediately: 6 canola oil dangers* [Blog post]. Retrieved March 19, 2017, from https://draxe.com/canola-oil-gm/.
(17) Mayo Clinic Staff. (2017). *Trans fat: Avoid this cholesterol double whammy*. Retrieved March 19, 2017, from www.mayoclinic.org/diseases-conditions/high-blood-cholesterol/in-depth/trans-fat/art-20046114.

Quality Control
(1) Mercola.com. (2008). *5 ways to keep BPA out of your food*. Retrieved March 17, 2017, from http://articles.mercola.com/sites/articles/archive/2008/10/07/5-ways-to-keep-bpa-out-of-your-food.aspx.
(2) HealthyInfoNetwork.com. (n.d.). *Cacao vs. cocoa: Are you eating the healthiest chocolate?* Retrieved Dec. 24, 2017, from http://healthyinfonetwork.com/2017/12/24/cacao-vs-cocoa-eating-healthiest-chocolate/.
(3) Oaklander, M. (2016, Jan. 20). *92% of restaurant meals have too many calories: Study*. *Time*. Retrieved from http://time.com.
(4) Fisk, M. (2015). *Fast food & bad health side effects* [Blog post]. Retrieved March 17, 2017, from www.livestrong.com/article/353199-fast-food-bad-health-side-effects/.
(5) Mercola.com. (2015, July 1). *7 top 'healthy' foods to avoid*. Retrieved March 17, 2017, from http://articles.mercola.com/sites/articles/archive/2015/07/01/7-healthy-foods-to-avoid.aspx.
(6) Hari, V. (2018, Sept. 17). *Why microwave popcorn is an absolute health nightmare* [Blog post]. Retrieved Jan. 20, 2019, from https://foodbabe.com/microwave-popcorn/.
(7) Goldberg, M. (2013, Nov. 30). *The health risks of eating conventional potatoes*. Retrieved March 18 2017, from http://livingmaxwell.com/health-risks-conventional-potatoes.
(8) Pesticide Action Network. (n.d.) *What's on my food: Potatoes*. Retrieved Jan. 20, 2019, from www.whatsonmyfood.org/food.jsp?food=PO.
(9) Leech, J. (2017, June 6). *13 ways that sugary soda is bad for your health*. Retrieved Jan. 20, 2019, from https://authoritynutrition.com/13-ways-sugary-soda-is-bad-for-you/.
(10) Price, A. (2017, Jan. 19). *Phosphoric acid: The dangerous hidden additive you've probably consumed*. Retrieved June 20, 2017, from draxe.com/phosphoric-acid/.
(11) Sircus, M. (2012, Dec. 31). *Sugar and cancer growth research*. Retrieved March 17, 2017, from http://drsircus.com/medicine/cancer/sugar-cancer-growth-research.
(12) Brandon. (2011, March 29). *The 76 dangers of sugar* [Blog post]. Retrieved March 17, 2017, from http://thehealthyadvocate.com/2011/03/29/the-76-dangers-of-sugar/.
(13) Mercola.com. (2009, Oct 13). *Artificial sweeteners—More dangerous than you ever imagined*. Retrieved March 17, 2017, from http://articles.mercola.com/sites/articles/archive/2009/10/13/artificial-sweeteners-more-dangerous-than-you-ever-imagined.aspx.
(14) Shell, E. R. (2015, April 1). Artificial sweeteners may change our gut bacteria in dangerous ways. *Scientific American*. Retrieved from www.scientificamerican.com.
(15) Zerbe, L. (2018, March 15). *21 'health' foods you should never eat*. Retrieved Jan. 20, 2019, from https://draxe.com/health-foods-you-should-never-eat/?utm_source=nurture&utm_medium=email&utm_campaign=nurture.
(16) Axe, J. (2018, Oct. 12). *Top 6 essential health benefits of sea salt*. Retrieved March 18, 2017, from https://draxe.com/10-benefits-celtic-sea-salt-himalayan-salt/.

(17) Mercola.com. (2009, Sept. 5). *Bromines: Avoid this if you want to keep your thyroid healthy*. Retrieved Jan. 20, 2019, from articles.mercola.com/sites/articles/archive/2009/09/05/Another-Poison-Hiding-in-Your-Environment.aspx.

(18) Rose, G. (2015, Jan. 28). *Why isn't white bread good for you?* [Blog post]. Retrieved March 18, 2017, from www.livestrong.com/article/343850-why-isnt-white-bread-good-for-you/.

(19) RealFarmacy.com. (2016, Aug. 4). *The top 10 worst food ingredients to avoid like the plague*. Retrieved March 18, 2017, from www.realfarmacy.com/worst-ingredients/.

(20) Kobylewski, S., & Jacobson, M. (2010). *Food dyes: A rainbow of risks*. Washington, DC: Center for Science in the Public Interest.

(21) Parker, H. (2010). *A sweet problem: Princeton researchers find that high-fructose corn syrup prompts considerably more weight gain*. Retrieved March 17, 2017, from www.princeton.edu/news/2010/03/22/sweet-problem-princeton-researchers-find-high-fructose-corn-syrup-prompts.

(22) Axe, J. (2018, July 16). *How high fructose corn syrup destroys your body (it's NOT a pretty picture)*. Retrieved Jan. 20, 2019, from https://theheartysoul.com/high-fructose-corn-syrup-destroys-body-not-pretty-picture/.

(23) Juhasz, F. (2015, April 15). *Other names for MSG or monosodium glutamate* [Blog post]. Retrieved July 16, 2017, from www.livestrong.com/article/377482-other-names-for-msg-or-monosodium-glutamate/.

(24) Roccisano, D., Henneberg, M., & Saniotis, A. (2013). A possible cause of Alzheimer's dementia—Industrial soy foods. *Medical Hypotheses, 82*(3), 250-254. doi: 10.1016/j.mehy.2013.11.033.

(25) O'Shea, T. (n.d.). *The magic bean*. Retrieved March 18, 2017, www.thedoctorwithin.com/soy/magic-bean/.

(26) Mercola.com. (2008, July 17). *Soy: This 'miracle health food' has been linked to brain damage and breast cancer*. Retrieved July 16, 2017, from http://articles.mercola.com/sites/articles/archive/2008/07/17/the-whole-soy-story-the-dark-side-of-america-s-favorite-health-food.aspx.

(27) Mercola.com. (2010, Sept. 18). *The truth about soy foods: Can soy damage your health?* Retrieved March 18, 2017, from http://articles.mercola.com/sites/articles/archive/2010/09/18/soy-can-damage-your-health.aspx.

Juicing and Smoothies

(1) Lawenda, B. D. (2014, Jan. 24). *Juicing*. Retrieved March 19, 2017, from https://integrativeoncology-essentials.com/2014/01/juicing-and-blending-anticancer-turbocharging/juicing/.

(2) Cross, J. (2017, Jan. 26). *Juicing vs. blending: Everything you need to know* [Blog post]. Retrieved March 19, 2017, from www.rebootwithjoe.com/juicing-vs-blending-facts/.

(3) Dr. Sears Wellness Institute. (n.d.). *Juicing vs. blending*. Retrieved Jan. 20, 2019, from www.drsearswellnessinstitute.org/blog/juicing-vs-blending/.

(4) AllAboutJuicing.com. (n.d.). *Top 15 fruits and vegetables to juice—You definitely don't want to skip these*. Retrieved March 19, 2017, from www.all-about-juicing.com/best-fruits-and-vegetables.html.

The Dangers of Sugar

(1) Vocabulary.com. (n.d.). *Temptation*. Retrieved April 1, 2017, from www.vocabulary.com/dictionary/temptation.

(2) HumanKinetics.com. (n.d.). *Endurance sports nutrition: The body's fuel sources*. Retrieved April 1, 2017, from www.humankinetics.com/excerpts/the-bodyrsquos-fuel-sources.

(3) Traister, J. (n.d.). *The function of disaccharides* [Blog post]. Retrieved Oct. 3, 2017, from www.livestrong.com/article/535273-the-function-of-disaccharides/.

(4) Cancer Treatment Centers of America. (2016, Aug. 9). *Natural vs. refined sugars: What's the difference?* [Blog post]. Retrieved Apr. 1, 2017, from www.cancercenter.com/discussions/blog/natural-vs-refined-sugars-whats-the-difference/.

(5) Healthline.com. (2016, Aug. 18). *11 reasons why too much sugar is bad for you*. Retrieved April 1, 2017, from https://authoritynutrition.com/10-disturbing-reasons-why-sugar-is-bad/.

(6) Organics.org. (2017, Feb. 10). *Natural vs. processed sugars*. Retrieved April 1, 2017, from http://organics.org/natural-vs-processed-sugars/.

(7) Welsh, J. (2012). The terrifying truth about how much sugar Americans eat [Infographic]. *Business Insider*. Retrieved from www.businessinsider.com.

(8) Espat, A. (2015). *Does sugar cause cancer?* Retrieved April 1, 2017, from www.mdanderson.org/publications/focused-on-health/may-2015/FOH-cancer-love-sugar.html.

(9) Silberstein, S. (2014, March 9). *5 reasons cancer and sugar are best friends*. Retrieved April 1, 2017, from http://beatcancer.org/2014/03/5-reasons-cancer-and-sugar-are-best-friends/.

(10) Norris, J. (2009, June 25). *Sugar is a poison, says UCSF obesity expert*. Retrieved April 1, 2017, from www.ucsf.edu/news/2009/06/8187/obesity-and-metabolic-syndrome-driven-fructose-sugar-diet.

(11) American Heart Association. (n.d.). *Frequently asked questions about sugar*. Retrieved April 1, 2017, from www.heart.org/HEARTORG/HealthyLiving/HealthyEating/HealthyDietGoals/Frequently-Asked-Questions-About-Sugar_UCM_306725_Article.jsp#.WN8mk1dIFEw.

(12) Mercola.com. (2016, Jan. 13). *How sugar destroys your liver and brain*. Retrieved April 1, 2017, from http://articles.mercola.com/sites/articles/archive/2016/01/13/sugar-destroys-liver-brain.aspx.

(13) Department of Health and Human Services, State Government of Victoria, Australia. (n.d.). *Liver*. Retrieved Jan. 20, 2019, from www.betterhealth.vic.gov.au/health/conditionsandtreatments/liver.

(14) Women's International Pharmacy. (n.d.). *The liver's role in hormone balance*. Retrieved April 1, 2017, from www.womensinternational.com/connections/liver.html.

(15) Natural Balance Foods. (n.d.). *What are empty calories?* Retrieved April 1, 2017, www.naturalbalancefoods.co.uk/community/healthy-living/what-are-empty-calories/.

(16) Haas, E. M., & Chace, D. (2004). *The new detox diet: The complete guide for lifelong vitality with recipes, menus, and detox plans*. Berkeley, CA: Celestial Arts.

(17) Academy of Nutrition and Dietetics. (n.d.). *Sugar and cancer*. Retrieved April 1, 2017, from www.oncologynutrition.org/erfc/healthy-nutrition-now/sugar-and-cancer/.

(18) Mercola.com. (n.d.). *What happens in your body when you eat too much sugar?* Retrieved April 1, 2017, http://articles.mercola.com/sugar-side-effects.aspx.

(19) Seward, M. (2017, Feb. 20). *6 surprising benefits of maple syrup*. Retrieved April 1, 2017, from https://healthyfocus.org/benefits-of-maple-syrup/.

(20) The Dr. Oz Show. (n.d.). *Easy ways to kick your sugar addiction*. Retrieved April 1, 2017, from www.doctoroz.com/article/kick-your-sugar-addiction.

(21) Rodale's Organic Life. (2015, Oct. 23). *Trying to lose weight? Stay away from artificial sweeteners*. Retrieved April 1, 2017, from www.rodalesorganiclife.com/food/trying-lose-weight-stay-away-artificial-sweeteners.

Reviewing to Meet the Code

(1) U.S. Department of Health and Human Services, National Institutes of Health, Office of Dietary Supplements. (n.d.). *Vitamin A*. Retrieved April 21, 2017, from https://ods.od.nih.gov/factsheets/VitaminA-HealthProfessional/.

(2) McDermott, N. (2016, July 14). *The benefits of vitamin B complex*. Retrieved April 21, 2017, from http://dailyburn.com/life/health/benefits-vitamin-b-complex/.

(3) University of Maryland Medical Center. (n.d.). *Vitamin C (ascorbic acid)*. Retrieved April 21, 2017, from www.umm.edu/health/medical/altmed/supplement/vitamin-c-ascorbic-acid.

(4) Mayo Clinic Staff. (2018, Oct. 3). *Calcium and calcium supplements: Achieving the right balance*. Retrieved Jan. 20, 2019, from www.mayoclinic.org/healthy-lifestyle/nutrition-and-healthy-eating/in-depth/calcium-supplements/art-20047097.

(5) Levy, J. (2018, May 11). *What is choline? Benefits, sources, and signs of a deficiency*. Retrieved Jan. 20, 2019, https://draxe.com/what-is-choline/.

(6) Oregon State University. (2017, Jan. 3). *Copper*. Retrieved April 21, 2017, http://lpi.oregonstate.edu/mic/minerals/copper.

(7) Ware, M. (2017, Nov. 13). *Vitamin D: Health benefits, facts and research*. Retrieved April 21, 2017, from www.medicalnewstoday.com/articles/161618.php.

(8) Editors of Reader's Digest. (2007). *Fight back with food: Use nutrition to heal what ails you*. New York: Reader's Digest Association.

(9) Physicians Committee for Responsible Medicine. (n.d.). *Cancer: Reducing cancer risk with a plant-based diet*. Retrieved Jan. 20, 2019, from https://www.pcrm.org/health-topics/cancer.

(10) Spritlzer, F. (2018, Sept. 3). *10 evidence-based health benefits of magnesium*. Retrieved Jan. 20, 2019, from https://authoritynutrition.com/10-proven-magnesium-benefits/.

(11) Harvard P. H. Chan School of Public Health. (n.d.). *Omega-3 fatty acids: An essential contribution*. Retrieved April 21, 2017, from www.hsph.harvard.edu/nutritionsource/omega-3-fats/.

(12) The George Mateljan Foundation. (n.d.). *Phosphorus*. Retrieved April 21, 2017, from www.whfoods.com/genpage.php?tname=nutrient&dbid=127.
(13) Ware, M. (2018, Jan. 12). *Selenium: What it does and how much you need*. Retrieved Jan. 20, 2019, from www.medicalnewstoday.com/articles/287842.php.

Inspecting the Electric
(1) Patil, K. (2018, Dec. 30). *10 interesting benefits of arugula*. Retrieved Jan. 20, 2019, from www.organicfacts.net/health-benefits/vegetable/health-benefits-of-arugula.html.
(2) Ware, M. (2018, Aug. 22). *The health benefits of bok choy*. Retrieved April 8, 2017, www.medicalnewstoday.com/articles/280948.php.
(3) Harrington, D. (2012, May 30). *9 health benefits of broccoli*. April 8, 2017, www.care2.com/greenliving/love-it-or-hate-it-broccoli-is-good-for-you.html.
(4) Mercola.com. (2014, Nov. 16). *What's new and beneficial about Brussels sprouts?* Retrieved April 8, 2017, from http://articles.mercola.com/sites/articles/archive/2014/11/16/benefits-brussels-sprouts.aspx.
(5) Patil, K. (2019, Jan. 3). *20 amazing benefits and uses of cabbage*. Retrieved Jan. 20, 2019, from www.organicfacts.net/health-benefits/vegetable/health-benefits-of-cabbage.html.
(6) Patil, K. (2018, Oct. 25). *20 amazing benefits of cauliflower*. Retrieved Jan. 20, 2019, from www.organicfacts.net/health-benefits/vegetable/health-benefits-of-cauliflower.html.
(7) FoodFacts.Mercola.com. (2016, Oct. 13). *What are collard greens good for?* Retrieved April 8, 2017, http://foodfacts.mercola.com/collard-greens.html.
(8) The CanCure Foundation. (n.d.). *Cancer fighting foods/spices*. Retrieved April 8, 2017, from www.cancure.org/12-links-page/37-cancer-fighting-foods-spices.
(9) Lewis, A. (2012, April 2). *Top 10 health benefits of eating kale*. Retrieved April 8, 2017, from www.mindbodygreen.com/0-4408/Top-10-Health-Benefits-of-Eating-Kale.html.
(10) Patil, K. (2018, Dec. 7). *20 surprising benefits of radish*. Retrieved Jan. 20, 2019, from www.organicfacts.net/health-benefits/vegetable/health-benefits-of-radish.html.
(11) Patil, K. (2019, Jan. 3). *15 impressive benefits of spinach*. Retrieved Jan. 20, 2019, from www.organicfacts.net/health-benefits/vegetable/health-benefits-of-spinach.html.
(12) Forberg, C. (n.d.). *5 powerful health benefits of asparagus you probably didn't know* [Blog post]. Retrieved April 8, 2017, from www.eatingwell.com/blogs/health_blog/5_powerful_health_benefits_of_asparagus_you_probably_didn_t_know.
(13) Mercola.com. (2014, Jan. 25). *Benefits of beets*. Retrieved April 8, 2017, from http://articles.mercola.com/sites/articles/archive/2014/01/25/beets-health-benefits.aspx.
(14) Kapadia, G. J., Rao, G. S., Ramachandran, C., Iida, A., Suzuki, N., & Tokuda, H. Synergistic cytotoxicity of red beetroot (Beta Vulgaris L.) extract with doxorubicin in human pancreatic, breast, and prostate cancer cell lines. *Journal of Complementary & Integrative Medicine, 10*(1), 113-122. doi: 10.1515/jcim-2013-0007.
(15) Herrington, D. (n.d.). *10 benefits of carrots: The crunchy powerfood*. Retrieved April 8, 2017, from www.care2.com/greenliving/10-benefits-of-carrots.html.
(16) The George Mateljan Foundation. (n.d.). *What's new and beneficial about celery*. Retrieved Jan. 20, 2019, from www.whfoods.com/genpage.php?tname=foodspice&dbid=140.
(17) Tremblay, S. (2018, Nov. 21). What are the health benefits of jalapeno peppers? *SF Gate*. Retrieved from http://healthyeating.sfgate.com.
(18) Tremblay, S. (2018, Nov. 21). What are the health benefits of jalapeno peppers? *SF Gate*. Retrieved from http://healthyeating.sfgate.com.
(19) Mercola.com. (2014, Aug. 23). *9 amazing health benefits of cucumbers*. Retrieved April 8, 2017, from http://articles.mercola.com/sites/articles/archive/2014/08/23/health-benefits-cucumbers.aspx.
(20) Staughton, J. (2018, Dec. 5). *10 amazing benefits of eggplant*. Retrieved April 8, 2017, www.organicfacts.net/health-benefits/vegetable/health-benefits-of-eggplant.html.
(21) National Cancer Institute. (n.d.). *Garlic and cancer prevention*. Retrieved, April 8, 2017, www.cancer.gov/about-cancer/causes-prevention/risk/diet/garlic-fact-sheet.
(22) Patel, S., & Goyal, A. (2012). Recent developments in mushrooms as anti-cancer therapy: A review. *3 Biotech, 2*(1), 1-15. doi: 10.1007/s13205-011-0036-2.
(23) Axe, J. (2018, July 19). *Mushroom nutrition benefits: Cancer fighters and cell renewers*. Retrieved Jan. 20, 2019, from https://draxe.com/mushroom-nutrition-benefits/.
(24) Thompson, J. (n.d.). *Healing power of onions: Can onions absorb bacteria, viruses, and flu?* Retrieved Jan. 20, 2019, from http://healthybliss.net/healing-power-of-onions-can-onions-absorb-bacteria-viruses-and-flu/.
(25) Mateljan, G. (2007). *The world's healthiest foods: Essential guide for the healthiest way of eating*. Seattle, WA: George Mateljan Foundation.
(26) HealingCancerNaturally.com. (n.d.). *The importance of minerals and trace elements for health and cancer prevention*. Retrieved April 8, 2017, from www.healingcancernaturally.com/importance-minerals-trace-elements.html.
(27) Staughton, J. (2018, Dec. 30). *7 amazing benefits of squash*. Retrieved Jan. 20, 2019, from www.organicfacts.net/health-benefits/fruit/squash.html.
(28) American Cancer Society, Cancer Survivors Network. (2012, Feb. 25). *NCI says what you eat can hurt you or it can help you fight cancer: List of foods with cancer-fighting properties follows*. Retrieved April 8, 2017, from https://csn.cancer.org/node/236257.
(29) Novek, D. (2012, May 2). 5 huge health benefits of sweet potatoes. *Natural News*. Retrieved from www.naturalnews.com.
(30) Levy, J. (2018, Dec. 5). *Tomato nutrition may help you fight cancer and inflammation*. Retrieved Jan. 20, 2019, from https://draxe.com/tomato-nutrition/.
(31) Jennings, K. (2018, Dec. 17). *10 impressive health benefits of apples*. Retrieved Jan. 21, 2019, from https://authoritynutrition.com/10-health-benefits-of-apples/.
(32) Patil, K. (2019, Jan. 3). *10 impressive benefits of apricots*. Retrieved Jan. 21, 2019, from www.organicfacts.net/health-benefits/fruit/apricots.html.
(33) Gunnars, K. (2018, June 30). *12 proven health benefits of avocado*. Retrieved Jan. 21, 2019, from https://authoritynutrition.com/12-proven-benefits-of-avocado/.
(34) Szalay, J. (2017, Oct. 25). *Bananas: Health benefits, risks, and nutrition facts*. Retrieved Jan. 21, 2019, from www.livescience.com/45005-banana-nutrition-facts.html.
(35) Group, E. (2018, April 6). *12 health benefits of acai berries*. Retrieved Jan. 21, 2019, from www.globalhealingcenter.com/natural-health/benefits-of-acai/.
(36) Nagdeve, M. (2019, Jan. 18). *15 best benefits of blackberry*. Retrieved Jan. 21, 2019, from www.organicfacts.net/health-benefits/fruit/blackberries.html.
(37) Ware, M. (2017, Dec. 19). *Everything you need to know about strawberries*. Retrieved Jan. 21, 2019, from www.medicalnewstoday.com/articles/271285.php.
(38) Link, R. (2018, April 30). *Top 7 health benefits of blueberries*. Retrieved Jan. 21, 2019, from https://draxe.com/health-benefits-blueberries/.
(39) NutritionAndYou.com. (n.d.). *Cranberries nutrition facts*. Retrieved April 9, 2017, from www.nutrition-and-you.com/cranberries.html.
(40) Levy, J. (2015, May 28). *Goji berries: Antioxidant and anti-inflammatory superfruit*. Retrieved April 8, 2017, from https://draxe.com/goji-berry-benefits/.
(41) Staughton, J. (2019, Jan. 11). *7 important benefits of cantaloupe*. Retrieved Jan. 21, 2019, from www.organicfacts.net/health-benefits/fruit/health-benefits-of-cantaloupe.html.
(42) Boucher, K. (2013, March 5). *Stop before you toss: 3 surprising health benefits of cantaloupe seeds*. Retrieved April 9, 2017, from https://mixwellness.com/health-benefits-of-cantaloupe-seeds/.
(43) Herrington, D. (n.d.). *11 health benefits of cherries*. Retrieved April 9, 2017, from www.care2.com/greenliving/11-health-benefits-of-the-beautiful-cherry.html.
(44) Barrett, M. (2013, March 5). *Health benefits of dates—Promoting heart, brain, and digestive health*. Retrieved April 9, 2017, from http://naturalsociety.com/health-benefits-of-dates-7-reasons-eat-date-fruit/.
(45) Patil, K. (2018, Dec. 27). *15 best benefits of figs or anjeer*. Retrieved Jan. 21, 2019, from www.organicfacts.net/health-benefits/fruit/health-benefits-of-figs-or-anjeer.html.
(46) Elliott, B. (2016, Oct. 3). *The 20 healthiest fruits on the planet*. Retrieved April 9, 2017, from www.healthline.com/nutrition/20-healthiest-fruits.
(47) NutritionAndYou.com. (n.d.). *Grapes nutrition facts*. Retrieved April 9, 2017, from www.nutrition-and-you.com/grapes.html.
(48) Ware, M. (2017, June 20). *Kiwifruit: Health benefits and nutritional information*. Retrieved Jan. 20, 2019, from www.medicalnewstoday.com/articles/271232.php.
(49) NeNa. (2016, April 20). *Top 10 health benefits of lemon water* [Blog post]. Retrieved April 9, 2017, from www.healthandlovepage.com/top-10-health-benefits-lemon-water.
(50) Arnarson, A. (2014, Oct. 21). *Oranges 101: Nutrition facts and health benefits*. Retrieved April 9, 2017, from https://authoritynutrition.com/foods/oranges/.
(51) The George Mateljan Foundation. (n.d.). *Papaya*. Retrieved April 9, 2017, from www.whfoods.com/genpage.php?tname=foodspice&dbid=47.
(52) Staughton, J. (2019, Jan. 3). *11 surprising benefits of pears* [Blog post]. Retrieved Jan. 21, 2019, from www.organicfacts.net/health-benefits/fruit/pears.html.
(53) Staughton, J. (2019, Jan. 16). *11 amazing benefits of pineapples* [Blog post]. Retrieved Jan. 21, 2019, from www.organicfacts.net/health-benefits/fruit/pineapples.html.

(54) Axe, J. (2018, Oct. 16). *7 bromelain benefits, uses, and best food sources*. Retrieved Jan. 21, 2019, from https://draxe.com/bromelain/.
(55) Patil, K. (2019, Jan. 3). *7 amazing benefits of pomegranates*. Retrieved Jan. 21, 2019, from www.organicfacts.net/health-benefits/fruit/health-benefits-of-pomegranate.html.
(56) Patil, K. (2018, Oct. 23). *9 amazing benefits of watermelon*. Retrieved Jan. 21, 2019, from www.organicfacts.net/health-benefits/fruit/watermelon.html.
(57) Mercola.com. (2014, July 7). *6 things you didn't know about watermelon*. Retrieved April 9, 2017, from http://articles.mercola.com/sites/articles/archive/2014/07/21/watermelon-nutrition.aspx.
(58) Jung, A. (2014, March 6). *5 health benefits of beans—And 5 surprising risks* Retrieved April 9, 2017, from www.rd.com/health/conditions/health-benefits-of-beans/.
(59) The George Mateljan Foundation. (n.d.). *What's new and beneficial about oats*. Retrieved April 9, 2017, from www.whfoods.com/genpage.php?tname=foodspice&dbid=.
(60) Kennedy, L. (2017, May 4). *Top 10 health benefits of brown rice* [Blog post]. Retrieved Jan. 21, 2019, from www.vegkitchen.com/brown-rice/.
(61) Levy, J. (2018, Dec. 12). *Lentils nutrition: Weight and blood sugar supporter or digestion disrupter?* Retrieved Jan. 21, 2019, from https://draxe.com/lentils-nutrition/.

Spices, Herbs, Seeds, and Nuts

(1) Fraser, C. (2013, June 16). *17 incredible health benefits of turmeric*. Retrieved March 21, 2017, from http://livelovefruit.com/incredible-health-benefits-of-turmeric/.
(2) Bollinger, T. (2016, June 12). The amazing cancer-fighting benefits of curcumin. Retrieved March 21, 2017, from https://thetruthaboutcancer.com/cancer-fighting-benefits-of-curcumin/.
(3) Axe, J. (2019, Jan. 18). *Turmeric and curcumin benefits: Can this herb really combat disease?* Retrieved Jan. 21, 2019, from https://draxe.com/turmeric-curcumin-benefits/.
(4) FoodFacts.Mercola.com. (2016, Nov. 14). *What is turmeric good for?* Retrieved March 21, 2017, from https://foodfacts.mercola.com/turmeric.html.
(5) CurcuminForHealth.com. (n.d.). *Turmeric vs. curcumin—What's the difference?* Retrieved March 21, 2017, from www.curcuminforhealth.com/the-difference-between-turmeric-and-curcumin/.
(6) Bollinger, T. (2016, June 12). *The amazing cancer-fighting benefits of curcumin*. Retrieved March 21, 2017, from https://thetruthaboutcancer.com/cancer-fighting-benefits-of-curcumin/.
(7) The George Mateljan Foundation. (n.d.). *Chili pepper, dried*. Retrieved Jan. 21, 2019, from http://whfoods.org/genpage.php?tname=foodspice&dbid=29.
(8) The George Mateljan Foundation. (n.d.). *What's new and beneficial about garlic*. Retrieved March 21, 2017, from www.whfoods.com/genpage.php?tname=foodspice&dbid=60.
(9) Nordqvist, J. (2017, Dec. 11). *What are the health benefits of oregano?* Retrieved Jan. 21, 2019, from www.medicalnewstoday.com/articles/266259.php.
(10) The George Mateljan Foundation. (n.d.). *Cinnamon, ground*. Retrieved March 21, 2017, from www.whfoods.com/genpage.php?dbid=68&tname=foodspice.
(11) FoodFacts.Mercola.com. (2016, Oct. 25). *What is ginger good for?* Retrieved March 21, 2017, from http://foodfacts.mercola.com/ginger.html.
(12) Bode, A. M., & Dong, Z. (2011). Chapter 7: The amazing and mighty ginger. In I. F. F. Benzie & S. Wachtel-Galor (Eds.), *Herbal Medicine: Biomolecular and Clinical Aspects (2nd ed)*. Boca Raton, FL: CRC/Taylor & Francis.
(13) University of Maryland Medical Center. (n.d.). *Peppermint*. Retrieved March 21, 2017, from http://umm.edu/health/medical/altmed/herb/peppermint.
(14) Mercola.com. (2016, Sept. 16). *Why curry will surprise you*. Retrieved Jan. 21, 2019, from https://articles.mercola.com/sites/articles/archive/2016/09/19/curry-spices.aspx.
(15) Herbal Information Center. (n.d.). *Aloe vera*. Retrieved March 21, 2017, from www.kcweb.com/herb/aloevera.htm.
(16) Cancer Research UK. (2018, Nov. 20). *Aloe*. Retrieved Jan. 21, 2019, from www.cancerresearchuk.org/about-cancer/cancers-in-general/treatment/complementary-alternative/therapies/aloe-vera.
(17) The George Mateljan Foundation. (n.d.). *Cumin seeds*. Retrieved March 21, 2017, from www.whfoods.com/genpage.php?tname=foodspice&dbid=91.
(18) Axe, J. (2018, April 22). *Top 10 benefits of flaxseed and how to add flaxseeds to your diet*. Retrieved Jan. 21, 2019, from https://draxe.com/10-flax-seed-benefits-nutrition-facts/.
(19) Mercola.com. (2015, July 6). *What are the health benefits of chia seeds?* Retrieved March 21, 2017, from http://articles.mercola.com/sites/articles/archive/2015/07/06/chia-seeds-benefits.aspx.
(20) Mercola.com. (2013, Sept. 30). *9 health benefits of pumpkin seeds*. Retrieved March 21, 2017, from http://articles.mercola.com/sites/articles/archive/2013/09/30/pumpkin-seed-benefits.aspx.
(21) Axe, J. (2017, May 17). *7 benefits of eating hemp seeds you won't believe*. Retrieved Jan. 21, 2019, from https://draxe.com/7-hemp-seed-benefits-nutrition-profile/.
(22) Levy, J. (2018, Aug. 24). *Sunflower seeds combat diabetes, heart disease, and maybe even cancer*. Retrieved Jan. 21, 2019, from https://draxe.com/sunflower-seeds/.
(23) Tan, S. Y., & Mattes, R. D. (2013). Appetitive, dietary, and health effects of almonds consumed with meals or as snacks: A randomized, controlled trial." *European Journal of Clinical Nutrition, 67*, 1205-1214. Retrieved from www.nature.com/ejcn/journal/v67/n11/full/ejcn2013184a.html.
(24) Staughton, J. (2018, Dec. 10). *21 surprising health benefits of Brazil nuts*. Retrieved April 9, 2017, from www.organicfacts.net/health-benefits/seed-and-nut/brazil-nuts.html.
(25) Bentley, P. (2015, Nov. 4). *Cashew nutrition: Absolute the best cure for depression without medication* [Blog post]. Retrieved March 21, 2017, from www.naturalnewsblogs.com/cashew-nutrition-absolute-best-cure-depression-without-medication/.
(26) Landry, G. (2016, June 19). *7 healthy reasons to snack on cashew nuts*. Retrieved March 21, 2017, www.1mhealthtips.com/7-healthy-reasons-to-snack-on-cashew-nuts/.
(27) Boldt, E. (2016, May 18). *Hazelnuts: 7 benefits of these heart-healthy, brain-boosting nuts*. Retrieved April 9, 2017, from https://draxe.com/hazelnuts/.
(28) Bosch, L. T. (2015, Oct. 14). *10 fascinating health benefits of macadamias*. Retrieved April 9, 2017, from www.foodmatters.com/article/10-fascinating-health-benefits-of-macadamias.
(29) NutritionAndYou.com. (n.d.). *Pecans nutrition facts*. Retrieved April 9, 2017, from www.nutrition-and-you.com/pecans.html.
(30) Krishan, S. (2012, Oct. 20). *8 incredible health benefits of pine nuts*. Retrieved April 9, 2017, from www.care2.com/greenliving/8-incredible-health-benefits-of-pine-nuts.html.
(31) Downey, M. (2015, December). *Walnuts: Abundant disease prevention benefits*. Retrieved March 21, 2017, from www.lifeextension.com/magazine/2015/12/walnuts-abundant-disease-prevention-benefits/page-01.
(32) Mercola.com. (2015, Oct. 19). *What are the best nuts and seeds?* Retrieved March 21, 2017, from http://articles.mercola.com/sites/articles/archive/2015/10/19/best-nuts-seeds.aspx. health-benefits-of-turmeric/>.
(2) "The Amazing Cancer-Fighting Benefits of Curcumin." *The Truth About Cancer*. N.p., 16 Nov. 2016. Web. 21 Mar. 2017. <https://thetruthaboutcancer.com/cancer-fighting-benefits-of-curcumin/>.
(3) "Turmeric Benefits Superior To 10 Medications At Reversing Disease." *Dr. Axe*. N.p., 27 Feb. 2017. Web. 21 Mar. 2017. <https://draxe.com/turmeric-benefits/>.
(4) "What Is Turmeric Good For?" *Mercola.com*, foodfacts.mercola.com/turmeric.html.
(5) "Turmeric vs. Curcumin - What's the Difference?" *Home: The Difference Between Turmeric and Curcumin : Curcumin For Health*, www.curcuminforhealth.com/the-difference-between-turmeric-and-curcumin/.
(6)"The Amazing Cancer-Fighting Benefits of Curcumin." *The Truth About Cancer*. N.p., 16 Nov. 2016. Web. 21 Mar. 2017. <https://thetruthaboutcancer.com/cancer-fighting-benefits-of-curcumin/>.
(7) N.p., n.d. Web. <http://www.whfoods.com/genpage.php?tname=foodspice&dbid=140>.
(8) "Garlic." *Garlic*. N.p., n.d. Web. 21 Mar. 2017. <http://www.whfoods.com/genpage.php?tname=foodspice&dbid=60>.
(9) Nordqvist, Joseph. "Oregano: Health Benefits, Side Effects." *Medical News Today*. MediLexicon International, n.d. Web. 21 Mar. 2017. <http://www.medicalnewstoday.com/articles/266259.php>.
(10) *Cinnamon, Ground*, www.whfoods.com/genpage.php?dbid=68&tname=foodspice.
(11) "What Is Ginger Good For?" *Mercola.com*. N.p., n.d. Web. 21 Mar. 2017. <http://foodfacts.mercola.com/ginger.html>.
(12) Bode, Ann M. "The Amazing and Mighty Ginger." *Herbal Medicine: Biomolecular and Clinical Aspects. 2nd Edition*. U.S. National Library of Medicine, 01 Jan. 1970. Web. 21 Mar. 2017. <http://www.ncbi.nlm.nih.gov/books/NBK92775/>.
(13) "Peppermint." *University of Maryland Medical Center*. N.p., n.d. Web. 21 Mar. 2017. <http://umm.edu/health/medical/altmed/herb/peppermint>.
(14) *Worldhealthpage.com*. N.p., n.d. Web. 21 Mar. 2017. <http://www.worldhealthpage.com/2016/03/27/curry-powder-health-benefits/>.

(15) "Herbal Information Center - Aloe Vera - Benefits, Usage, Side Effects, Dosage, General Store - Herbs." *Herbal Information Center - Aloe Vera - Benefits, Usage, Side Effects, Dosage, General Store - Herbs.* N.p., n.d. Web. 21 Mar. 2017. <http://www.kcweb.com/herb/aloevera.htm>.
(16) UK, Cancer Research. "Aloe." *Cancer Research UK.* N.p., n.d. Web. 21 Mar. 2017. <http://www.cancerresearchuk.org/about-cancer/cancers-in-general/treatment/complementary-alternative/therapies/aloe-vera>.
(17) "Cumin Seeds." *Cumin Seeds.* N.p., n.d. Web. 21 Mar. 2017. <http://www.whfoods.com/genpage.php?tname=foodspice&dbid=91>.
(18) "Natural Health: 10 Amazing Benefits of Consuming Flax Seed." *Dr. Axe.* N.p., 08 May 2016. Web. 21 Mar. 2017. <https://draxe.com/10-flax-seed-benefits-nutrition-facts/>.
(19) "8 Delicious Ways to Use Chia Seeds." *Mercola.com.* N.p., n.d. Web. 21 Mar. 2017. <http://articles.mercola.com/sites/articles/archive/2015/07/06/chia-seeds-benefits.aspx>.
(20) "9 Amazing Health Benefits of Pumpkin Seeds." *Mercola.com.* N.p., n.d. Web. 21 Mar. 2017. <http://articles.mercola.com/sites/articles/archive/2013/09/30/pumpkin-seed-benefits.aspx>.
(21) "Hemp Seed Benefits and Nutrition Profile." *Dr. Axe.* N.p., 16 June 2015. Web. 21 Mar. 2017. <https://draxe.com/7-hemp-seed-benefits-nutrition-profile/>.
(22) "Sunflower Seeds: Benefits, Nutrition & Recipes." *Dr. Axe.* N.p., 06 Dec. 2016. Web. 21 Mar. 2017. <https://draxe.com/sunflower-seeds/>.
(23) Tan, S. Y., and R. D. Mattes. "Appetitive, Dietary and Health Effects of Almonds Consumed with Meals or as Snacks: A Randomized, Controlled Trial." *Nature News.* Nature Publishing Group, 02 Oct. 2013. Web. 21 Mar. 2017. <http://www.nature.com/ejcn/journal/v67/n11/full/ejcn2013184a.html>.
(24) "9 Surprising Benefits of Brazil Nuts." *Organic Facts.* N.p., 28 Feb. 2017. Web. 09 Apr. 2017. <https://www.organicfacts.net/health-benefits/seed-and-nut/brazil-nuts.html>.
(25) "Cashew Nutrition: Absolute The Best Cure For Depression Without Medication." *NaturalNews Blogs.* N.p., 04 Nov. 2015. Web. 21 Mar. 2017. <http://www.naturalnewsblogs.com/cashew-nutrition-absolute-best-cure-depression-without-medication/>.
(26) Landry, Georgia. "Georgia Landry." *1mhealthtips.* N.p., 18 June 2016. Web. 21 Mar. 2017. <http://www.1mhealthtips.com/7-healthy-reasons-to-snack-on-cashew-nuts/>.
(27) "Hazelnuts Benefit the Heart, Brain & Skin." *Dr. Axe.* N.p., 05 Apr. 2017. Web. 09 Apr. 2017. <https://draxe.com/hazelnuts/>.
(28) Bosch, Laurentine Ten. "10 Fascinating Health Benefits Of Macadamias." *FOOD MATTERS®.* Food Matters, 17 Feb. 2017. Web. 09 Apr. 2017. <http://www.foodmatters.com/article/10-fascinating-health-benefits-of-macadamias>.
(29) "Pecans Nutrition Facts and Health Benefits." *Nutrition And You.com.* N.p., n.d. Web. 09 Apr. 2017. <http://www.nutrition-and-you.com/pecans.html>.
(30) "8 Incredible Health Benefits of Pine Nuts." *8 Incredible Health Benefits Of Pine Nuts | Care2 Healthy Living.* N.p., n.d. Web. 09 Apr. 2017. <http://www.care2.com/greenliving/8-incredible-health-benefits-of-pine-nuts.html>.
(31) "Walnuts: Abundant Disease Prevention Benefits." *LifeExtension.com.* N.p., n.d. Web. 21 Mar. 2017. <http://www.lifeextension.com/magazine/2015/12/walnuts-abundant-disease-prevention-benefits/page-01>.
(32) "What Are the Healthiest Nuts and Seeds?" *Mercola.com.* N.p., n.d. Web. 21 Mar. 2017. <http://articles.mercola.com/sites/articles/archive/2015/10/19/best-nuts-seeds.aspx>.

Meat, Eggs, and Fish
(1) U.S. Department of Health and Human Services, National Institutes of Health, National Library of Medicine. (2019, Jan. 15). *What are proteins and what do they do?* Retrieved Jan. 21, 2019, from https://ghr.nlm.nih.gov/primer/howgeneswork/protein.
(2) Ede, G. (n.d.). *Protein* [Blog post]. Retrieved April 22, 2017, from www.diagnosisdiet.com/food/protein/.
(3) Products.Mercola.com. (n.d.). *What you can't see in your beef should scare you the most.* Retrieved April 22, 2017, from http://products.mercola.com/grass-fed-beef/.
(4) Mercola.com. (2014, May 21). *Reasons to switch to grass-fed beef and dairy.* Retrieved April 22, 2017, from https://articles.mercola.com/sites/articles/archive/2014/05/21/grass-fed-beef-dairy.aspx.
(5) Asprey, D. (2017, April 13). *Grass-fed meat vs grain-fed meat: Part 1.* Retrieved April 22, 2017, www.bulletproofexec.com/grass-fed-meat-part-1.
(6) Daley, C. A., Abbott, A., Doyle, P.S., Nader, G. A., & Larson, S. A review of fatty acid profiles and antioxidant content in grass-fed and grain-fed beef. *Nutrition Journal, 9,* 10. doi: 10.1186/1475-2891-9-10.
(7) Gunnars, K. (2018, May 7). *Grass-fed vs grain-fed beef—What's the difference?* Retrieved Jan. 21, 2019, from https://authoritynutrition.com/grass-fed-vs-grain-fed-beef/.
(8) Flower, F. (2011). *What makes organic chicken organic?* Retrieved April 22, 2017, from www.wholefoodsmarket.com/blog/whole-story/what-makes-organic-chicken-organic.
(9) Lam, F. (2011, Jan. 21). What do "free range," "organic," and other chicken labels really mean? *Salon.* Retrieved from www.salon.com.
(10) CBSNews. (2010, March 16). "Shocking" reasons to go organic. *CBS News.* Retrieved from www.cbsnews.com.
(11) Long, C., & Alterman, T. (2007, October/November). Meet real free-range eggs. *Mother Earth News.* Retrieved from www.motherearthnews.com.
(12) Mercola.com. (2011, Sept. 2). *Another reason to ignore the warnings about eggs.* Retrieved April 22, 2017, from http://articles.mercola.com/sites/articles/archive/2011/09/02/why-does-this-commonly-vilified-food-actually-prevent-heart-disease-and-cancer.aspx.
(13) Michaelis, K. (n.d.). *Healthy seafood: What to buy* [Blog post]. Retrieved April 22, 2017, from www.foodrenegade.com/healthy-seafood-what-to-buy/.

Antioxidants
(1) Group, E. (2015, Oct. 14). *The health benefits of antioxidants* [Blog post]. Retrieved July 10, 2017, from www.globalhealingcenter.com/natural-health/health-benefits-of-antioxidants/.
(2) Axe, J. (2018, May 7). *Top 10 high antioxidant foods.* Retrieved Jan. 21, 2019, from https://draxe.com/top-10-high-antioxidant-foods/.
(3) U.S. Department of Health and Human Services, National Institutes of Health, National Cancer Institute. (2017, Feb. 6). Antioxidants and cancer prevention. Retrieved July 10, 2017, from www.cancer.gov/about-cancer/causes-prevention/risk/diet/antioxidants-fact-sheet.
(4) Lobo, V., Patil, A., Phatak, A., & Chandra, N. (2010). Free radicals, antioxidants, and functional foods: Impact on human health. *Pharmacognosy Reviews, 4*(8), 118-126. doi: 10.4103/0973-7847.70902.
(5) Sharma, H., & Clark, C. (1998). Free radicals: Effects, causes, and defenses. In *Contemporary Ayurveda.* Edinburgh: Churchill Livingstone.
(6) Parnes, R. B. (2002). *Antioxidants: What you need to know.* Retrieved July 10, 2017, from https://health.howstuffworks.com/wellness/food-nutrition/facts/antioxidant1.htm.
(7) Appleby, M. (n.d.). Does rich color in vegetables mean more antioxidants? *Healthy Eating | SF Gate.* Retrieved from https://healthyeating.sfgate.com.
(8) U.S. Department of Health and Human Services, National Institutes of Health, National Center for Complementary and Integrative Medicine. (2016, May 4). *Antioxidants: In depth.* Retrieved July 10, 2017 from https://nccih.nih.gov/health/antioxidants/introduction.htm.
(9) Harvard T. H. Chan School of Public Health. (2016, April 12). *Antioxidants: Beyond the hype.* Retrieved July 10, 2017, from www.hsph.harvard.edu/nutritionsource/antioxidants/.

Removing Toxins from the Temple
(1) Hyman, M. (2010, May 19). *Is there toxic waste in your body?* Retrieved April 26, 2017, from http://drhyman.com/blog/2010/05/19/is-there-toxic-waste-in-your-body-2/.
(2) Benjamin Associates. (n.d.). *The immune system.* Retrieved April 26, 2017, from http://immunedisorders.homestead.com/detoxification.html.
(3) Group, E. (2017, Feb. 22). *Body cleanse: 6 ways to do a body detox.* Retrieved April 26, 2017, from www.globalhealingcenter.com/natural-health/6-ways-to-body-detox/.
(4) LymphNotes.com. (n.d.). *The lymphatic system.* Retrieved April 26, 2017, from www.lymphnotes.com/article.php/id/151/.
(5) Jane. (2013, July 16). *Best/worst foods for a detox* [Blog post]. Retrieved April 26, 2017, from www.greeneatz.com/1/post/2013/07/best-and-worst-foods-for-a-detox-diet.html.
(6) Link, R. (2018, May 15). *Detox diet plan: How to detoxify the body and reset your health.* Retrieved Jan. 21, 2019, from https://draxe.com/detox-diet/.
(7) Palsdottir, H. (2018, Aug. 28). *11 probiotic foods that are super healthy.* Retrieved Jan. 21, 2019, from https://authoritynutrition.com/11-super-healthy-probiotic-foods/.
(8) Schmidt, D. (2017, Jan. 27). *Best foods and herbs to cleanse and detox the kidneys.* Retrieved Jan. 21, 2019, from www.naturalhealth365.com/liver_cleansing.html.

(9) Haas, E. M., & Chace, D. (2004). *The new detox diet: The complete guide for lifelong vitality with recipes, menus, and detox plans.* Berkeley, CA: Celestial Arts.

(10) Khalil, R., & Baker, L. (n.d.). *Asparagus: Extraordinary health benefits.* Retrieved April 30, 2017, from www.pureinsideout.com/asparagus-extraordinary-health-benefits.html.

Maintaining an Alkaline Diet

(1) Ströhle, A., Hahn, A., & Sebastian, A. (2009). Estimation of the diet-dependent net acid load in 229 worldwide historically studied hunter-gatherer societies. *The American Journal of Clinical Nutrition, 91*(2), 406-412. doi: 10.3945/ajcn.2009.28637.

(2) Schwalfenberg, G. K. (2012) The alkaline diet: Is there evidence that an alkaline pH diet benefits health? *Journal of Environmental and Pubic Health, 2012,* 727630. doi: 10.1155/2012/727630.

(3) Levy, J. (2018, May 21). *Alkaline diet: The key to longevity and fighting chronic disease?* Retrieved Jan. 21, 2019, from draxe.com/alkaline-diet/.

(4) Smith, S. R., Martin, P. A., & Edwards, R. H. (1991). Tumour pH and response to chemotherapy: An in vivo 31P magnetic resonance spectroscopy study in non-Hodgkin's lymphoma. *The British Journal of Radiology, 64*(766), 923-928. Retrieved from www.ncbi.nlm.nih.gov/pubmed/1954534/.

APPLE CIDER VINEGAR

(1) Mercola.com. (2009, June 2). *What the research really says about apple cider vinegar.* Retrieved April 22, 2017, from http://articles.mercola.com/sites/articles/archive/2009/06/02/apple-cider-vinegar-hype.aspx.

(2) Link, R. (2018, July 31). *20 apple cider vinegar uses + 6 health benefits.* Retrieved Jan. 21, 2019, from draxe.com/apple-cider-vinegar-uses/.

(3)   Jillee. (2017, Feb. 6). *28 surprising ways you can benefit from apple cider vinegar.* Retrieved April 22, 2017, from www.onegoodthingbyjillee.com/2013/09/28-health-and-beauty-benefits-of-apple-cider-vinegar.html.

(4) Zafar, J. (n.d.). *Apple cider vinegar health benefits.* Retrieved April 22, 2017, from www.homeremediesweb.com/apple_cider_vinegar_health_benefits.php.

(5) PeasHealth.com. (2013, July 10). *Sixty health benefits and home remedies of apple cider vinegar.* Retrieved April 22, 2017, from www.peashealth.com/sixty-health-benefits-and-home-remedies-of-apple-cider-.

Heating and Cooling the Temple

(1) Mercola.com. (2013, May 10). *Exercise could hold key to successful cancer and mental health treatment.* Retrieved April 28, 2017, from http://fitness.mercola.com/sites/fitness/archive/2013/05/10/exercise-may-help-cure-cancer.aspx.

(2) Grisham, J. (2014, Jan. 2). *What are the benefits of exercise during and after cancer treatment?* Retrieved April 28, 2017, from www.mskcc.org/blog/what-are-benefits-exercise-during-and-after-treatment.

(3) Science Daily. (2015, June 11). *Obesity associated with increased breast cancer risk in postmenopausal women.* Retrieved April 28, 2017, from www.sciencedaily.com/releases/2015/06/150611114404.htm.

(4) American Heart Association. (n.d.). *American Heart Association recommendations for physical activity in adults.* Retrieved July 17, 2017, from www.heart.org/HEARTORG/HealthyLiving/PhysicalActivity/FitnessBasics/American-Heart-Association-Recommendations-for-Physical-Activity-in-Adults_UCM_307976_Article.jsp#.WWznQ6OZPIF.

(5) American Diabetes Association. (n.d.). *What we recommend.* Retrieved July 17, 2017, from www.diabetes.org/food-and-fitness/fitness/types-of-activity/what-we-recommend.html.

(6) Mercola.com. (2015, July 31). *Exercise reduces your cancer risk.* Retrieved April 28, 2017, from http://fitness.mercola.com/sites/fitness/archive/2015/07/31/exercise-reduces-cancer-risk.aspx.

(7) Mayo Clinic Staff. (n.d.). *Strength training: Get stronger, leaner, healthier.* Retrieved April 22, 2016, from www.mayoclinic.org/healthy-lifestyle/fitness/in-depth/strength-training/art-20046670?pg=2.

(8) Fitness.Mercola.com. (2017, June 30). *Why strength training is so important for optimal health.* Retrieved Jan. 21, 2019, from fitness.mercola.com/sites/fitness/archive/2017/06/30/strength-training-importance.aspx.

(9) Schlinger, A. (2017, Aug. 24). *The do-it-anywhere HIIT workout you need to try.* Retrieved Aug. 29, 2017, from http://dailyburn.com/life/fitness/high-intensity-hiit-workout/.

Inviting the Presence of the Lord into the Temple

(1) Amiel, E, Ofir, R., Dudai, N., Soloway, E., Rabinskky, T., & Rachmilevitch, S. (2012). β-Caryophyllene, a compound isolated from the Biblical Balm of Gilead (commiphora gileadensis), is a selective apoptosis inducer for tumor cell lines. *Evidence-Based Complementary and Alternative Medicine, 2012,* 872394. doi: 10.1155/2012/872394.

(2) Zielinski, E. (2018, Nov. 14). *12 healing oils of the Bible.* Retrieved Jan. 21, 2019, from https://naturallivingfamily.com/12-healing-oils-of-the-bible/.

(3) Simple Life Abundant Life. (2013, Sept. 26). *What does the Bible say about essential oils?* Retrieved March 12, 2017, from http://simplelifeabundantlife.com/2013/09/26/biblical-look-use-essential-oils-can-apply-lives/.

(4) Stewart, D. (2007). *Healing oils of the Bible.* Marble Hill, MO: Care Publications.

(5) Knowing-Jesus.com. (n.d.). *38 Bible verses about anointing with oil.* Retrieved April 9, 2017, from http://bible.knowing-jesus.com/topics/Anointing-With-Oil.

How to Use Essential Oils

(1) Perez, S. (2011, Dec. 13). *Candles.* Retrieved April 22, 2017, from https://nourishingourchildren.org/2011/12/13/candles/.

(2) Neat Oil Essentials. (n.d.). *Distilling quality essential oils.* Retrieved Jan. 21, 2019, from http://neatoilessentials.com/distilling-quality-essential-oils/.

(3) Axe, J. (2018, July 25). *Cinnamon oil: 10 proven benefits and uses.* Retrieved Jan. 21, 2019, from https://draxe.com/cinnamon-oil/.

(4) Patil, K. (2019, Jan. 3). *23 surprising benefits of clove oil.* Retrieved Jan. 21, 2019, from www.organicfacts.net/health-benefits/essential-oils/health-benefits-of-clove-oil.html.

(5) Axe, J. (2018, June 30). *What is frankincense good for? 8+ essential oil uses and benefits for healing.* April 22, 2017, from https://draxe.com/what-is-frankincense/.

(6) Mercola.com. (2016, June 2). *Frankincense oil: The 'king' of oils.* Retrieved April 22, 2017, from http://articles.mercola.com/herbal-oils/frankincense-oil.aspx.

(7) Patil, K. (2018, Dec. 11). *10 wonderful benefits of grapefruit essential oil.* Retrieved Jan. 21, 2019, from www.organicfacts.net/health-benefits/essential-oils/grapefruit-essential-oil.html.

(8) Patil, K. (2018, Sept. 4). *10 amazing benefits of lemon oil.* Retrieved Jan. 21, 2019, from www.organicfacts.net/health-benefits/essential-oils/health-benefits-of-lemon-oil.html.

(9) Zielinkski, E. (2019, Jan. 16). *Best essential oils for healing: The top 10 and how to use them!* Retrieved Jan. 21, 2019, from https://naturallivingfamily.com/best-essential-oils/.

(10) Ramsey, T. (2012, April 25). *Dr. Theresa Ramsey: Homeopathic remedies for common conditions* [Video]. Retrieved April 22, 2017, from www.drramsey.com/treating-infections-naturally-2/.

(11) Deckard, A. (2016, May 28). *11 proven peppermint essential oil benefits.* Retrieved April 22, 2017, from https://healthyfocus.org/proven-peppermint-essential-oil-benefits/.

(12) Doctors Health Press. (2017, Feb. 14). *Roman chamomile essential oil uses and benefits.* Retrieved April 22, 2017, from www.doctorshealthpress.com/general-health-articles/roman-chamomile-essential-oil-uses-benefits.

(13) Fernández, L. F., Palomino, O. M., & Frutos, G. (2014). Effectiveness of rosmarinus officinalis essential oil as antihypotensive agent in primary hypotensive patients and its influence on health-related quality of life. *Journal of Ethnopharmacology, 151*(1), 509-516. doi: 10.1016/j.jep.2013.11.006.

(14) Bollinger, T. (2016, Sept. 1). *Do you know these 6 health benefits and uses for rosemary essential oil?* Retrieved April 22, 2017, from https://thetruthaboutcancer.com/rosemary-essential-oil/.

(15) Patil, K. (2019, Jan. 3). *15 amazing benefits of sandalwood essential oil.* Retrieved Jan. 21, 2019, from www.organicfacts.net/health-benefits/essential-oils/sandalwood-essential-oil.html.

(16) Spritzler, F. (2017, April 21). *14 everyday uses for tea tree oil.* Retrieved April 22, 2017, from https://authoritynutrition.com/tea-tree-oil/.

Removing Chemicals from the Temple
(1) Ternes, T. (2016, July 8). *Your skin: It absorbs!* Retrieved April 29, 2017, from www.downtoearth.org/health/general-health/your-skin-it-absorbs.
Cleaning the Temple
(21) Steinemann, A. C. (2008). Fragranced consumer products and undisclosed ingredients. *Environmental Impact Assessment Review, 2008*. doi: 10.1016/j.eiar.2008.05.002.
(2) Organic Consumers Association. (n.d.). *How toxic are your household cleaning supplies?* Retrieved April 29, 2017, from www.organicconsumers.org/news/how-toxic-are-your-household-cleaning.
(3) Svanes, O., Bertelsen, R. J., Lygre, S. H. L., Carsin, A. E., Antó, J. M., ... Svanes, C. (2018). Cleaning at home and at work in relation to lung function decline and airway obstruction. *American Journal of Respiratory and Critical Care Medicine, 197*(9), 1099-1101. doi: 10.1164/rccm.201706-1311OC.
(4) Dovey, D. (2017, Sept. 11). Common cleaning products may increase your risk of chronic lung diseases, study shows. *Newsweek.* Retrieved from www.newsweek.com. DVD

Resources

Resources I have found helpful and recommend them if you want to delve deeper into a subject you find interesting and want to learn more.

Diet
The Daniel Plan: 40 Days to a Healthier Life by Rick Warren, Daniel Amen, and Mark Hyman
Foods to Fight Cancer: Essential Foods to Help Prevent Cancer by Richard Beliveau
Forks Over Knives directed by Lee Fulkerson
Food Inc. directed by Robert Kennar
The World's Healthiest Foods (2- ed.): The Force for Change to Health-Promoting Foods and New Nutrient-Rich Cooking by George Mateljan
The World's Healthiest Foods website, www.whfoods.com/foodstoc.php, by George Mateljan
Fight Back with Food: Use Nutrition to Ease What Ails You by the Editors of Reader's Digest
Superfood Kitchen: Cooking with Nature's Most Amazing Foods by Julie Morris
1° of Change The Standard Process 21-Day Purification Program Cookbook (3- ed.) by George Nab

Juicing and smoothies
The Juicing Bible (2- ed.) by Pat Crocker
The Big Book of Juices: More Than 400 Natural Blends for Health and Vitality Every Day by Natalie Savona

Detoxing
The Blood Sugar Solution 10-Day Detox Diet: Activate Your Body's Natural Ability to Burn Fat and Lose Weight Fast by Mark Hyman
The New Detox Diet the Complete Guide for Lifelong Vitality with Recipes, Menus, & Detox Plans by Elson M. Haas

Cleaning
https://experiencelife.com/article/8-hidden-toxins-whats-lurking-in-your-cleaning-products/
https://www.organicconsumers.org/news/how-toxic-are-your-household-cleaning-supplies
https://wellnessmama.com/4733/cleaning-checklist/

Made in the USA
Lexington, KY
14 August 2019